MIDLAND HUMOR

A HARVEST OF FUN
AND FOLKLORE

MIDLAND HUMOR

A HARVEST OF FUN AND FOLKLORE

EDITED BY

JACK CONROY

NEW YORK
CURRENT BOOKS, INC.
A· A· WYN, PUBLISHER

1947

The selections "Gold-seeking" and "Machinery" by Finley Peter Dunne are reprinted from MR. DOOLEY AT HIS BEST (1943), edited by Elmer Ellis, with the permission of Charles Scribner's Sons. "Our First Circus" by E. W. Howe is reprinted from HER FIFTH MARRIAGE AND OTHER STORIES, copyright 1928 by the Haldeman-Julius Company, with the permission of E. Haldeman-Julius. "Discretion Is Necessary to Success," "The Conceited Donkey," "The Lightning Bug Who Thought He Was the Whole Thing," "The Fice and the Moon," "The Kissing Bug and the Wax Figure," "The Rhinoceros and the Mosquitoes," "The Tough Spring Chicken," "The Tiger and the Cat," "The Cricket and the Opera Singer," and "The Ant and the Robin" by T. A. McNeal are reprinted from TOM MCNEAL'S FABLES (1900), by permission of his daughter, Louise McNeal. "Mister Hop-Toad" is reprinted from HOME FOLKS, by James Whitcomb Riley, copyright 1900. Used by special permission of the publishers, the Bobbs-Merrill Company. "Was Solomon Wise?" by Mark Twain is reprinted from THE ADVENTURES OF HUCKLEBERRY FINN, by permission of Harper and Brothers. "Il Janitoro" by George Ade is reprinted by permission of the *Chicago Daily News* and of Franklin J. Meine, editor of STORIES OF THE STREETS AND OF THE TOWN, copyright 1941 by the Caxton Club, Chicago. "The Heroes" by Nelson Algren is reprinted from THE NEON WILDERNESS, copyright 1933, 1934, 1941, 1942, 1943, 1944, 1947 by Nelson Algren, by permission of Doubleday & Company, Inc. "Momma Gest and the Irisher" is reprinted from the novel LAMPS AT HIGH NOON, copyright 1941 and published by Modern Age, by permission of the author, J. S. Balch. "When Mrs. Martin's Booker T.," "At the Hairdresser's," and "The Date" by Gwendolyn Brooks are reprinted from A STREET IN BRONZEVILLE, copyright 1944 by Gwendolyn Brooks Blakely, and are used by permission of the publishers, Harper and Brothers. "The Sissy from the Hardscrabble County Rock Quarries" by Jack Conroy appeared in A TREASURY OF AMERICAN FOLKLORE, copyright 1944 by B. A. Botkin, and published by Crown Publishers. "Different Cultural Levels Eat Here" by Peter DeVries is used by permission of the author. Originally published in *The New Yorker*. Copyright 1946 The F-R. Publishing Corporation. "A Hawk in the Loop" is reprinted from THE MURMUR OF WINGS by Leonard Dubkin (1945), where it appeared as "How a Bird Threw a Great City into a Turmoil," by permission of the publishers, Whittlesey House, copyright, 1946, by the McGraw-Hill Book Company, Inc. "Ballad of Kansas City" by C. L. Edson is reprinted by permission of the *Kansas City Star*. "Alice in Justice-Land" by Jake Falstaff is reprinted by permission of Hazel Fetzer. "Plainsville's First Hossless Kerridge" is reprinted from FOR HERE IS MY FORTUNE by Amos R. Harlin, with the permission of the publishers, Whittlesey House; copyright, 1946, by the McGraw-Hill Book Company, Inc. "Author's Prefaces" and "Hats Off to These Lovelies" by Sidney J. Harris are reprinted from the *Chicago Daily News*, with the permission of that newspaper and the author. "The Light of the World" is reprinted from THE FIFTH COLUMN AND THE FIRST FORTY-NINE STORIES, copyright 1938 by Ernest Hemingway; used by permission of the publishers, Charles Scribner's Sons. Selections from BARBED WIRE and ABE MARTIN'S BROADCAST by Kin

Hubbard, copyright respectively 1928 and 1930, are used by special permission of the publishers, the Bobbs-Merrill Company. "Benny the Bummer" by Ben Krit, which appeared in the *Chicago Daily News* in 1940 as "Such a Life," is printed here by permission of that newspaper and of the author. "Nora" is reprinted from ROUND UP, by Ring Lardner, copyright 1929 by Charles Scribner's Sons; used by permission of the publishers. "Dogs" and "Colleges for Cops" are reprinted from FIRST AND LAST, by Ring Lardner, copyright 1926 by Charles Scribner's Sons; used by permission of the publishers. "Michigan Political Rally" by Della T. Lutes is reprinted from COUNTRY SCHOOLMA'AM, copyright 1941 by Della T. Lutes, by permission of Little, Brown and Company. "No Tears, No Good" by Ruth McKenney is reprinted from MY SISTER EILEEN, copyright 1937, 1938, 1939, by Ruth McKenney, by permission of Harcourt, Brace and Company, Inc., the publishers. "Kansas Grasshoppers" by Kenneth W. Porter is reprinted from NO RAIN FROM THESE CLOUDS, copyright 1946 by Kenneth W. Porter, with permission of the publishers, The John Day Company. "Button, Button, Who Has the Button?" "An Awful Responsibility," "The Liberators," and "Heart Blobs" by Keith Preston are reprinted from POT SHOTS FROM PEGASUS, copyright 1929 by Covici-Friede, Inc., by permission of Crown Publishers. "The Feather-Grafter" by Vance Randolph is reprinted from FROM AN OZARK HOLLER, copyright 1933 by Vanguard Press, Inc., by permission of the publishers. "They Have Yarns" is reprinted from THE PEOPLE, YES, by Carl Sandburg, copyright 1936, by permission of the publishers, Harcourt, Brace and Company, Inc. "Asa Hearthrug Joins Alpha Cholera" is reprinted from BAREFOOT BOY WITH CHEEK, by Max Shulman, copyright 1943, by special permission of the publishers, Doubleday & Company, Inc. "Hell, Said the Duchess" and "Embattled Virgin" by Vincent Starrett are reprinted from AUTOLYCUS IN LIMBO, copyright 1943 by Vincent Starrett, by permission of the publishers, E. P. Dutton & Co. "Penrod and Harold Ramorez" is reprinted from PENROD by Booth Tarkington, published by Doubleday & Company, Inc., copyright 1914, 1942, by Booth Tarkington, by permission of Brandt & Brandt. "Gilded Fairy Tales," "The London Busman Story," and "Mr. Dubbe's Program Study Class" by Bert Leston Taylor are reprinted from THE SO-CALLED HUMAN RACE (1922) with the permission of Emma Taylor. "The Day the Dam Broke" and "University Days" are reprinted from MY LIFE AND HARD TIMES by James Thurber, copyright 1933 by James Thurber, with the permission of Mr. Thurber and Harper and Brothers, the publishers. "The Fat Women of Boone" by Raymond Weeks, originally printed in *Midland*, January, 1925, is reprinted here from THE HOUND-TUNER OF CALLAWAY, copyright 1927 by Columbia University Press, with permission of the publishers. "Essence of Rural Humor" by Charles Morrow Wilson is reprinted from BACKWOODS AMERICA by permission of the University of North Carolina Press. Copyright, 1934, by the University of North Carolina Press. "Odyssey" by Howard Wolf appeared in slightly different form as "The Old Man's Odyssey" in the September, 1939, issue of *Esquire*. "When Life Comes in the Door" by Robert M. Yoder is reprinted from THERE'S No FRONT LIKE HOME, copyright 1942, 1943, 1944, by Robert M. Yoder, with the permission of Houghton Mifflin Company, the publishers.

PRINTED IN THE UNITED STATES OF AMERICA
AMERICAN BOOK—STRATFORD PRESS, INC. NEW YORK

Introduction

AMERICAN humor in its more robust aspects is geared to events and actualities rather than purely cerebral exercises, or artificially contrived situations, such as those which occupied the attention of most of the British "wits" who were still forgathering in drawing rooms while the Yankee colonists were wrestling with reality far past the outposts of civilization. It is a proud and true boast of Americans that they can laugh as loudly and heartily at their own absurdities as they do at the silliness of others. With considerable smugness, colonial writers of the Atlantic Coast area laughed at the frontiersmen; the frontiersmen soon learned to laugh back, with a great deal more raucousness. The iconoclastic funny men of the Middle West frontier helped vitally in forging the concepts of humor now generally accepted throughout America. They have leavened beneficially the heritage left by pallid Brahmins and grim Puritans; they have scorned hollow inanity, shallow pretense, and pompous humbuggery. At first the East was impervious to the seminal influence of Midwestern writers and even Mark Twain was regarded with dubiety. Since his day many humorists have arisen from the rich Midland soil. A great many of them have pulled out for New York and remained there, mostly because of the superior advantages for the writing craft in the big city, but their role has been like that of the honeybee, which, in Midwest folk belief, dies after once stinging the object of its wrath. They inject a powerful virus that lives and works beyond their time.

The editor of a regional collection of humor is confronted with a two-headed difficulty, for both chronological and geographical distance may lend disenchantment to a joke. A good many of the pioneer Midwest writers who found time to be humorous among their more pressing concerns were men with an ax to grind and their work was utilitarian (or propagandistic, as we'd call it today) in that it was a vehicle for the contempt, or perhaps the sublimated envy, of the rugged outlander, compelled to brave the rigors of the wilderness, far from the comparatively civilized surroundings of those fortunate enough to live on the Eastern Seaboard. The Easterners were in constant and direct contact with the mother country and thus with its books, music, art, and other cultural manifestations.

Nothing seemed more comically ineffectual to the Midwest funny men than an Eastern dandy transplanted in untamed regions where physical courage, knowledge of woodcraft and of plant and animal life, and skill with firearms, or with a hunting knife for close quarters, were vastly more important than any amount of learning in the more sedate fields of literature or art. Men with pretensions to "book larnin'" or with smug pride in their material possessions became targets of ridicule in the stories written by such men as Joseph M. Field and John S. Robb, both of whom had knocked about the country quite a bit. Visiting Easterners, cocksure and arrogant, fell into swamps, were assailed by wild beasts, or, at the best, were stung severely by wasps and mosquitoes. They had a fatal propensity for losing their way after having made smart alecky aspersions about the low mental capacity of the natives and in the end had to be rescued by the same rude hinds for whom they had evinced such lofty disdain and scorn. Field was particularly incensed when, during a trip to Washington, he was privileged to look down from a gallery upon the deliberations of Congress. The immaculately clad, bewigged, and scented gentlemen were passing laws regulating the lives of the frontiersmen, who, if they were to survive, had to make their own laws to avoid being done to death by the legislation conceived by some remote and comfortably sheltered statesman with only the faintest idea as to the practical problems of the backwoods settlements.

There being no copyright arrangement, the best works of European writers could be pirated without any legal consequences. Quite reasonably, the publishers and newspaper editors in America preferred the work of a well-known English writer at no cost whatsoever to material written by a native American who was not so skilled a technician and who might in addition demand at least a small payment for his wares. Frontier wits found grist for their sarcastic mills in the English tales of hothouse ladies who were wont to swoon at any fairly severe emotional crisis. The contrast between these delicately nurtured females and the rough-and-ready dames of the frontier, willing and able to engage in mortal combat with Indians, "varmints," and other natural foes gave opportunity for comic exaggeration such as we find in the admiring account of the prowess of Sal Fink, "the Mississippi Screamer," who "fought a duel once with a thunderbolt, an' came off without a singe, while at the fust fire she split the thunderbolt all to flinders, an' gave the pieces to Uncle Sam's artillerymen to touch off their cannon with." As a tot of six Sal "used to ride down the river on an alligator's back, standing upright, an' dancing 'Yankee Doodle,' and could leave all the steamers behind."

Far from yearning for the lot of their more sheltered sisters, such Amazons gloried in their state, as may be learned from this letter written by the "first sweetheart" of "Harry Macarthy, the Arkansas Comedian" and printed in *His Book of Original Songs, Ballads and Anecdotes:*

> You just ought to see me rigged out in my best. My bonnet is a hornet's nest, garnished with wolves' tails and eagles' feathers. My gown's made of a whole bear's hide, with the tail for a train. I can drink from the branch without a cup, shoot a wild goose flying, wade the Mississippi without getting wet, out-scream a catamount, and jump over my own shadow.

. . . I can dance down any fellow in Arkansas, and cut through the bushes like a pint of whisky among forty men.

The ring-tailed roarers and Salt River screamers of the half-horse and half-alligator breed, both male and female, were ordinarily combinations of physical might and mother wit which enabled them to outsmart invaders from other regions. The celebrated dialogue in the traditional piece called *The Arkansas Traveler* is more or less duplicated in Opie Read's "An Englishman's Night" and this note persists today in a folk story current in Missouri and southern Illinois about a stranger on horseback who seeks to have some fun at the expense of a barefoot urchin engaged in hoeing corn, but finds the tables turned on him.

In the middle period came the literary comedians whose chief humorous device was the grotesque misspelling of words and deliberate violence to grammar. In a great many cases these funny men were wandering printers to begin with and had not acquired a large store of formal learning. Their work was another form of the frontier revolt, and found its most popular expression in the writings of Artemus Ward and Petrolem V. Nasby. The "goaks" of Artemus Ward, if put into ordinary English, would seem pretty tepid today, but they were highly pleasing to a public still entertaining the Jacksonian conception of the superior man: one endowed with low but robust wit and with rugged, homespun qualities more to be esteemed than the learned lumber of schools.

More urbane burlesques of polite society and the pretensions of the pork-and-beef millionaires who began to flourish late in the nineteenth century were written by Ten Eyck White, a newspaper columnist once widely read, but now so completely forgotten that neither the newspaper for which he worked nor the publisher that printed his book has any information about him. Not so completely submerged in oblivion is Robert J. Burdette, much in demand at one time both as an author and lecturer. Known as the "Burlington

Hawkeye Man," Burdette made his reputation in the small Iowa city. A number of other men in out-of-the-way places did not find it necessary to go to the large centers of population in order to win a following.

A more sophisticated era in Midwest humor was ushered in during the early years of this century by men who continued to write until many of the present-day practitioners were well on their way. These include George Ade, with his *Stories of the Streets and of the Town* and, later, his *Fables in Slang;* Finley Peter Dunne, whose philosophic bartender, Mr. Dooley, vouchsafed his ideas about many matters far afield from his Archey Road saloon; and Kin Hubbard, with his sly aphorisms of Abe Martin, from Brown County, Indiana. Booth Tarkington's Penrod is a more credible and tractable (and complex) youngster than George W. Peck's Bad Boy, whose fiendish pranks antedated Little Lord Fauntleroy by three years.

Perhaps our Midland humor as conceived by such interpreters of it as James Thurber, Ruth McKenney, Max Shulman, and Wendell Wilcox has less of the tang of river and prairie about it, less of the urgency that impelled the comedians of an earlier period to offense or defense for a culturally backward community. There may be fewer distinctive characteristics since the same gags emerge from radios in Walla Walla, Washington, and Bangor, Maine; the ubiquitous screen comedies may have had some standardizing effect upon our concepts of what's funny. But the present-day writers have compensatory subtleness for whatever they have lost in uniquely regional flavor. All of them represented here do reflect in some manner the impress of their environment. Nelson Algren, born in Detroit and reared in Chicago, travels to Europe with the United States Army and comes back to remember such phrases as "the beauty part of it—" a Midwest heritage from which he'll never be separated. The Middle West has received and assimilated many people of many cultural inheritances. These may be, and are, modified by the section in which they live, but they are not inevitably remolded into a standardized cast of speech and behavior.

The selections herein are arranged into approximate chronological periods, but there is some overlapping, of course. Some attempt has been made to supply a sense of historical progression. I have attached biographical and other information to the pieces themselves, believing it to be of more specific relevance there than in an introduction. A great deal of thought, care, and labor have been expended in the task of compilation, but no claim is made that the collection is all-inclusive or encyclopedic.

Even a listing of the many people who have assisted me generously by offering suggestions and making available otherwise inaccessible material would occupy more space than this foreword. I should like, however, to express my heavy debt of gratitude to all those who did help. Max Siegel and Lawrence Hill deserve commendation for giving the impetus that projected the book from idea to reality. Special credit is due Tom Conroy for invaluable editorial aid, James Light for his research labors, and Margaret Jean Swartz for her devotion to the preparation of the manuscript.

JACK CONROY

Contents

PART THREE

YESTERDAY AND TODAY

*Modern Voices, Some of Them Re-
capturing the Past*

PART ONE

BEGINNINGS

*Trappers, Path Makers, Land Clearers,
Scouts, Rivermen, and Ring-tailed
Roarers*

Anonymous

"The Harp of a Thousand Strings" is of indeterminate authorship
and origin, though it has been widely reprinted in anthologies
and on broadsides since its first appearance in a Mississippi newspaper in the 1850's. It has been attributed to several writers, including Henry T. Lewis and Van Dyke Browne (William P.
Brannan), the latter claiming it in a volume entitled THE HARP OF
A THOUSAND STRINGS; WITH AN AUTOBIOGRAPHY OF THE AUTHOR,
JABEZ FLINT *(1865)*. Its metaphorical language and accentuation
of the final syllable with an "ah!" is typical of Hard-Shell Baptist
preachers of the Mississippi Valley region in an earlier era. It is
still a favorite with rural mimics and I have heard it rendered to
appreciative audiences in a number of Midwestern communities,
as late as the summer of 1946 in Moberly, Missouri.

The Harp of a Thousand Strings

A Hard-Shell Baptist Sermon

I MAY say to you my brethring, that I am not an edicated man, an' I am not one of them as believes that edication is necessary for a Gospel minister, for I believe the Lord edicates his preachers jest as he wants 'em to be edicated; an' although I say it that oughtn't to say it, yet in the State of Indianny, whar I live, thar's no man as gets bigger congregations nor what I gits.

Thar may be some here to-day, my brethring, as don't know what persuasion I am uv. Well, I must say to you, my brethring, that I'm a Hard Shell Baptist. Thar's some folks as don't like the Hard Shell Baptist, but I'd rather have a hard shell as no shell at all. You see me here to-day, my brethring, dressed up in fine clothes; you mout think I was proud, but I am not proud, my brethring, and although I've been a preacher of the gospel for twenty years, an' although I'm capting of the flatboat that lies at your landing, I'm not proud, my brethring.

I am not gwine to tell edzactly whar my tex may be found; suffice to say, it's in the Bible, and you'll find it somewhar between the first chapter of the book of Generations, and the last chapter of the book of Revolutions, and ef you'll go and search the Scriptures, you'll not only find my tex thar, but a great many other texes as will do you good to read, and my tex, when you shall find it, you shill find it to read thus:—

"And he played on a harp uv a thousand strings—sperits uv jest men made perfeck."

My tex, my brethring, leads me to speak of sperits. Now, thar's a great many kind of sperits in the world—in the fuss place, thar's the sperits as some folks call ghosts, and thar's the sperits uv turpentine, and thar's the sperits as some folks

3

call liquor, an' I've got as good an artikel of them kind of sperits on my flatboat as ever was fotch down the Mississippi river; but thar's a great many other kinds of sperits, for the tex says, "He played on a harp uv a *t-h-o-u-s*-and strings, sperits uv jest men made perfeck."

But I'll tell you the kind uv sperits as is meant in the tex, is FIRE. That's the kind uv sperits as is meant in the tex, my brethring. Now thar's a great many kinds of fire in the world. In the fuss place there's the common sort of fire you light your cigar or pipe with, and then thar's foxfire and campfire, fire before you're ready, and fire and fall back, and many other kind uv fire, for the tex says, "He played on the harp uv a *thous*and strings, sperits of jest men made perfeck."

But I'll tell you the kind of fire as is meant in the tex, my brethring—it's HELL FIRE! an that's the kind uv fire as a great many uv you'll come to, ef you don't do better nor what you have been doin'—for "He played on a harp uv a *thous*and strings, sperits uv jest men made perfeck."

Now, the different sorts of fire in the world may be likened unto the different persuasions of Christians in the world. In the first place we have the Piscapalions, an' they are a high sailin' and high-falutin' set, and they may be likened unto a turkey buzzard, that flies up into the air, and he goes up, and up, and up, till he looks no bigger than your finger nail, and the fust thing you know, he cums down, and down, and down, and is a fillin' himself on the carkiss of a dead hoss by the side of the road, and "He played on a harp uv a *thous*and strings, sperits uv jest men made perfeck."

And then thar's the Methodis, and they may be likened unto the squirril runnin' up into a tree, for the Methodis beleeves in gwine on from one degree of grace to another, and finally on to perfection, and the squirrel goes up and up, and up and up, and he jumps from limb to limb, and branch to branch, and the fust thing you know he falls, and down he cums kerflumix, and that's like the Methodis, for they is allers fallen from grace, ah! and "He played on a harp uv a *thous*and strings, sperits of jest men made perfeck."

And then, my brethring, thar's the Baptist, ah! and they have been likened unto a possum on a 'simmon tree, and thunders may roll and the earth may quake, but that possum clings thar still, ah! and you may shake one foot loose, and the other's thar, and you may shake all feet loose, and he laps his tail around the limb, and clings and he clings furever, for "He played on the harp uv a *thous*and strings, sperits uv jest men made perfeck."

The Crockett Almanacs

Between *1835* and *1856* there appeared in various cities of the United States a number of crudely illustrated comic almanacs devoted to the lurid exploits of Colonel Davy Crockett. These tall tales, written by several professional humorists, burlesqued the brag and hyperbole of the "half horse and half alligator" breed. As meretricious as the radio gag writers of our day, the tongue-in-cheek biographers of Crockett coined words awkwardly and indulged in labored witticisms that must have seemed feeble even when they were written. Nevertheless, they were successful in cultivating a spirit of crude vigor and suggesting in some measure the flavor of the Homeric period when Crockett was the bull of the woods and Mike Fink the bully of the Ohio. Walter Blair and Franklin J. Meine have achieved an admirable synthesis of the Mike Fink legends in their MIKE FINK, KING OF THE KEELBOATMEN *(1933)*, while Richard M. Dorson has published generous samplings of the rare Crockett almanacs in DAVY CROCKETT, AMERICAN COMIC LEGEND *(1939)*. "Col. Crockett Beat at a Shooting Match" is from THE CROCKETT ALMANAC, *Volume 2, No. 2, published in Nashville by Ben Harding, 1840.* I am indebted to Franklin J. Meine for the use of this material from his extensive collection of the scarce publications. "Sal Fink, the Mississippi Screamer," reprinted here from the Dorson collection, originally appeared in THE CROCKETT ALMANAC *(1854).*

Col. Crockett Beat at a Shooting Match

I EXPECT, stranger, you think old Davy Crockett war never beat at the long rifle; but he war tho. I expect there's no man so strong, but what he will find some one stronger. If you havent heerd tell of one Mike Fink, I'll tell you some thing about him, for he war a helliferocious fellow, and made an almighty fine shot. Mike was a boatman on the Mississip, but he had a little cabbin on the head of the Cumberland, and a horrid handsome wife, that loved him the widkedest that ever you see. Mike only worked enough to find his wife in rags, and himself in powder, and lead, and whiskey, and the rest of the time he spent in nocking over bar and turkeys, and bouncing deer, and sometimes drawing a lead on an Injun. So one night I fell in with him in the woods, where him and his wife shook down a blanket for me in his wigwam. In the morning sez Mike to me, "I've got the handsomest wife, and the fastest horse, and the sharpest shooting iron in all Kentuck, and if any man dare doubt it, I'll be in his hair quicker than hell could scorch a feather." This put my dander up, and sez I, "I've nothing to say agin your wife, Mike, for it can't be denied she's a shocking handsome woman, and Mrs. Crockett's in Tennessee, and I've got no horses. Now, Mike, I dont exactly like to tell you you lie about what you say about your rifle, but I'm d——d if you speak the truth, and I'll prove it. Do you see that are cat sitting on the top rail of your potato patch, about a hundred and fifty yards off? If she ever hears agin, I'll be shot if it shant be without ears." So I blazed away, and I'll bet you a horse, the ball cut off both the old tom cat's ears close to his head, and shaved the hair off clean across the skull, as slick as if I'd done it with a razor, and the critter

never stirred, nor knew he'd lost his ears till he tried to
scratch 'em. "Talk about your rifle after that, Mike!" sez I.
"Do you see that are sow away off furder than the end of
the world," sez Mike, "with a litter of pigs round her" and
he lets fly. The old sow give a grunt, but never stirred in her
tracks, and Mike falls to loading and firing for dear life, till he
hadn't left one of them are pigs enough tail to make a toothpick on. "Now," sez he, "Col. Crockett, I'll be pretticularly
obleedged to you if you'll put them are pig's tails on again,"
sez he. "That's onpossible, Mike," sez I "but you've left one
of 'em about an inch to steer by, and if it had a-been my
work, I wouldn't have done it so wasteful. I'll mend your
shot," and so I lets fly, and cuts off the apology he'd left the
poor cretur for decency. I wish I may drink the whole of
Old Mississip without a drop of the rale stuff in it, if you
wouldn't have thort the tail had been drove in with a hammer. That made Mike a kinder sorter wrothy, and he sends
a ball after his wife as she was going to the spring after a
gourd full of water, and nocked half her coom out of her
head, without stirring a hair, and calls out to her to stop for
me to take a blizzard at what was left on it. The angeliferous
critter stood still as a scarecrow in a cornfield, for she'd got
used to Mike's tricks by long practiss. "No, no, Mike," sez I,
"Davy Crockett's hand would be sure to shake if his iron war
pointed within a hundred mile of a shemale, and I give up
beat, Mike, and as we've had our eye-openers a-ready, we'll
now take a flem-cutter, by way of an anti-fogmatic, and
then we'll disperse."

Sal Fink, the Mississippi Screamer

I DARE SAY you've all on you, if not more, frequently heard this or that great she-human crittur boasted of, an' pointed out as "one o' the gals"—but I tell you what, stranger, you have never really set your eyes on "one o' the gals" till you have seen Sal Fink, the Mississippi screamer.

She fought a duel once with a thunderbolt, an' came off without a singe, while at the fust fire she split the thunderbolt all to flinders, an' gave the pieces to Uncle Sam's artillerymen to touch off their cannon with. When a gal about six years old, she used to play see-saw on the Mississippi snags, and arter she war done she would snap 'em off, an' so cleared a large district of the river. She used to ride down the river on an alligator's back, standing upright, an' dancing "Yankee Doodle," and could leave all the steamers behind. But the greatest feat she ever did, positively outdid anything that ever was did.

One day when she war out in the forest, making a collection o' wildcat skins for her family's winter bedding, she war captered in the most all-sneakin' manner by about fifty Injuns, an' carried by 'em to Roastflesh Hollow, whar the blood-drinkin' wild varmints determined to skin her alive, sprinkle a leetle salt over her, an' devour her before her own eyes. So they took an' tied her to a tree, to keep till mornin' should bring the rest o' thar ring-nosed sarpints to enjoy the fun. Arter that, they lit a large fire in the holler, turned the bottom o' thar feet towards the blaze, Injun fashion, and went to sleep to dream o' thar mornin's feast. Well, arter the critturs got into a somniferous snore, Sal got into an all-lightnin' of a temper, and burst all the ropes about her like

9

an apron string. She then found a pile o' ropes, took and tied all the Injun's heels together all around the fire; then fixin' a cord to the shins of every two couple, she, with a sud-denachous jerk, that made the entire woods tremble, pulled the entire lot o' sleepin' red-skins into that ar great fire fast together—an' then sloped * like a panther out of her pen, in the midst o' the tallest yellin', howlin', scramblin' and singin', that war ever seen or heerd on, since the great burnin' o' Buffalo prairie!

* Left hastily.

Joseph M. Field

Joseph M. Field (1810–1856) was born probably in Dublin, but came to America as a small boy. Making his way to Saint Louis, he attained prominence as an actor, first as a tragedian and later as a comedian, in various cities along the Mississippi River. He also tried his hand as an impressario and theatrical manager and was more than a little successful as a contributor to the Saint Louis REVEILLE, *where his pieces were usually signed* EVERPOINT. *The following selections are reprinted from* THE DRAMA IN POKER-VILLE; THE BENCH AND BAR OF JURYTOWN, AND OTHER STORIES *(1847). They have a historical significance in that they indicate the sort of material to which professional funnymen of the day turned. "Going to Bed at Honey Run" poses a popular dilemma in the literature of the period—how to preserve the proprieties when the two sexes are compelled, by the circumstance that many houses of the period had but one room, to get between the bed covers with as much decorum as possible (see M. Quad's "A Particular Girl," page 108 in this collection). A familiar story is the one attributed to Judge Stephen Douglas in which the young Douglas, desperately sleepy but hesitant about climbing into bed before the young lady who is his hostess, finally disrobes quickly and essays a desperate leap when her back is turned. Safe beneath the quilts, he hears the charmer comment without evident perturbation, "Mr. Douglas, you have got a mighty small chance of legs there." The frontiersman or rustic in comic bewilderment among the newfangled complexities of city life (represented in this case by what we know now as an ordinary bathtub), described in "A Sucker in a Warm Bath," has always been sure-fire.*

Going to Bed at Honey Run

(The experience of a Missouri politician)

THERE IS a spot in the south-western part of this State, known as *The Fiery Fork of Honey Run!*—a delicious locality, no doubt, as the *run* of honey is of course accompanied by a corresponding flow of "milk," and a mixture of milk and honey, or at any rate, honey and "peach," is the evidence of sublunary contentment, every place where they have preaching.

"Honey Run," further Christianized by the presence of an extremely hospitable family whose mansion, comprising *one apartment*—neither more nor less—is renowned for being never shut against the traveller, and so our friend found it during the chill morning air, at the expense of a rheumatism in his shoulder, its numerous unaffected cracks and spaces clearly showing that dropping the latch was a useless formality. The venerable host and hostess, in their one apartment, usually enjoy the society of two sons, four daughters, sundry dogs, and as many lodgers as may deem it prudent to risk the somewhat equivocal allotment of sleeping partners. On the night in question, our friend, after a hearty supper of ham and eggs and a canvass of the *Fiery Forkers*, the old lady having pointed out his bed, felt very weary, and only looked for an opportunity to "turn in," though the mosquitoes were trumping all sorts of wrath, and no net appeared to *bar* them. The dogs flung themselves along the floor, or again rose and sought the door-step; the old man stripped unscrupulously and sought his share of the one collapsed-looking pillow, and the sons, cavalierly followed his example, leaving the old woman, "gals," and "stranger," to settle any question of delicacy that might arise.

13

The candidate yawned, looked at his bed, went to the door, looked at the daughters; finally, in downright recklessness, seating himself upon "the downy," and pulling off his coat. Well, he *pulled* off his coat—and he folded his coat—and then he yawned—and then he whistled—and then he called the old lady's attention to the fact that it would *never* do to sleep in his muddy trousers—and then he *undid* his vest—and then he whistled again—and then, suddenly, an idea of her lodger's possible embarrassment seemed to flash upon the old woman, and she cried—

"*Gals*, just turn your backs round 'till the *stranger* gits into bed."

The backs were turned, and the stranger *did* get into bed in "less than no time," when the hostess again spoke.

"Reckon, stranger, as you aint used to us, you'd better *kiver up* till the *gals* undress, hadn't you?"

By this time our friend's sleepy fit was over, and though he did "kiver up" as desired, somehow or other, the old counterpane was equally kind in hiding his blushes, and favoring his sly glances. The nymphs were soon stowed away, for there were neither bustles to unhitch nor corsets to unlace, when their mamma, evidently anxious not to smother her guest, considerately relieved him.

"You can *unkiver* now, stranger; I'm *married folks*, and you aint afeared o' *me*, I reckon!"

The stranger happened to be "married folks," himself; he *unkivered* and turned his back with true connubial indifference as far as the ancient lady was concerned, but, with regard to the "gals," he declares that his half-raised curiosity inspired the most tormenting dreams of *mermaids* that ever he experienced.

A Sucker in a Warm Bath

OUR FRIEND Louis, of the "Italian Baths," St. Louis, has just about the nicest arrangements in the shape of a bath that an up-river man can desire; but still he hasn't, after all, got the "latest touch" in the way of his cocks, and that we found out recently at the St. Charles, New Orleans. We called in to see our old acquaintance, the Irish lady, who *does the towels*, &c., and who—more stretch to her girdle—resembles nothing fleshly in petticoats, except it be Falstaff, disguised as "the fat woman of Bentford," in the Merry Wives. We were shown into a bathing-room, and there we discovered that an entire new plan of letting in and letting off the water had been introduced. We saw a shining brass plate with three polished handles, having a "crank" turn, and elegantly lettered beneath, "Hot," "Cold," "Waste."

"D'ye understand the cocks?" said Mrs. McTowell. "Oh, certainly," said we, for the credit of St. Louis and the Italian Baths. The fat mistress of the mysteries shut herself out. We went to work very confidently at the handles; heard a desperate *gug*gling up through polished gratings in the bottom of the "tub," prepared ourselves leisurely for the luxury, and—but we have another story to tell about the matter, and, as that is rather the richer of the two, we shall only say that, between "hot" and "cold," we were never so *cocked* in our life. Having managed to get a bath on the improved plan without exposing our ignorance, we left the place and were met at the corner by a rough, but estimable friend from northern Illinois—one who has made a fortune among the "diggings," and one who can afford to take a "splurge" every now and then—so he terms his occasional visits to the large cities.

"You hain't been taking a bath, hev ye?" said he.

"Oh, yes," was the reply.

"In them there brass handle concerns?"

"Yes," said we—"a great improvement—obviates the inconvenience of the noise and dash of the old plan." We hope that this public confession may prove some atonement, but we certainly did talk to our more ingenious friend with an unblushing face upon the occasion. He roared out laughing, and gave us his own experience of the matter.

"Old Mrs. Cornfed, there," said he, 'asked me if I knew the cocks, and I told her yes, *in* course, cause I'd bathed a few, I reckon, though not with them kind o' fixins,—and I takes and turns them all, and there was all kinds of splutter below; but when I was ready, there wasn't a mite of water in the blasted thing! It just nat'rally run out as fast as it run in, and then I know'd what 'waste' meant. Well, I just fusses with it, fust up, and then down, and then one side, and then t'other, till I allowed I'd shut the derned thing up, cause the tub began to fill. Well, it kept fillin', and fillin', till I reckoned it was about right, and in I went, one leg—but, holy Egypt! Out I came again, howling! The cussed, eternal 'cold' one hadn't worked, I s'pose, and I couldn't a cum out wuss from a seven biler explosion! Old seven hundred weight knocked at the door; 'Perhaps yes don't understand the cocks?' says she. 'Cock thunder!' I sung out,—but I didn't want *her* in to laugh at me; and I wa'n't exactly fit to be seen by a lady, either, if she *was* fat; so I said it was nothin', and tried again to get the hang of the consarned handles, but by this time the tub was quite full, and *bi*lin', at that, and I kept turnin' and wagglin', till I rather guess I must a started the *cold* one, without stoppin' the *hot*, and, as it was *b*rimmin' before, it jest now nat'rally overrun, and *p*rehaps there was the derndest *rise* all over that carpet in about two minutes that you ever *did* see.

"The cussed cocks *wouldn't* stop, none of 'em; and I was hoppin' about in the water, and had to sing out for old *fatty*, any how! I'd rather a gin a farm, by thunder, but out I sung, and half opened the door 'fore I recollected about my *cos-toome!* Back went old *fatty* against the center-table, and broke a pitcher, and I hopped on to a chair, and into my skin; and then I broke for one of the opposite bathing-rooms, and locked myself in, and told the old woman I'd give her ten dollars if she would swob up, hand me my shirt, and say nothing about it! I don't know whether she did or not, but I almost die a laffin, spite of my sore leg, whenever I think of it. I tell you what," added our sucker friend, "I don't mind *your* havin' a laff, but if you go to publishin', I'll shoot you, by gosh!"

We beg to assure our friend that we consider ourselves shot!

Caroline Kirkland

Caroline Kirkland (1801–1864), born Caroline Matilda Stansbury, was a native of New York State. She accompanied her husband to his extensive and undeveloped tract of land in the Michigan backwoods and her three year sojourn in the untamed region afforded grist for the most enduring products of a rather prolific literary mill, notably A NEW HOME—WHO'LL FOLLOW?; OR, GLIMPSES OF WESTERN LIFE *(1839), animated epistolatory sketches admittedly in the style of Mary Mitford's* OUR VILLAGE, *published under the pseudonym "Mrs. Mary Clavers, an Actual Settler." Other results of the Michigan experience are* FOREST LIFE *(1842) and* WESTERN CLEARINGS *(1846). "A Reminiscence of the Land-Fever" is reprinted from the latter volume.*

A Reminiscence of the Land-fever

"SEEING is believing," certainly, in most cases; but in the days of the land-fever, we, who were in the midst of the infected district, scarcely found it so. The whirl, the fervor, the flutter, the rapidity of step, the sparkling of eyes, the beating of hearts, the striking of hands, the utter *abandon* of the hour, were incredible, inconceivable. The "man of one idea" was everywhere; no man had two. He who had no money, begged, borrowed, or stole it; he who had, thought he made a generous sacrifice if he lent it a cent per cent. The tradesman forsook his shop; the farmer his plough; the merchant his counter; the lawyer his office; nay, the minister his desk, to join the general chase. Even the schoolmaster, in his longing to be "abroad" with the rest, laid down his birch, or in the flurry of his hopes plied it with diminished unction.

> Tramp! tramp! along the land they rode.
> Splash! splash! along the sea!

The man with one leg, or he that had none, could at least get on board a steamer, and make for Chicago or Milwaukee: the strong, the able, but above all, the "enterprising," set out with his pocket-map and his pocket-compass to thread the dim woods and see with his own eyes. Who would waste time in planting, in building, in hammering iron, in making shoes, when the path to wealth lay wide and flowery before him?

A ditcher was hired by the job to do a certain piece of work in his line. "Well, John, did you make anything?"

"Pretty well; I cleared about two dollars a day; but I should have made more by *standing round*;" i.e., watching the land-market for bargains.

This favorite occupation of all classes was followed by its legitimate consequences. Farmers were as fond of "standing around" as anybody; and when harvest time came, it was discovered that many had quite forgotten that the best land requires sowing; and grain, and of course other articles of general necessity, rose to an unprecedented price. The hordes of travellers flying through the country in all directions were often cited as the cause of the distressing scarcity; but the true source must be sought in the diversion, or rather suspension, of the industry of the entire population. Be this as it may, of the wry faces made at the hard fare, the travellers contributed no inconsiderable portion; for they were generally city gentlemen, or at least gentlemen who had lived long enough in the city to have learned to prefer oysters to salt pork. This checked not their ardor, however; for the golden glare before their eyes had power to neutralize the hue of all present objects. On they pressed, with headlong zeal; the silent and pathless forest, the deep miry marsh, the gloom of night, and the fires of noon beheld alike the march of the speculator. Such searching of trees for town lines! Such ransacking of the woods for section corners, ranges, and base line! Such anxious care in identifying spots possessing particular advantages! And then, alas! after all, such precious blunders!

These blunders called into action another class of operators, who became popularly known as "land-lookers." These met you at every turn, ready to furnish "water power," "pine lots," "choice farming tracts," or anything else, at a moment's notice. Bar-rooms and street-corners swarmed with these prowling gentry. It was impossible to mention any part of the country which they had not personally surveyed. They would tell you, with the gravity of astrologers, what sort of timber predominated on any given tract, drawing sage deductions as to the capabilities of the soil. Did you incline to city property? Lo! a splendid chart, setting forth the advantages of some unequalled site, and your confidential friend, he land-looker, able to tell you more than all about it or to ccompany you to the happy spot; though that he would not dvise; "bad roads," "nothing fit to eat," etc.; and all this rom a purely disinterested solicitude for your welfare.

These amiable individuals were, strange to tell, no favorites vith actual settlers. If they disliked the gentleman specu- ator, they hated with a perfect hatred him who aided by his ocal knowledge the immense purchases of non-residents. These short-sighted and prejudiced persons forgot the honor ind distinction which must result from their insignificant arms being surrounded by the possessions of the magnates of he land. They saw only the solitude which would probably oe entailed on them for years; and it was counted actual reason in a settler to give any facilities to the land-looker, of vhatever grade. "Let the land-shark do his own hunting," vas their frequent reply to applications of this kind; and ome thought them quite right. Yes, this state of feeling among he hard-handed, was not without its inconvenient results to :ity gentlemen, as witness the case of our friend Mr. Wil- oughby, a very prim and smart bachelor from——.

It was when the whirlwind was at its height, that a gentle- nan wearing the air of a bank director, at the very least—in other words, that of an uncommonly fat pigeon—drew bridle it the bars in front of one of the roughest log houses in the :ounty of——. The horse and his rider were loaded with all hose unnecessary defences and cumbrous comforts which he fashion of the time prescribed in such cases. Blankets, valise, saddlebags, and holsters nearly covered the steed; a nost voluminous enwrapement of India-rubber cloth com- oletely enveloped the rider. The gallant sorrel seemed indeed fit for his burden. He looked as if he might have swam any stream in Michigan,

> Barded from counter to tail,
> And the rider arm'd complete in mail;

yet he seemed a little jaded, and hung his head languidly while his master accosted the tall and meagre tenant of the log-cabin.

This individual and his dwelling resembled each other in an unusual degree. The house was, as we have said, of the roughest; its ribs scarcely half filled in with clay; its "looped and windowed raggedness" rendered more conspicuous by the tattered cotton sheets which had long done duty as glass, and which now fluttered in every breeze; its roof of oak shingles, warped into every possible curve; and its stick chimney, so like its owner's hat, open at the top, and jammed in at the sides; all shadowed forth the contour and equipment of the exceedingly easy and self-satisfied person who leaned on the fence, and snapped his long cart-whip, while he gave such answers as suited him to the gentleman in the India-rubbers, taking especial care not to invite him to alight.

"Can you tell me, my friend,—" civilly began Mr. Willoughby.

"Oh! *friend!*" interrupted the settler; "Who told you I was your friend? Friends is scuss in these parts."

"You have at least no reason to be otherwise," replied the traveller, who was blessed with a very patient temper, especially where there was no use in getting angry.

"I don't know that," was the reply. "What fetch'd you into these woods?"

"If I should say 'my horse,' the answer would perhaps be as civil as the question."

"Jist as you like," said the other, turning on his heel, and walking off.

"I wished merely to ask you," resumed Mr. Willoughby, talking after the nonchalant son of the forest, "whether this is Mr. Pepper's land?"

"How do you know it ain't mine?"

"I'm not likely to know at present, it seems," said the traveller, whose patience was getting a little frayed. And taking out his memorandum-book, he ran over his minutes: "South half of north-west quarter of section fourteen—Your name is Leander Pepper, is it not?"

"Where did you get so much news? you ain't the sheriff, be ye?"

"Pop!" screamed a white-headed urchin from the house, "Mam says supper's ready."

"So ain't I," replied the papa: "I've got all my chores to do yet." And he busied himself at a log pigsty on the opposite side of the road, half as large as the dwelling-house. Here he was soon surrounded by a squealing multitude with whom he seemed to hold a regular conversation.

Mr. Willoughby looked at the westering sun, which was not far above the dense wall of trees that shut in the small clearing; then at the heavy clouds which advanced from the north, threatening a stormy night; then at his watch, and then at his note-book; and after all, at his predicament—on the whole, an unpleasant prospect. But at this moment a female face showed itself at the door. Our traveller's memory reverted at once to the testimony of Layard and Mungo Park; and he had also some floating and indistinct poetical recollections of woman's being useful when a man was in difficulties, though hard to please at other times. The result of these reminiscences, which occupied a precious second, was that Mr. Willoughby dismounted, fastened his horse to the fence, and advanced with a brave and determined air to throw himself upon female kindness and sympathy.

He naturally looked at the lady as he approached the door, but she did not return the compliment. She looked at the pigs and talked to the children, and Mr. Willoughby had time to observe that she was the very duplicate of her husband; as tall, as bony, as ragged, and twice as cross-looking.

"Malviny Jane!" she exclaimed, in no dulcet treble, "be done a-paddlin' in that'ere water! If I come there, I'll—"

"You'd better look at Sophrony, I guess!" was the reply.

"Why, what's she a-doin'?"

"Well, I guess if you look, you'll see!" responded Miss Malvina, coolly, as she passed into the house, leaving at every step a full impression of her foot in the same black mud that covered her sister from head to foot.

The latter was saluted with a hearty cuff as she emerged from the puddle; and it was just at the propitious moment when her shrill howl aroused the echoes that Mr. Willoughby, having reached the threshold, was obliged to set about making the agreeable to the mamma. And he called up for the occasion all his politeness.

"I believe I must become an intruder on your hospitality for the night, madam," he began. The dame still looked at the pigs. Mr. Willoughby tried again, in less courtly phrase.

"Will it be convenient for you to lodge me to-night, ma'am? I have been disappointed in my search for a hunting-party whom I had engaged to meet, and the night threatens a storm."

"I don't know nothin' about it; you must ask the old man," said the lady, now for the first time taking a survey of the newcomer; "with *my* will, we'll lodge nobody."

This was not very encouraging, but it was a poor night for the woods; so our traveller persevered, and, making so bold a push for the door that the lady was obliged to retreat a little, he entered and said he would await her husband's coming.

And in truth he could scarcely blame the cool reception he had experienced when he beheld the state of affairs within those muddy precincts. The room was large, but it swarmed with human beings. The huge open fire-place, with its hearth of rough stone, occupied nearly the whole of one end of the apartment; and near it stood a long cradle containing a pair of twins, who cried—a sort of hopeless cry, as if they knew it would do no good, yet could not help it. The school-master (it was his week) sat reading a tattered novel and rocking the cradle occasionally when the children cried *too* loud. An old gray-headed Indian was curiously crouched over a large tub, shelling corn on the edge of a hoe; but he ceased his noisy employment when he saw the stranger, for no Indian will ever willingly be seen at work, though he may be sometimes compelled by the fear of starvation or the longing for whiskey to degrade himself by labor. Near the only window was placed the work-bench and entire paraphernalia of the shoemaker, who in these regions travels from house to house, shoeing the family and mending the harness as he goes, with various interludes of songs and jokes, ever new and acceptable. This one, who was a little, bald, twinkling-eyed fellow, made the smoky rafters ring with the burden of that favorite ditty of the west:

"All kind of game to hunt, my boys, also the buck and doe,
  All down by the banks of the river O-hi-o;"

and the children of all sizes, clattering in all keys, completed the picture and the concert.

The supper-table, which maintained its place in the midst of this living and restless mass, might remind one of the square stone lying bedded in the bustling leaves of the acanthus; but the associations would be any but those of Corinthian elegance. The only object which at that moment diversified its dingy surface was an iron hoop into which the mistress of the feast proceeded to turn a quantity of smoking hot potatoes, adding afterward a bowl of salt and another of pork fat, by courtesy denominated gravy; plates and knives dropped in afterward, at the discretion of the company.

Another call of "Pop! pop!" brought in the host from the pigsty; the heavy rain which had now begun to fall having, no doubt, expedited the performance of the chores. Mr. Willoughby, who had established himself resolutely, took advantage of a very cloudy assent from the proprietor to lead his horse to a shed and to deposit in a corner his cumbrous outer gear; while the company used in turn the iron skillet which served as a wash-basin, dipping the water from a large trough outside, overflowing with the abundant dripping of the eaves. Those who had no pocket handkerchiefs contented themselves with a nondescript article, which seemed to stand for the family towel; and when this ceremony was concluded, all seriously addressed themselves to the demolition of the potatoes. The grown people were accommodated with chairs and chests; the children prosecuted a series of flying raids upon the good cheer, snatching a potato now and then as they could find an opening under the raised arm of one of the family, and then retreating to the chimney corner, tossing the hot prize from hand to hand and blowing it stoutly the while. The old Indian had disappeared.

To our citizen, though he felt inconveniently hungry, this primitive meal seemed a little meagre; and he ventured to ask if he could not be accommodated with some tea.

"Ain't my victuals good enough for you?"

"Oh!—the potatoes are excellent, but I'm very fond of tea."

"So be I, but I can't have everything I want—can you?"

This produced a laugh from the shoemaker, who seemed to think his patron very witty; while the schoolmaster, not knowing but the stranger might happen to be one of his examiners next year, produced only a faint giggle, and then reducing his countenance instantly to an awful gravity, helped himself to his seventh potato.

The rain which now poured violently, not only outside but through many a crevice in the roof, naturally kept Mr. Willoughby cool; and finding that dry potatoes gave him the hiccough, he withdrew from the table, and, seating himself on the shoemaker's bench, took a survey of his quarters.

Two double-beds and the long cradle seemed all the sleeping apparatus; but there was a ladder which doubtless led to a lodging above. The sides of the room were hung with abundance of decent clothing, and the dresser was well stored with the usual articles, among which a teapot and canister shone conspicuous; so that the appearance of inhospitality could not arise from poverty, and Mr. Willoughby concluded to set it down to the account of rustic ignorance.

The eating ceased not until the hoop was empty, and then the company rose and stretched themselves, and began to guess it was about time to go to bed. Mr. Willoughby inquired what was to be done with his horse.

"Well! I s'pose he can stay where he is."

"But what can he have to eat?"

"I reckon you won't get nothing for him, without you turn him out on the mash."

"He would get off, to a certainty!"

"Tie his legs."

The unfortunate traveller argued in vain. Hay was "scuss," and potatoes were "scusser;" and in short the "mash" was the only resource, and these natural meadows afford but poor picking after the first of October. But to the "mash" was the good steed despatched, ingloriously hampered, with the privilege of munching wild grass in the rain after his day's journey.

Then came the question of lodging for his master. The lady, who had by this time drawn out a trundle-bed and packed it full of children, said there was no bed for him unless he could sleep "up chamber" with the boys.

Mr. Willoughby declared that he should make out very well with a blanket by the fire.

"Well! just as you like," said his host; "but Solomon sleeps there, and if you like to sleep by Solomon, it is more than I should."

This was the name of the old Indian, and Mr. Willoughby once more cast woeful glances toward the ladder.

But now the schoolmaster, who seemed rather disposed to be civil, declared that he could sleep very well in the long cradle, and would relinquish his place beside the shoemaker to the guest, who was obliged to content himself with this arrangement, which was such as was most usual in those times.

The storm continued through the night, and many a crash in the woods attested its power. The sound of a storm in a dense forest is almost precisely similar to that of a heavy surge breaking on a rocky beach; and when our traveller slept it was only to dream of wreck and disaster at sea and to wake in horror and affright. The wild rain drove in at every crevice and wet the poor children in the loft so thoroughly that they crawled shivering down the ladder and stretched themselves on the hearth, regardless of Solomon, who had returned after the others were in bed.

But morning came at last; and our friend, who had no desire farther to test the vaunted hospitality of a western settler, was not among the latest astir. The storm had partially subsided; and although the clouds still lowered angrily and his saddle had enjoyed the benefit of a leak in the roof during the night, Mr. Willoughby resolved to push on as far as the next clearing, at least, hoping for something for breakfast besides potatoes and salt. It took him a weary while to find his horse, and when he had saddled him and strapped on his various accoutrements he entered the house and inquired what he was to pay for his entertainment—laying somewhat of a stress on the last word.

His host, nothing daunted, replied that he guessed he would let him off for a dollar.

Mr. Willoughby took out his purse, and, as he placed a silver dollar in the leathern palm outspread to receive it, happened to look toward the hearth. There he perceived preparations for a very substantial breakfast, and the long pent-up vexation burst forth.

"I really must say, Mr. Pepper—" he began. His tone was certainly that of an angry man, but it only made his host laugh.

"If this is your boasted western hospitality, I can tell you—"

"You'd better tell me what the dickens you are peppering me up this fashion for? My name isn't Pepper, no more than yours is! May be that *is* your name; you seem pretty warm."

"Your name not Pepper! Pray what is it, then?"

"Ah! there's the thing, now! You land-hunters ought to know sich things without asking."

"Land-hunter! I'm no land-hunter!"

"Well! you're a land shark, then—swallowin' up poor men's farms. The less I see of such cattle, the better I'm pleased."

"Confound you!" said Mr. Willoughby, who waxed warm, "I tell you I've nothing to do with land. I wouldn't take your whole State for a gift."

"What did you tell my woman you was a land-hunter for, then?"

And now the whole matter became clear in a moment; and it was found that Mr. Willoughby's equipment, with the mention of a "hunting-party," had completely misled both host and hostess. And to do them justice, never were regret and vexation more heartily expressed.

"You needn't judge our new-country-folks by me," said Mr. Handy, for such proved to be his name; "any man in these parts would as soon bite off his own nose as to snub a civil traveller that wanted a supper and a night's lodging. But somehow or other, your lots o' fixin' and your askin' after that 'ere Pepper—one of the worst land-sharks we've ever had here—made me mad; and I know I treated you worse than an Indian."

"Humph!" said Solomon.

"But," continued the host, "you shall see whether my old woman can't set a good breakfast when she's a mind to. Come, you shan't stir a step till you've had breakfast; and just take back this plaguy dollar. I wonder it didn't burn my fingers when I took it!"

Mrs. Handy set forth her very best, and a famous breakfast it was, considering the times. And before it was finished the hunting-party made their appearance, having had some difficulty in finding their companion, who had made a very common mistake as to section corners and town-lines.

"I'll tell you what," said Mr. Handy, confidentially, as the cavalcade with its baggage-ponies, loaded with tents, gun-cases, and hampers of provisions, was getting into order for a march to the prairies, "I'll tell you what; if you've occasion to stop any where in the bush, you'd better tell 'em at the first goin' off that you ain't land-hunters."

But Mr. Willoughby had already had "a caution."

John S. Robb

John S. Robb was one of the regular contributors to Charles Keemle's Saint Louis WEEKLY REVEILLE *(1844–1850) a valuable repository for such Midwestern literature as then existed. Robb, a wandering printer, had traveled in the West and Southwest before he wrote* STREAKS OF SQUATTER LIFE, AND FAR WESTERN SCENES *(1846), humorous sketches, most of which had appeared in the* WEEKLY REVEILLE *under his pen name* SOLITAIRE. KAAM; OR, DAYLIGHT *(1847) is less imposing. "The Standing Candidate" is one of the pieces in* STREAKS OF SQUATTER LIFE. *The circumstances and time of Robb's birth and death—in fact, the principal details of his life—remain shrouded in mystery.*

The Standing Candidate

AT BUFFALO HEAD, Nianga County, State of Missouri, during the canvass of 1844, there was held an extensive political *Barbecue*, and the several candidates for Congress, legislature, county offices, etc., were all congregated at this southern point for the purpose of making an *immense* demonstration. Hards, softs, whigs and Tylerites were represented, and to hear their several expositions of State and general policy, a vast gathering of the Missouri sovereigns had also assembled. While the impatient candidates were awaiting the signal to mount the "stump," an odd-looking old man made his appearance at the brow of a small hill bounding the place of meeting.

"Hurrah for old *Sugar!*" shouted an hundred voices, while on, steadily, progressed the object of the cheer.

Sugar, as he was familiarly styled, was an old man, apparently about fifty years of age, and was clad in a coarse suit of brown linsey-woolsey. His pants were patched at each knee, and around the ankles they had worn off into picturesque points—his coat was not of the modern close-fitting cut, but hung in loose and easy folds upon his broad shoulders, while the total absence of buttons upon this garment exhibited the owner's contempt for the storm and tempest. A coarse shirt, tied at the neck with a piece of twine, completed his body covering. His head was ornamented with an old woolen cap of divers colors, below which beamed a broad, humorous contenance, flanked by a pair of short, funny little gray whiskers. A few wrinkles marked his brow, but time could not count them as sure chroniclers of his progress, for *Sugar's* hearty, sonorous laugh oft drove them from their hiding-place. Across his shoulder was thrown a sack, in each

33

end of which he was bearing to the scene of political action a keg of *bran new whiskey* of his own manufacture, and he strode forward on his moccasin-covered feet, encumbered as he was, with all the agility of youth. *Sugar* had long been the *standing candidate* of Nianga County for the legislature, and founded his claim to the office upon the fact of his being the first "squatter" in that county—his having killed the first *bar* there ever killed by a white man, and, to place his right beyond cavil, he had *'stilled* the first keg of whiskey! These were strong claims which, urged in his comic rhyming manner, would have swept the "diggins," but *Sugar*, when the canvass opened, always yielded his claim to some liberal purchaser of his *fluid*, and duly announced himself a candidate for the *next* term.

"Here you air, old fellar!" shouted an acquaintance, "allays on hand 'bout 'lection."

"Well, Nat," said *Sugar*, "you've jest told the truth as easy as ef you'd taken sum of my mixtur—

> Whar politicians congregate,
> I'm allays thar, at any rate!

"Set him up!—set the old fellar up somewhar, and let us take a univarsal liquor!" was the general shout.

"Hold on, boys,—keep cool and shady," said old *Sugar*, "whar's the candidates?—none of your splurgin round till I get an appropriation for the sperits. Send 'em along, and we'll negotiate fur the *fluid*, arter which I shall gin 'em my instructions, and they may then *per-cede* to

> Talk away like all cre-*a*-tion,
> What they knows about the nation.

The candidates were accordingly summoned up to pay for *Sugar's* portable grocery, and to please the crowd and gain the good opinion of the owner, they made up a purse, and gathered round him. *Sugar* had placed his two kegs upon a broad stump, and seated himself astride of them with a small tin cup in his hand and a paper containing brown sugar lying before him—each of his kegs was furnished with a *spigot*, and as soon as the money for the whole contents was paid in, *Sugar* commenced addressing the crowd as follows:

"Boys, fellars, and candidates," said he, "I, *Sugar*, am the furst white man ever seed in these yeur diggins—I killed the furst *bar* ever a white skinned in this country, and I kalkilate I hev hurt the feelings of his relations sum sence, as the *bar-skin* linin' of my cabin will testify;—'sides that, I'm the furst manufacturer of whiskey in the range of this district, and powerful mixtur it is, too, as the bilin' of fellars in this crowd will declar';—and more'n that, I'm a candidate for the legislatur', and intend to gin up my claim *this* term to the fellar who can talk the *pooteyst;* now, finally at the eend, boys, this mixtur of mine will make a fellar talk as iley as goose-grease,—as sharp as lightnin', and as *per*suadin' as a young gal at a quiltin', so don't spar it while it lasts, and the candidates can drink furst, 'cause they've got to do the talkin'!"

Having finished his charge, he filled the tin cup full of whiskey, put in a handful of brown sugar, and with his fore-finger stirred up the sweetening, then surveying the candidates, he pulled off his cap, remarking, as he did so:

"Old age, allays, afore beauty!—your daddy furst, in course," then holding up the cup he offered a toast, as follows:

"Here is to the string that binds the states; may it never be bit apart by political *rats!*" Then holding up the cup to his head, he took a hearty swig, and passed it to the next oldest looking candidate. While they were tasting it, *Sugar* kept up a fire of lingo at them:

"Pass it along lively, gentle*men*, but don't spar the *fluid*. You can't help tellin' truth arter you've swaller'd enough of my mixtur, jest fur this reason, it's been 'stilled in honesty, rectified in truth, and poured out with wisdom! Take a *leetle* drop more," said he to a fastidious candidate, whose stomach turned at thought of the way the "mixtur" was mixed. "Why, Mister," said *Sugar*, coaxingly,

> Ef you war a babby just new born,
> 'Twould do you good this juicy *corn!*

"No more, I thank you," said the candidate, drawing back from the proffer.

Sugar winked his eye at some of his cronies, and muttered— "He's got an *a*-ristocracy stomach, and can't go the *native licker*." Then, dismissing the candidates, he shouted,—"crowd up, constitoo-*ents*, into a circle, and let's begin fair—your daddy furst, allays; and mind, no changin' places in the circle to git the sugar in the bottom of the cup. I know you're arter it, Tom Williams, but none on your Yankeein' round to get the sweetnin'—it's all syrup, fellars, 'cause *Sugar* made and mixed it. The gals at the frolicks allays git me to prepar' the cordials, 'cause they say I make it mighty drinkable. Who next? What *you*, old Ben Dent!—Well, hold your hoss for a minit, and I'll strengthen the tin with a speck more, jest because you can kalkilate the valee of the licker, and do it jestiss!"

Thus chatted *Sugar*, as he measured out and sweetened up the contents of his kegs, and until all who would drink had taken their share, and then the crowd assembled around the speakers. We need not say that the virtues of each political party were duly set forth to the hearers—that follows as a matter of course, candidates dwell upon the strong points of their argument, always. One among them, however, more than his compeers, attracted the attention of our friend *Sugar*, not because he had highly commended the contents of his kegs, but because he painted with truth and feeling the claims of the western *pioneers!* Among these he ranked the veteran

Col. Johnson and his compatriots, and as he rehearsed their struggles in defence of their firesides, how they had been trained to war by conflict with the ruthless savage, their homes oft desolated, and their children murdered,—yet, still ever foremost in the fight, and last to retreat, winning the heritage of these broad valleys for their children, against the opposing arm of the red man, though aided by the civilized power of mighty Britain, and her serried cohorts of trained soldiery! We say, as he dwelt upon these themes, *Sugar's* eye would fire up, and then at some touching passage of distress dwelt upon by the speaker, tears would course down his rude cheek. When the speaker concluded, he wiped his eyes with his hard hand, and said to those around him:—

"That are true as the yearth!—thar's suthin' like talk in that fellar!—he's the right breed, and his old daddy has told him about them times. So did mine relate 'em to me, how the only sister I ever had, when a baby, had her brains dashed out by one of the red-skinned devils! But didn't we pepper them fur it! Didn't I help the old man, afore he grew too weak to hold his shootin' iron, to send a few on 'em off to rub out the account? Well, I *did!—Hey!*" and shutting his teeth together he yelled through them the exultation of full vengeance.

The speaking being done, candidates and hearers gathered around old Sugar, to hear his comments upon the speeches, and to many inquiries of how he liked them, the old man answered:—

"They were all pooty good, but that tall fellar they call Tom, from St. Louis; *you,* I mean, *stranger,*" pointing at the same time to the candidate, "you jest scart up my feelin's to the right pint—you jest made me feel wolfish as when I and old dad war arter the red varmints; and now what'll *you* take? I'm goin' to publicly *de*-cline in your favor."

Pouring out a tin full of the liquor, and stirring it as before, he stood upright upon the stump, with a foot on each side of his kegs, and drawing off his cap, toasted:—

"The memory of the Western *pioneers!*"

A shout responded to his toast, which echoed far away in
the depths of the adjoining forest, and seemed to awaken a
response from the spirits of these departed heroes.

"That's the way to sing it out, boys," responded old *Sugar*,
"sich a yell as that would *scar* an inimy into ager fits, and
make the United States Eagle scream, 'Hail Columby.'"

"While you're up, *Sugar*," said one of the crowd, "give us
a stump speech yourself."

"Bravo!" shouted a hundred voices, "a speech from *Sugar*."

"Agreed, boys," said the old man, "I'll jest gin a few words
to wind up with, so keep quiet while your daddy's talkin';

> Sum tell it out jest like a song,
> I'll gin it to you sweet and strong.

"The only objection ever made to me in this arr county,
as a legislatur', was made by the *wimin* 'cause I war a *bachelor*, and I never told you afore why I *re*-mained in the state
of number *one*—no fellar stays single *pre*-meditated, and, in
course, a hansum fellar like me, who all the gals declar' to be
as enticin' as a jay bird, warn't goin' to stay alone, ef he could
help it. I did see a creatur' once, named *Sofy Mason*, up the
Cumberland, nigh unto Nashville, Tennes*see*, that I took an
orful hankerin' arter, and I sot in to lookin' anxious fur matrimony, and gin to go reglar to meetin', and took to dressin'
tremengeous finified jest to see ef I could get her good
opinion. She did git to lookin' at me, and one day, cumin'
from meetin', she was takin' a look at me a kind of shy, just
as a hoss does at something he's scared at, when arter champin'
at a distance fur awhile, I sidled up to her, and blarted out a
few words about the sarmin'—she said yes, but cuss me ef I
knew whether that war the right answer or not, and I'm
a thinkin' she didn't know then, nuther! Well, we larfed and
talked a leetle all the way along to her daddy's, and thar I

gin her the best bend I had in me, and raised my bran new
hat as peert and *per*lite as a minister, lookin' all the time so
enticin' that I sot the gal tremblin'. Her old daddy had a
powerful numerous lot of healthy niggers, and lived right
adjinin' my place, while on tother side lived Jake Simons—
a sneakin' cute varmint, who war wusser than a miser for
stinginess; and no sooner did this cussed sarpint see me sidlin'
up to Sofy, than he went to slickin' up, too, and sot himself
to work to cut me out. That arr wur a struggle ekill to the
battle of Orleans. Furst sum new fixup of Jake's would take
her eye, and then I'd sport suthin' that would outshine him,
until Jake at last gin in tryin' to outdress me, and sot thinkin'
of suthin' else. Our farms wur just the same number of acres,
and we both owned three niggers a-piece. Jake knew that
Sofy and her dad kept a sharp eye out fur the main chance,
so he thort he'd clar me out by buyin' another nigger; but
I jest follor'd suit, and bought one the day arter he got his,
so he had no advantage thar; he then got a *cow*, and so did I,
and jest about then both on our *pusses* gin out. This put Jake
to his wit's eend and I war a wunderin' what in the yearth
he would try next. We stood so, hip and thigh, fur about two
weeks, both on us talkin' sweet to Sofy, whenever we could
git her alone. I thort I seed that Jake, the sneakin' cuss, wur
gittin' a mite ahead of me, 'cause his tongue wur so iley;
howsever, I didn't let on, but kep a top eye on him. One Sunday mornin' I wur a leetle mite late to meetin', and when I
got thar, the first thing I seed war Jake Simons, sittin' close
bang up agin Sofy, in the same pew with her daddy! I biled
a spell with wrath, and then tarned sour; I could taste myself!
Thar they wur, singin' *himes* out of the same book. Je-e-
eminy, fellars, I war so *enormous* mad that the new silk hand-
kercher round my neck lost its color! Arter meetin', out they
walked, linked arms, a smilin' and lookin' as pleased as a young
couple at thar furst christenin', and Sofy tarned her 'cold
shoulder' at me so orful pinted that I wilted down, and gin up

right straight—Jake had her, thar wur no disputin' it! I headed toward home, with my hands as fur in my trowsers pockets as I could push 'em, swarin' all the way that she war the last one would ever git a chance to rile up my feelin's. Passin' by Jake's plantation I looked over the fence, and thar stood an explanation of the matter, right facin' the road whar every one passin' could see it—his consarned *cow* was tied to a stake in the gardin' *with a most promising calf along side of her!* That *calf* jest soured my milk, and made Sofy think, that a fellar who war allays gittin' ahead like Jake, wur a right smart chance for a lively husband!"

A shout of laughter here drowned *Sugar's* voice, and as soon as silence was restored he added, in a solemn tone, with one eye shut, and his forefinger pointing at his auditory:—

"What is a cussed slight wusser than his gettin' Sofy war the fact, that he *borrowed that calf the night before from Dick Hardley!* Arter the varmint got Sofy hitched, he told the joke all over the settlement, and the boys never seed me arterwards that they didn't *b-a-h* at me fur lettin' a *calf* cut me out of a gal's affections. I'd a shot Jake, but I thort it war a free country, and the gal had a right to her choice without bein' made a widder, so I jest sold out and travelled! I've allays thort since then, boys, that *wimin* were a good deal like *licker*, ef you love 'em too hard thar sure to throw you some way:

> Then here's to *wimin*, then to *licker*,
> Thar's nuthin' swimmin' can be slicker!

Alphonso Wetmore

Alphonso Wetmore (1793–1849), who lost an arm in the War of 1812, was the first Missouri writer to depict the frontier environment with any degree of literary skill. As an army paymaster, he traveled during the early 1820's gathering material for his GAZETTEER OF THE STATE OF MISSOURI *(1837), a compendium giving geographical and other information. Interspersed with the data are asides by the author, often of a humorous or dramatic nature. "The Heroine of Cote sans Dessein" is one of these contrapuntal anecdotes.*

The Heroine of Cote sans Dessein

COTE SANS DESSEIN (a hill without design) is the site of an ancient French village. This place has its name from an isolated hill that is standing, as if by accident, on the river-bank, in an extensive bottom. It appears that some convulsion of nature may have cut it off from the hills at the mouth of the Osage, on the opposite bank of the Missouri, and given passage to this last mentioned river, between it and the base of its kindred hills. The village of Cote sans Dessein was settled in 1808, and was once a populous place. The old inhabitants have generally removed across the Missouri, and settled there. This ancient village had its share of the Indian wars incident to the settlement of the country, and furnishes an instance of gallantry in the defence of the place, equal to anything recorded in the history of manly firmness. The principal actor in this achievement was a Frenchman, whose name was Baptiste Louis Roi. He chanced to be in the block-house, with only two men and as many women, when the attack commenced. With this small command he made a successful defence against a numerous and very determined band of Indians. One of his men, observing the great disparity of force, was panic-struck, and rendered no assistance in the conflict. He devoted himself to prayer and *very* humble penitence throughout the siege. The women, the wife and sister-in-law of the gallant Roi, lent efficient and indispensable aid to the two soldiers, their husbands. The defenders of the blockhouse had not been sufficiently provident in their supply of ammunition, so as to have a sufficient quantity of balls on hand at the beginning of the attack. While the men were firing, the women made it their business to cast balls and cut patches, so as to keep up the defence in a steady and uninterrupted manner. The consequence was, that these two riflemen numbered fourteen Indians in their report of killed, without being able to form any correct account of the wounded. But they had the satisfaction to continue the fight until the balance of their foes was among the missing. After the extreme suffering which the assailants endured, they became desperate in their determination to take or destroy the block-house. They made several bold attempts to storm, but were always driven back with reduced numbers. This taught them circumspection, and they determined to set fire to the house. To effect this in security, they fastened combustible matter to their arrows, and, having lighted this, their missives were shot into the roof of the block-house; as often as this occurred, the women made it a business to extinguish the blaze by the application of the little water they had within the building. The place of defence was near the river-bank, but the garrison was too weak to justify a sally for additional supplies. It was with appalling interest that the little band observed the rapid expenditure of their small stock as the incendiaries repeated their experiments. Their torches were sent up with fearful accuracy from the shelter of a ravine, and each new blaze was accompanied with the demoniac yells of the assailants. The women continued to apply the water with parsimonious regard to economy—not a drop was wasted. The fiery arrows were still showered upon the devoted house, and at each discharge the warwhoop was redoubled. At last the water was exhausted, the last bucket was drained of the last drop! another discharge succeeded. The roof was blazing over their heads; and when despair was settling on the hitherto buoyant spirits of the little band, one of the females produced a gallon of milk. This was sufficient to protract destruction, but no security against a recurrence of imminent peril. There was a pause after the last blaze had been extinguished. The defenders were watching with acute sensibility every movement of the enemy, hoping that their fruitless efforts had discouraged them, and that in this they would win impunity. But when they began to respire freely with hope of safety, another discharge broke on their view; the fiery arrows hurled in the air, and the roof blazed again with fearful clearness! A mighty shout arose from a hundred wild and startling voices. Even Baptiste Roi himself, whose visage was the mirror of a hero's soul, looked aghast at the companions of his peril, until his wife, with an angel's smile upon her face, produced, from the urinal then replenished, the fluid that proved the salvation of the garrison. The fire was again extinguished. Then it was that the elastic spirits of the little party sent forth an answering shout of joy, and another of defiance, hurled with spirit in the face of savage exultation! Thrice did these women supply from the same fountain a fluid for the extinguishment of wicked hopes; when, at last, the baffled bloodhounds ran off, screaming a bitter howl of mingled resentment and despair. When the achievement above described was talked over, long after the war, some of the young gentlemen in St. Louis united in the expense of procuring a rifle, of fine finish, to present to Monsieur Louis Baptiste Roi, for his Spartan gallantry in the defence of Cote sans Dessein. He was flattered with the compliment intended, when it had been intimated that he was to receive it as soon as the gun could be completed. No expense was spared to render the transaction agreeable to the soldier, and the present suitable to the character and liberal sentiments of the donors. During the time employed in manufacturing the rifle, and in some of the conversations that the interesting subject produced, it was playfully suggested that the ladies deserved a present for the spirited share they had taken in the conflict, and some thoughtless young man remarked that a silver *urinal* should be presented to Madame Roi. This unfortunate remark was reported to her husband. When, therefore, the committee waited on him with a complimentary communication, and requested that he would accept an expensive rifle, one of

CREAMER's best, he explained his views something to the following effect:—

"Gentlemen—it is a *fuzee* of beautiful proportions—containing very *much* gold in de pan, and silver *on his breeches; he is a very gentleman gun for kill de game*. I *tank* you. I shall not take him. Some gentleman have considered to give *ma chere ami* one *urinal silvare!* I tell you, sare, I take care of *dem tings myself*—go to h—ll, anybody, by d——n sight! ! ! "

And with this expression of resentment for the freedom that the young man had unwittingly taken in discussion of the affair, he departed with manly indignation, in perfect keeping with his admirable character.

PART TWO

THE MIDDLE YEARS

*From River to Railroad. Cracker-barrel
Philosophers and Newspaper Comedians*

Robert Jones Burdette

Robert Jones Burdette (1844–1914) typifies the newspaper humorist who used to lend distinction and liveliness to newspapers in remote sections of the country before syndicated features, syndicated gags, and syndicated comics and even syndicated editorials tended to merge all our journals into a pale gray of mediocre unanimity. Burdette, born in Pennsylvania, spent his boyhood in Cumminsville, Ohio, and Peoria, Illinois. He worked for the Peoria REVIEW *until its suspension in 1874, then went to Burlington, Iowa, to join the staff of the* HAWKEYE. *His "Hawkeyetems" won him a national reputation as "The* BURLINGTON HAWKEYE *Man," and he eventually became a popular lecturer, his "Rise and Fall of the Mustache" being particularly relished by audiences. He moved East to facilitate his lecture business, then settled in California to end his days as a preacher. His books include* THE RISE AND FALL OF THE MUSTACHE AND OTHER HAWKEYE-TEMS *(1877), from which the selections herein were taken;* SCHOONERS THAT PASS IN THE DARK *(1894); and* CHIMES FROM A JESTER'S BELLS *(1897).*

The Demand for Light Labor

ONE MORNING, just as the rush of house cleaning days was beginning to abate, a robust tramp called at a house on Barnes Street, and besought the inmates to give him something to eat, averring that he had not tasted food for nine days.

"Why don't you go to work?" asked the lady to whom he proffered his petition.

"Work!" he ejaculated. "Work! And what have I been doing ever since the middle of May but hunting work? Who will give me work? When did I ever refuse work?"

"Well," said the woman, "I guess I can give you some employment. What can you do?"

"Anything!" he shouted, in a kind of delirious joy. "Anything that any man can do. I'm sick for something to fly at. Why, only yesterday I worked all day, carrying water in an old sieve from Flint River an' emptying it into the Mississippi, just because I was so tired of having nothing to do, that I had to work at something or I would have gone ravin' crazy. I'll do anything, from cleaning house to building a steamboat. Jest give me work, ma'am, an' you'll never hear me ask for bread agin."

The lady was pleased at the willingness and anxiety of this industrious man to do something, and she led him to the wood pile.

"Here," she said, "you can saw and split this wood, and if you are a good, industrious worker, I will find work for you to do, nearly all Winter."

"Well, now," said the tramp, while a look of disappointment stole over his face, "that's just my luck. Only three days ago I was pullin' a blind cow out of a well for a poor widow

49

woman who had nothin' in the world but that cow to support her, an' I spraint my right wrist till I hain't been able to lift a pound with it sinst. You kin jest put your hand on it now and feel it throb, it's so painful and inflamed. I could jest cry of disappointment, but it's a Bible fact, ma'am, that I couldn't lift that ax above my head ef I died fur it, and I'd jest as lief let you pull my arm out by the roots as to try to pull that saw through a lath. Jest set me at something I kin do, though, if you want to see the dust fly."

"Very well," said the lady, "then you can take these flower beds, which have been very much neglected, and weed them very carefully for me. You can do that with your well hand, but I want you to be very particular with them, and get them very clean, and not injure any of the plants, for they are all very choice and I am very proud of them."

The look of disappointment that had been chased away from the industrious man's face when he saw a prospect of something else to do, came back deeper than ever as the lady described the new job, and when she concluded, he had to remain quiet for a moment before he could control his emotion sufficiently to speak.

"If I ain't the most onfortnit man in Ameriky," he sighed. "I'm jest dyin' for work, crazy to get somethin' to do, and I'm blocked out of work at every turn, I jest love to work among flowers and dig in the ground, but I never dassent do it fur I'm jest blue ruin among the posies. Nobody ever cared to teach me anythin' about flowers and its a Gospel truth, ma'am, I can't tell a violet from a sunflower nor a red rose from a dog fennel. Last place I tried to git work at, woman of the house set me to work weedin' the garden, an' I worked about a couple of hours, monstrous glad to get work, now you bet, an' I pulled up every last livin' green thing in that yard. Hope I may die ef I didn't. Pulled up all the grass, every blade of it. Fact. Pulled up a vine wuth seventy-five dollars, that had roots reachin' cl'ar under the cellar and into the cistern, and I yanked 'em right up, every fiber of 'em. Woman was so heart broke when she come out and see the yard just as bare as the floor of a brick yard that they had to put her to bed. Bible's truth, they did, ma'am; and I had to work for that house three months for nothin' and find my board, to pay fur the damage I done. Hope to die ef I didn't. Jest gimme suthin' I kin do, I'll show you what work is, but I wouldn't dare to go foolin' around no flowers. You've got a kind heart ma'am, gimme some work; don't send a despairin' man away hungry for work."

"Well," the lady said, "you can beat my carpets for me. They have just been taken up, and you can beat them thoroughly, and by the time they are done, I will have something else ready for you."

The man made a gesture of despair and sat down on the ground, the picture of abject helplessness and disappointed aspirations.

"Look at me now," he exclaimed. "What is goin' to become o' me? Did you ever see a man so down on his luck like me? I tell you ma'am, you must give me somethin' I can do. I wouldn't no more dare for to tech them carpets than nothin' in the world. I'd tear 'em to pieces. I'm a awful hard hitter, an' the last time I beat any carpets was for a woman out at Creston, and I just welted them carpets into string and carpet rags. I couldn't help it. I can't hold in my strength. I'm too glad to get to work, that's the trouble with me, ma'am, it's a Bible fact. I'll beat them carpets if you say so, but I won't be responsible fur 'em; no makin me work for nothin' fur five or six weeks to pay fur tearin 'em into slits yer know. I'll go at 'em if you'll say the word and take the responsibility, but the fact is, I'm too hard a worker to go foolin' around carpets, that's just what I am."

The lady excused the energetic worker from going at the carpets, but was puzzled what to set him at. Finally she asked him what there was he would like to do and could do, with safety to himself and the work.

"Well, now," he said, "that's considerit in ye. That's real considerit, and I'll take a hold and do something that'll give ye the wuth of your money, and won't give me no chance to destroy nothin' by workin' too hard at it. If ye'll jest kindly fetch me out a rockin' chair, I'll set down in the shade and keep the cows from liftin' the latch of the front gate and gettin' into the yard. An' I'll do it well and only charge you reasonable for it, fur the fact is I'm so dead crazy fur work that it isn't big pay I want so much as a steady job."

And when he was rejected and sent forth, jobless and breakfastless, to wander up and down the cold, unfeeling world in search of work, he cast stones at the house and said, in dejected tones,

"There, now, that's just the way. They call us a bad lot, and say we're lazy and thieves, and won't work, when a feller is just crazy to work and nobody won't give him nary job that he can do. Won't work! Land alive, they won't give us work, an' when we want to an' try to, they won't let us work. There ain't a man in Ameriky that 'ud work as hard an' as stiddy as I would if they'd gimme a chance."

Selling the Heirloom

ONE AFTERNOON, about a week after the big Fourth of July, a hungry-looking man made his appearance down near the postoffice corner, carrying in his arms an old-fashioned clock, about four feet high, with some ghastly looking characters scrawled across the dial, like the photograph of a fire-cracker label with the delirium tremens. He set the clock down, and in loud tones called upon the passers-by to pause, as he was about to make a sacrifice that would break the heart of the oldest horologer living. He was going to sell that clock, he said. An old family heirloom, and a genuine curiosity of antiquity, which he would not ordinarily take thousands of dollars for, but which he sold now because he was out of work, penniless; and when his wife and children cried to him for bread, he could not say them nay when he had that in his possession that would, in any intelligent community, bring them food and plenty.

"Gentlemen," he said, "look at that clock. A relic of antiquity. One of the oldest Chinese clepsydras in the world. Bamboo case and sandal-wood running gear. Not an ounce of metal in its construction. Made in China by the eminent horologer Tchin Pitshoo, as near as can be ascertained, three hundred years after the flood. Worth a thousand dollars if it's worth a cent; but of course I don't expect to get half its value in these hard times. The inscription on the face is the characters of the purest Confucian Chinese, and the interpretation of them is, "Time flies and money is twelve per cent." Now what are you going to give me for that clock? Who will buy this clock, and present it to the Iowa Historical Society or the Burlington Library? How much? Start her up; send her ahead at something, gentlemen; there's a woman and five children that haven't had a bite to eat for two days, and can't get a crumb till the money for this clock is in my pocket. A marvelous time-piece; never lost—"

A man in brown overalls and a dirty face lounged up to the clock, and after scratching the case with a pin, to assure himself that it was really a genuine Chinese clepsydra, bid ten cents.

"Ten cents!" roared the man, rolling his eyes—"Heaven, hold back your lightnings! Don't strike him dead just yet! Give him time to repent. Ten cents to buy food for a starving woman and five children. Ten cents for a d——" He choked with emotion, and could not go on for a moment. "Ten cents! Why, that clock only has to be wound once a month, and it records every minute of time; tells just how long it will take you to get to the depot; tells when the train starts, and when the children are late to school. This clock, gentlemen, will tell when the oldest boy has played hookey and gone off fishing; it tells how late the hired girl's beau stays Sunday night, and it will register the exact minute of your oldest daughter's arrival and departure at and from the front gate after ten o'clock at night. Why, after you've had it six weeks you'll not take six hundred dollars for it. It runs fast all day and slow all night, giving a man fourteen hours' sleep in the Winter and sixteen hours' sleep in the Summer, without disturbing the accurate average of the day a minute. Ten cents for such a clock as that! Gentlemen, this is robbery; it's cold-blooded murder. At ten cents; at ten, at ten, atten, atten, attenat-tennit-tennit-tennet-tenatenatenaten a-a-ten cents only am I offered, twenty do I hear? At ten—"

An old rag man, after a critical examination of the marvel, bid fifteen cents, and was instantly regarded as a mortal enemy by the first bidder.

"Fifteen cents!" exclaimed the seller. "Gentlemen, knock me down and rob me of my clothes, strip me naked if you will, but don't plunder a gasping, starving woman and five weak, helpless babes. Don't rob the dying. Fifteen cents. Why, I've suffered more than three hundred dollars' worth of privation and sorrow and misery, rather than sell this clock at all. Fifteen cents. Why, you set that clock where the sun shines on it, and it will indicate a rain storm three days in advance, and will tell where the lightning is going to strike. Why, you could make millions by buying this clock to bet on. It will tell, just three weeks before election, who is going to beat. It's a credit to any household, and will run the whole family on tick. Fifteen cents! why, it won't pay for the shelf you stand it on. Fifteen cents for a clock that used to be

owned by an emperor! Fifteen cents. Oh, kill me dead. At
fifteen cents. Fifteen, fiftn, fiftn, fift, nfit, nfit, nfitnfitnfift,
ta-a-a-t fifteen cents for a clock that can't be duplicated this
side of the Yangste Kiang. At fifteen ce—thank you sir,
twenty cents I have; twenty cents to feed a starving family of
seven souls; twenty cents for a barefooted woman and five
ragged children that haven't tasted food since Monday morning; twenty cents, from a city of thirty thousand inhabitants,
for a starving family; there's Christian philanthropy for you.
Twenty cents from the commercial capital of Iowa, for a
clock that would be snapped up anywhere else in the world at
hundreds, merely for its antiquity; there's intelligent appreciation of the arts and culture for you. Gentlemen, I can't
stand this much longer, my heart is breaking. Twenty cents,
twenty cents, twenty, twent, twen, twen, twentwentwen, and
sold—a thousand-dollar clock, starving woman, dying children, heart-broken man, and all to the second-hand-store man
for twenty cents."

He took his money, a ragged shinplaster and two street car
nickels, and walked away with a dejected, heart-broken air.
He stopped in at a bakery with frosted windows and transient
doors, to buy bread for his starving wife and babes, and his
voice was husky with emotion as he said to the natty-looking
baker, whose diamond pin glittered over the walnut counter,

"Gimme a plain sour."

Finley Peter Dunne

Finley Peter Dunne (1867–1936) was born in Chicago, in the vicinity of Archey Road, a neighborhood later to be made famous by the sage utterances of Martin Dooley, Irish-American saloon keeper and philosopher. Mr. Dooley was created for the readers of the Chicago POST, *but he could not be confined to such narrow limits. His humorous dissection of spreadeagling politicians, sword-clanking military men, and other pompous frauds, originally poured into the attentive but not always assenting ear of Hennessy, eventually was enjoyed by a national audience. A number of "Mr. Dooley" volumes appeared. The following selections are from* MR. DOOLEY AT HIS BEST *(1943), edited by Elmer Ellis.*

Gold-seeking

"WELL sir," said Mr. Hennessy, "that Alaska sure is the gr-reat place. I thought 'twas nawthin' but an iceberg with a few seals roostin' on it, an' wan or two hundherd Ohio Politicians that can't be killed on account iv th' threaty iv Pawrs. But here they tell me that 'tis fairly smothered in goold. A man stubs his toe on th' ground, an' lifts th' top off iv a goold mine. Ye go to bed at night, an' ye wake up with goold fillin' in ye'er teeth."

"Yes," said Mr. Dooley, "Clancy's son was in here this mornin', an' he says a frind iv his wint to sleep out in th' open wan night an' whin he got up his pants assayed four ounces iv goold to th' pound, an' his whiskers panned out as much as thirty dollars net."

"If I was a young man an' not tied down here," said Mr. Hennessy, "I'd go there: I wud so."

"I wud not," said Mr. Dooley. "Whin I was a young man in th' ol' counthry, we heerd th' same story about all America. We used to set be th' tur-rf fire o' nights, kickin' our bare legs on th' flure an' wishin' we was in New York, where all ye had to do was to hold ye'er hat an' th' goold guineas'd dhrop into it. An' whin I got to be a man, I come over here with a ham and a bag iv oatmeal, as sure that I'd dhrive me own ca-ar as I was that me name was Martin Dooley. An' that was a cinch.

"But, faith, whin I'd been here a week, I seen that there was nawthin' but mud undher th' pavement—I larned that be means iv a pick-axe at tin shillin's th' day—an' that, though there was plenty iv goold, thim that had it were froze to it; an' I come west, still lookin' f'r mines. Th' on'y mine I

57

sthruck at Pittsburg was a hole f'r sewer pipe. I made it. Siven
shillin's th' day. Smaller thin New York, but th' livin' was
cheaper, with Mon'gahela rye at five a throw, put ye'er hand
around th' glass.

"I was still dreamin' goold, an' I wint down to Saint Looey.
Th' nearest I come to a fortune there was findin' a quarther
on th' sthreet as I leaned over th' dashboord iv a car to whack
th' off mule. Whin I got to Chicago, I looked around f'r the
goold mine. They was Injuns here thin. But they wasn't anny
mines I cud see. They was mud to be shovelled an' dhrays to
be dhruv an' beats to be walked. I chose th' dhray; f'r I was
niver cut out f'r a copper, an' I'd had me fill iv excavatin'.
An' I dhruv th' dhray till I wint into business.

"Me experyence with goold minin' is it's always in th' nex'
county. If I was to go to Alaska, they'd tell me iv th' finds in
Seeberya. So I think I'll stay here. I'm a silver man, annyhow;
an' I'm contint if I can see goold wanst a year, whin some
prominent citizen smiles over his newspaper. I'm thinkin' that
ivry man has a goold mine undher his own durestep or in his
neighbor's pocket at th' farthest."

"Well, annyhow," said Mr. Hennessy, "I'd like to kick up
th' sod, an' find a ton iv goold undher me fut."

"What wud ye do if ye found it?" demanded Mr. Dooley.

"I—I dinnaw," said Mr. Hennessy, whose dreaming had not
gone this far. Then, recovering himself, he exclaimed with
great enthusiasm, "I'd throw up me job an'—an' live like a
prince."

"I tell ye what ye'd do," said Mr. Dooley. "Ye'd come back
here an' sthrut up an' down th' sthreet with ye'er thumbs in
ye'er armpits; an' ye'd dhrink too much, an' ride in sthreet
ca-ars. Thin ye'd buy foldin' beds an' piannies, an' start a reel
estate office. Ye'd be fooled a good deal an' lose a lot iv ye'er
money, an' thin ye'd tighten up. Ye'd be in a cold fear night
an' day that ye'd lose ye'er fortune. Ye'd wake up in th' middle iv th' night, dhreamin' that ye was back at th' gas-house

with ye'er money gone. Ye'd be prisidint iv a charitable society. Ye'd have to wear ye'er shoes in th' house, an' ye'er
wife'd have ye around to rayciptions an' dances. Ye'd move
to Mitchigan Av-noo, an' ye'd hire a coachman that'd laugh
at ye. Ye'er boys'd be joods an' ashamed iv ye, an' ye'd support ye'er daughters' husbands. Ye'd rackrint ye'er tinants an'
lie about ye'er taxes. Ye'd go back to Ireland on a visit, an'
put on airs with ye'er cousin Mike. Ye'd be a mane, close-
fisted, onscrupulous ol' curmudgeion; an' whin ye'd die, it'd
take half ye'er fortune f'r rayqueems to put ye r-right. I don't
want ye iver to speak to me whin ye get rich, Hinnissy."

"I won't," said Mr. Hennessy.

Machinery

Mr. Dooley was reading from a paper. " 'We live,' " he says,
" 'in an age iv wondhers. Niver befure in th' histhry iv th'
wurruld has such pro-gress been made.'

"Thrue wurruds an' often spoken. Even in me time things
has changed. Whin I was a la-ad Long Jawn Wintworth cud
lean his elbows on th' highest buildin' in this town. It took two
months to come here fr'm Pittsburgh on a limited raft an'
a stage coach that run fr'm La Salle to Mrs. Murphy's hotel.
They wasn't anny tillygraft that I can raymimber an' th'
sthreet car was pulled be a mule an' dhruv be an engineer be
th' name iv Mulligan. We thought we was a pro-grissive people. Ye bet we did. But look at us today. I go be Casey's house
tonight an' there it is a fine storey-an'-a-half frame house
with Casey settin' on th' dure shtep dhrinkin' out iv a pail. I
go be Casey's house to-morrah an' it's a hole in th' groun'.

I rayturn to Casey's house on Thursdah an' it's a fifty-eight storey buildin' with a morgedge onto it an' they're thinkin' iv takin' it down an' replacin' it with a modhren sthructure. Th' shoes that Corrigan th' cobbler wanst wurruked on f'r a week, hammerin' away like a wood pecker, is now tossed out be th' dozens fr'm th' mouth iv a masheen. A cow goes lowin' softly in to Armours an' comes out gluc, beef, gela- tine, fertylizer, celooloid, joolry, sofy cushions, hair restorer, washin' sody, soap, lithrachoor an' bed springs so quick that while aft she's still cow, for'ard she may be annything fr'm buttons to Pannyma hats. I can go fr'm Chicago to New York in twinty hours, but I don't have to, thank th' Lord. Thirty years ago we thought 'twas marvelous to be able to tillygraft a man in Saint Joe an' get an answer that night. Now, be wireless tillygraft, ye can get an answer befur ye sind th' tillygram if they ain't careful. Me frind Macroni has done that. Be manes iv his wondher iv science a man on a ship in mid-ocean can sind a tillygram to a man on shore, if he has a confid'rate on board. That's all he needs. Be mechanical science an' thrust in th' op'rator annywan can set on th' shore iv Noofoundland an' chat with a frind in th' County Kerry. . . .

"What's it done f'r th' wurruld? says ye. It's done ivry- thing. It's give us fast ships an' an autymatic hist f'r th' hod, an' small flats an' a taste iv solder in th' peaches. If annybody says th' wurruld ain't betther off thin it was, tell him that a masheen has been invinted that makes honey out iv pethrolyum. If he asts ye why they ain't anny Shakesperes today, say: 'No, but we no longer make sausages be hand.' . . .

"I sometimes wondher whether pro-gress is anny more thin a kind iv a shift. It's like a merry-go-round. We get up a speckled wooden horse an' th' mechanical pianny plays a chune an' away we go, hollerin'. We think we're thravellin' like th' divvle but th' man that doesn't care about merry-go- rounds knows that we will come back where we were. We get out dizzy an' sick an' lay on th' grass an' gasp: 'Where am I? Is this th' meelin-yum?' An' he says: 'No, 'tis Ar-rchey Road.' Father Kelly says th' Agyptians done things we cudden't do an' th' Romans put up skyscrapers an' aven th' Chinks had tillyphones an' phonygrafts.

"I've been up to th' top iv th' very highest buildin' in town, Hinnissy, an' I wasn't anny nearer Hivin thin if I was in th' sthreet. Th' stars was as far away as iver. An' down beneath is a lot iv us runnin' an' lapin' an' jumpin' about, pushin' each other over, haulin' little sthrips iv ir'n to pile up in little buildin's that ar-re called skyscrapers but not be th' sky; wur-rukin' night an' day to make a masheen that'll carry us fr'm wan jack-rabbit colony to another an' yellin', 'Prog-gress!' Pro-gress, oho! I can see th' stars winkin' at each other an' sayin': 'Ain't they funny! Don't they think they're playin' hell!' . . ."

"What d'ye think iv th' man down in Pinnsylvanya who says th' Lord an' him is partners in a coal mine?" asked Mr. Hennessy, who wanted to change the subject.

"Has he divided th' profits?" asked Mr. Dooley.

Eugene Field

Eugene Field (1850–1895) was born in Saint Louis. His mother died when he was six and Eugene dallied with the higher learning at several universities before his father died in 1869, leaving him an eight-thousand-dollar legacy. He spent the money on a European trip, and returned to Missouri to take a reporting job on the Saint Joseph GAZETTE. *He later worked in a similar capacity in Saint Louis, Kansas City, and Denver, where his tenure on the* TRIBUNE *suggested a title for the sardonic* TRIBUNE PRIMER *(1882), from which the following items are taken. A year after this, his first book, was published, he moved to Chicago to write the "Sharps and Flats" column for the* MORNING NEWS, *called the* RECORD *after 1890. A merry wit, a practical joker, a judge of good liquor, a translator from Horace, and author of more than slightly bawdy verses, Eugene Field had many other strings to his bow than the one twanged so sweetly and lachrymosely in "Little Boy Blue."*

Excerpts from *The Tribune Primer*

THE COAL-HOD

Oh, how nice and Black the Coal-Hod is! Run, children, Run quick and put your Little Fat hands in it. Mercy me, your Hands are as Black as the Coal-Hod now! Hark! Mamma is Coming. She will spank you when she Finds your Hands so Dirty. Better go and Rub the Black Dirt off on the Wall Paper before she Comes.

THE FOOLISH ROACH

This is a Cock Roach. He is Big, Black, and Ugly. He is Crawling over the Pillow. Do not Say a Word, but lie still and Keep your Mouth open. He will Crawl into Your Mouth and You can Bite him in Two. This will Teach him to be more Discreet in Future.

THE BOTTLE

This is a Bottle. What is in the Bottle? Very bad Whiskey. It has been Sent to the Local Editor. He did not Buy it. If he had Bought it the Whiskey would have been Poorer than it is. Little Children, you Must never Drink Bad Whiskey.

THE UNFORTUNATE MOUSIE

Poor little Mouse! He got into the Flour Barrel and Made Himself dead. The Cook baked him in a Loaf of Bread, and here he lies on the Table cut in two by the Sharp bread Knife. But we will not Eat poor Mouse. We will eat the Bread, but we will take the Mousie and Put him in the Cistern.

THE GUN

This is a gun. Is the Gun loaded? Really, I do not know. Let us Find out. Put the Gun on the table, and you, Susie, blow down one barrel, while you, Charlie, blow down the other. Bang! Yes, it was loaded. Run quick, Jennie, and pick up Susie's head and Charlie's lower Jaw before the Nasty Blood gets over the New carpet.

THE APPLE

The Apple is in a Basket. A worm is in the Apple. It is a juicy little White Worm. Suppose you Eat the Apple, where will the Worm be?

THE DEEP WELL

The Well is very Dark and Deep. There is Nice Cool Water in the Well. If you Lean way Over the Side, maybe you will Fall in the Well and down in the Dear Water. We will Give you some Candy if you will Try. There is a Sweet Little Birdie in the bottom of the Well. Your Mamma would be Surprised to find you in the Well, would she not?

THE CATERPILLAR

The Caterpillar is Crawling along the Fence. He has pretty Fur all over his Back, and he Walks by Wrinkling up his Skin. He is Full of Nice yellow Custard. Perhaps you had better take him into the house, where it is warm, and Mash him on the Wall Paper with Sister Lulu's Album. Then the Wall Paper will Look as if a Red Headed Girl had been leaning Against it.

OUR ESTEEMED CONTEMPORARY

This Awkward sheet is our Esteemed Contemporary. It is Run by an Unhung Felon. We would not Give him a Glass of Water to Save his life, but we would Take a Beer with him if we were Properly Approached. Our esteemed Contemporary has no Circulation and its influence is Correspondingly Small. It cuts Advertising Rates and is So Mean it would Skin a Skunk to Save a Scent. If we had Our Way, we would

Suspend our Esteemed Contemporary and Put its Editors and Reporters in Jail where they belong.

THE LOBSTER

This is not a Big Spider. It is a Lobster. He is Green now, but when he Gets into Hot Water he will look Red and Feel Blue. The Lobster carries his teeth on his Arm. Pat him on the Teeth. Maybe the Teeth will Kind of Take to You.

THE INK BOTTLE

Can you See the Ink Bottle on the Table? It is Full of Nice Black Ink. If you Want to, you can Pour the Ink out on the Carpet. It makes the Carpet look Black, too, does it not? Sit down on the Carpet and Put both of your Little Paddies in the Ink. See, your Fingers are Covered with the Ink. What a Nice picture you can Make on the Wall Paper now, Make a Picture of a Big Man and a Little Girl. Do you want to Put Some Ink on the Lace Curtain? Very well, Put it on Carefully, for you Should never Waste the Ink or anything else. This will be Quite a Surprise to Mamma when she Comes in.

THE CONCENTRATED LYE

What a Pretty Can it is. What do you Suppose is in the Can? Open it and see. Goodness me, it is Concentrated Lye! How Nice! Are you not Glad? Let us eat it. Taste it and See how Warm it is. If you will Eat it you will not Want anything More to Eat For a Long Time.

THE BLIND MAN

The old Man is Blind and cannot See. He holds his Hat in his Hand and there is a Dime in the Hat. Go up quietly and Take the Dime out of the Hat. The Man cannot See you. Next Sunday you can put the Dime in the Sabbath School box and the Teacher will Praise you. Your Papa will put some Money in the Contribution box, too. He will put More in than you do. But his Opportunities for Robbing are better than yours.

John Hay

John Hay (1838–1905) was born in Salem, Indiana, and graduated from Brown University in 1858. While studying law in Springfield, Illinois, he met Abraham Lincoln, who took him along to Washington as a member of the White House secretarial staff. It was the beginning of a long governmental and diplomatic career culminating in Hay's presence in the cabinets of both William McKinley and Theodore Roosevelt as Secretary of State. In his PIKE COUNTY BALLADS *(1871), from which "Banty Tim" is selected, Hay employed the Pike County dialect and the concept of the Pike County man, rude and unlettered but with definite ideas of his own, presented by Bret Harte in his* EAST AND WEST POEMS, *also published in 1871. Though there are Pike Counties in Missouri, Illinois, and Arkansas, the literary territory of Pike is rather vague as to limits, the Pike County man becoming a certain Midwestern type rather than being by strict necessity an actual resident of any of the three counties bearing the name. Many Pike County men made their way to the California gold fields.*

Banty Tim

Remarks of Sergeant Tilmon Joy to the White Man's Committee of Spunky Point, Illinois

I reckon I git your drift, gents,—
    You 'low the boy sha'n't stay;
This is a white man's country;
    You're Dimocrats, you say;
And whereas, and seein', and wherefore,
    The time bein' all out o' j'int,
The nigger has got to mosey
    From the limits o' Spunky P'int!

Le's reason the thing a minute:
    I'm an old-fashioned Dimocrat too,
Though I laid my politics out o' the way
    For to keep till the war was through.
But I come back here, allowin'
    To vote as I used to do,
Though it gravels me like the devil to train
    Along o' sich fools as you.

Now dog my cats ef I kin see,
    In all the light of the day,
What you've got to do with the question
    Ef Tim shill go or stay.
And furder than that I give notice,
    Ef one of you tetches the boy,
He kin check his trunks to a warmer clime
    Than he'll find in Illanoy.

Why, blame your hearts, jest hear me!
    You know that ungodly day
When our left struck Vicksburg Heights, how ripped
    And torn and tattered we lay.

When the rest retreated I stayed behind,
  Fur reasons sufficient to me,—
With a rib caved in, and a leg on a strike,
  I sprawled on that cursed glacee.

Lord! how the hot sun went for us,
  And br'iled and blistered and burned!
How the Rebel bullets whizzed round us
  When a cuss in his death-grip turned!
Till along toward dusk I seen a thing
  I couldn't believe for a spell:
That nigger—that Tim—was a-crawlin' to me
  Through that fire-proof, gilt-edged hell!

The Rebels seen him as quick as me,
  And the bullets buzzed like bees;
But he jumped for me, and shouldered me,
  Though a shot brought him once to his knees;
But he staggered up, and packed me off,
  With a dozen stumbles and falls,
Till safe in our lines he drapped us both,
  His black hide riddled with balls.

So, my gentle gazelles, thar's my answer,
  And here stays Banty Tim:
He trumped Death's ace for me that day,
  And I'm not goin' back on him!
You may rezoloot till the cows come home,
  But ef one of you tetches the boy
He'll wrastle his hash to-night in hell,
  Or my name's not Tilmon Joy.

E. W. Howe

Edgar Watson Howe (1853–1937), born in Indiana, traveled as a child with his parents via covered wagon to Missouri. Settling later in Kansas, he edited and owned the Atchison GLOBE *from 1877 to 1911, when he turned the paper over to his sons in order to devote his attention to* E. W. HOWE'S MONTHLY, *a journal of personal opinion which he conducted until his death. His* THE STORY OF A COUNTRY TOWN *(1883), printed at his own expense, antedated Sinclair Lewis'* MAIN STREET *in its caustic revelation of the spiritual meanness and cultural paucity of the Midwestern small town. Howe was familiarly known as "The Sage of Potato Hill."* PLAIN PEOPLE *(1929) is his autobiography. "Our First Circus" is reprinted from* HER FIFTH MARRIAGE AND OTHER STORIES *(1928).*

Our First Circus

WHEN I was a boy, living on a farm, my father returned from the country town where he had been several days, and announced that he had bought the weekly paper printed there. I had no idea what a printing office was like, but soon had opportunity to find out, for the next morning I was taken to town, and turned over to the foreman, who was told to make a printer of me.

The man who taught me the trade was an old-fashioned printer named Martin, who had a bed in the office, and who wrote stories for the New York *Mercury*, played the guitar, sang ballads, and took part in amateur theatricals.

My brother Jim worked with me, and we worshipped Mr. Martin. He gave us little suppers in the office at night, when we had rare things to eat we had heard of, but never hoped to taste; including cove oysters with little round crackers, instead of the big square kind. At the conclusion of these suppers, Mr. Martin told us stories. Usually we became so sleepy that he was compelled to drag us into his bed, and spend the night himself on a pallet on the floor.

Among other things this wonderful man told us about was the circus; he had seen one, although there had never been one in the town where we lived. But one day, after Mr. Martin had gone away for good, and Jim and I were doing the mechanical work on the paper with the assistance of the editor, the advance agent of a circus came to town in a wagon; in those days circuses traveled overland, there being few railroads, and none at all in our section.

We were tremendously excited, as Mr. Martin had said printers always received free tickets. Much to our dismay, however, father had a quarrel with the agent. Father was a preacher, and said circuses were immoral; therefore no picture of an elephant should appear in his paper. What was more, he said he would use his influence to keep people away from the circus man's demoralizing exhibition.

It was a terrible blow, but father kept his word: he attacked the circus with as much violence as he attacked the institution of slavery, a question then prominent. So Jim and I looked at the bills, and wondered if we should be able to see the show.

When circus day arrived, father told us we were to work all day, and not see the crowds or the parade. The attack of the editor on the circus did not do it any harm; indeed, early on the morning of circus day, the town was crowded with country people from many miles around. And every farmer who came into the printing office to pay his subscription made jokes with the editor, who was somewhat surly because his good advice had not been taken. It was the town's first circus, and we soon discovered that it was also the town's greatest crowd. Teams began arriving in the vacant lot back of the printing office at an early hour; the horses were hurriedly unhitched, and the owners went away to see and mingle in the excitement. In the front office the editor was having an uncomfortable time with farmers who thought it a great joke on the paper that its abuse of the circus had brought an enormous crowd.

While the editor was arguing angrily with a number of men about the iniquity of the circus, and the men were laughing merrily, I told Jim I intended to make a sneak, and see the circus, if I died for it. Jim was a good boy, and warned me not to, but when he saw I was determined, he accompanied me in the wild run we made for liberty.

When we reached the street, we found the circus had not yet arrived, so we set out with a number of other boys to meet it. We knew it was to come in on The Falls road; every boy knew that, somehow, so we traveled that way until we

became suspicious, and turned back. Reaching town, tired
and hungry, we found the circus had arrived by another road,
and that the parade, and the afternoon performance, were
over.

We were hungry, but didn't dare go home, so we hunted
up a woman we had known in the country, and she gave us
something to eat. Then we started out to borrow money with
which to attend the evening performance. But we didn't make
any progress, so when the band struck up for the night show,
we decided to crawl under the tent. It seemed easy, and I was
about in when a man caught me by the heels, and pulled me
out. While the circus man was cuffing me, I saw another circus
man cuffing Jim, about twenty feet away; he had also failed.

Then we met a man named McCurry, a member of my
father's church; a good man who did not intend to witness the
wicked performance, but who was nevertheless walking
around outside, to see the crowds, and hear the band. We
appealed to him; we said we had run off, and would get a
whipping, but that it would be terrible to get a beating, and
not see the performance.

Mr. McCurry looked around, to see no one was watching,
and said:

"Well, I don't want your father to know it, but I'll loan you
the money."

A few minutes later we were on the inside of the palace of
pleasure, whistling with the other boys, and demanding that
the circus men appear, for the performance had not yet commenced. But when it did begin, it was all we expected, and
more. It was Miles Orton's circus, I remember, and the clown
was a merry fellow called Doctor Gilkerson.

Delight succeeded delight for an hour, when the proceed-
ings were interrupted by a drunken man. We didn't know
him; there was only one drunkard, Fin Wilkerson, in our
neighborhood. We supposed the new drunkard had wandered
into town from some other neighborhood, owing to the cir-

cus, and were in sympathy with the ring master, who attempted to throw the man out. But the man wouldn't be thrown out, and seemed determined to make trouble. He said he had known the clown, Doctor Gilkerson, when they were boys, and wanted to talk to him.

About this time, Doctor Gilkerson came in, and said he didn't know the dissipated man. But the man insisted, and finally they patched up an acquaintance. We were disposed at first to be annoyed by the interruption of the stranger, but when Doctor Gilkerson shook hands with him, and threw him head over heels, we roared with laughter.

It seemed Doctor Gilkerson had known the fellow very well; they had gone to school together as boys, somewhere, and after they had talked awhile, Doctor Gilkerson asked:

"By-the-way, what has become of old Howe, who used to teach school down there?"

"Why," replied the drunken man, "don't you know? He's running a newspaper about the size of a postage stamp here, and has become so good that he won't print circus advertisements."

It was the first joke on a citizen ever heard in a show in the town, and the people almost suffocated with merriment, they were so pleased. The show was brought to a standstill by the merriment of the people over the joke on the editor, and Jim and I were amused, too; we were getting something to offset the whipping we expected later.

At last the people were satisfied with the joke on the editor, and we thought the performance would be resumed. But the clown's friend still insisted on being sociable with the show people, and there were cries of "Put him out!" But the man wouldn't go out, and wanted to ride a horse that stood in the ring. I had been thinking I could ride it, as the horse had a big flat pad on its back. Doctor Gilkerson was in favor of letting the intruder ride, but the ring master said he would kill himself.

"All right," said the merry man, "let him kill himself. That's a good way to get rid of him."

It was finally agreed to let the stranger try, and away went the horse and the band, with the drunken man on the horse's back. It was tremendously exciting; the man reeled and staggered a good deal, and the people in the audience were mightily pleased that a man from the country, and drunk at that, could do it.

Then the man managed to stand on his feet, and take off his coat. This was exciting; but a dreadful thing happened at that time: the man being intoxicated, and not knowing what he was doing, began taking off his pants! Much to my surprise, the circus men did not stop him, and before we all died of mortification, the man got his pants off, and turned out to be a circus rider in tights.

We felt mighty cheap when we realized we had been beautifully fooled, but we enjoyed that, too, along with the joke on the editor, and everybody had a good time.

But at last the show was over, and Jim and I hung around an hour or more, dreading to go home; we knew what was coming to us. There was a sideshow, and the barker was busy while the main tent was being torn down. I wanted to see the sideshow, but had no money, and finally thought of a scheme: I had heard that if a printer displayed his rule to the doorkeeper of a show, the doorkeeper would let him in free. I tried it, and the doorkeeper in an amused way, looked at me, laughed, and said:

"Well, it's all right! Go on in!"

Probably he had been a printer's devil himself; anyway, he let me in. He tried to stop Jim, who hadn't his rule with him, but I said: "That's all right; he has one, but left it at home."

"Give me your honor as a gentleman that he is entitled to the courtesies of the profession," the man said, "and I'll pass him."

I suppose he was making game of me, but I didn't care, and gave him the assurance.

So Jim got in free, too, and I felt mighty important. The sideshow didn't amount to much; it was nothing more than a lot of stereopticon views of the war, then going on, and we were soon confronted with the necessity of going home, and taking our whipping. On the way, I got into a row with a boy belonging to the circus, and he pushed me, and I pushed as hard as he did, and said if he wanted any more, to come on. Jim thought I was a tremendous dare devil. Jim was older than I, but he always followed me everywhere; had I stirred up a fight with the circus men, he would have followed me and done the best he could, but he couldn't have done much, as he was always a weakly boy.

The last wagon drove away about two o'clock in the morning, and then there was nothing left for us but to go home. So we sneaked in at the kitchen door; we imagined mother would leave that open for us, and found she had. After entering the kitchen, there was a door leading into the sitting room, and then a stairway leading up to our room. We had gone around the house, and noted a light in the sitting room; that's where we expected trouble. After entering the kitchen, we tried the knob of the sitting room door, and attempted to turn it quietly. Ever notice how a door knob squeaks when you try to turn it quietly? That door knob squeaked, and when we turned it, opened the door, and went into the sitting room, there sat the editor, waiting for us. I went in first, and Jim sneaked in behind me.

"Well," father said, "you've been to the circus?"

There was no use trying to deceive him; I was willing to try, but knew it was impossible, so I replied, meekly:

"Yes, sir."

He thought awhile, as though trying to decide just how hard he would whip us, and finally inquired:

"How did you like it?"

I was too wise a boy to be enthusiastic, under the circumstances, so I replied:

"O, I didn't think it amounted to much." (I did, though; it was the very best show I ever saw in my life.)

For some reason the editor didn't grab us, and begin the punishment we expected, and he had no switch.

"Did they say anything about me?" he asked.

I hadn't thought of that before, but evidently he had been expecting an attack. I repeated what the clown had said, making it as mild as possible.

"How did the people take it?" he asked again.

Then I had an idea so I replied with animation:

"Well, sir, you should have been there, and seen how the people took it! Bill Hillman, the sheriff, walked down to the ring, and shook his fist at the clown, and said the people wouldn't stand for low circus people abusing a prominent man like you. And Mr. Cuddy, the banker, he walked down to the ring, too, and told the circus men what he thought of them. He said you were one of the most useful men in this town, and that people looked up to you, and that they didn't want to hear any more of that."

The editor was evidently pleased; still he delayed the whipping.

"Well," he said at last, after thinking a while, "hurry up to bed. We've a big day's work ahead of us tomorrow."

When we got into bed, we chuckled softly, and Jim nudged me with his elbow, and said I was certainly the boldest, wisest boy the country ever produced.

And we paid back Mr. McCurry next day, with ducks we stole from mother, and later we fixed it all right with her: she never was hard on us as father was. When we told her how we fooled father, she said it was a shame, but we caught her laughing about it afterwards.

T. A. McNeal

Thomas Allen McNeal (1853–1942) was born on a farm near Iberia, Ohio, and was educated at Oberlin College. He came to Kansas in 1879, settling at Medicine Lodge where he began a long newspaper career, interrupted by several years spent as a lawyer. In 1894 he moved to Topeka, where he remained for the rest of his life. He founded the KANSAS BREEZE, *but sold it after two years to Arthur Capper, then owner of the* NORTH TOPEKA MAIL. *It was the beginning of a relationship with Capper and his publications that endured until McNeal's death. Aside from* TOM MCNEAL'S FABLES *(1900), from which the following selections are reprinted, he wrote* WHEN KANSAS WAS YOUNG *(1922) and* STORIES BY TRUTHFUL JAMES *(1925).*

Fables

DISCRETION IS NECESSARY TO SUCCESS

IN A certain hotel a large colony of bugs had taken possession of the beds, where they lay in wait for the weary travelers. On one occasion a large, fat traveling-man registered and called for a room. And the bug whose business it was to watch the register immediately carried the news to the rest of the tribe that there was extra good picking in sight. Pleased with the prospect, the bugs had a hilarious time for a little while and then waited impatiently for the fat traveler to appear. When he finally came to his room he turned down the bed-covers, and saw there a dozen bugs or such a matter sitting on the sheet waiting to get in their work. But instead of getting into bed as the bugs had expected, the fat traveler swore a loud and vociferous swear, and then, taking a cover off the bed, he shook it, wrapped it about his person, and lay down to sleep on the floor. And when the leader of the bugs saw that the prey had escaped, he turned loose on the other bugs as follows: "If you infernal fools had lain low and hidden out until that man had got to bed, we might all have had a feed. You have ruined the whole business by being too greedy and too previous."

MORAL.—To work a graft with success requires some discretion.

THE CONCEITED DONKEY

It chanced that a horse and a donkey were being shipped to market in the same car, and as they were passing through a certain town the donkey, who was in love with his voice, remarked to the horse that while they were waiting for the trainmen to do some switching he would entertain the people

79

with a few vocal selections from his repertoire. Then after inflating his lungs, he turned loose with a wild, weird bray that could be heard for a mile. And when this had gone on for about two minutes the brakeman appeared on the scene with a large elm club and biffed the donkey several times. When the brakeman had finally gone away, the donkey turned to the horse for sympathy, but that wise animal simply said: "If you had kept your fool mouth shut you would not only have saved yourself this beating, but the people generally around this neighborhood would not have known that I had an ass for a companion."

MORAL.—Many a chump has gotten into trouble by working his mouth when there was no occasion for doing so.

THE LIGHTNING-BUG WHO THOUGHT HE WAS THE WHOLE THING

A lightning-bug who had fallen into the error of supposing that he was the whole thing, suspended his light for a moment while he engaged in conversation with a pincher-bug that was passing by. At that moment there was some hitch in the works at the electric-light plant, and the whole city was suddenly in darkness. And the lightning-bug, thinking that it all came about because he shut off his glow, pompously remarked: "Excuse my mentioning it, but you observe, I suppose, what shape this town would be in if I were to move out of it."

MORAL.—There is a vast difference between the real value of many people and the estimate they place on themselves.

THE FICE AND THE MOON

A scrawny, stub-tailed fice, seeing the rising moon, began to bark a furious criticism of the queen of night; but the moon continued to sail right along as if nothing had happened. Finally the fice's mother, who had acquired some wisdom from experience, called the pup into the woodshed where they slept, and said: "My son, your yelping doesn't change the course of the moon any, but if you had kept your fool mouth shut you wouldn't have ruined the reputation of the family for common-sense."

MORAL.—Many a fool might have a fair reputation for wisdom if his mouth were only put in the hands of a receiver.

THE KISSING BUG AND THE WAX FIGURE

A kissing-bug, which was flitting along the street of a town, noticed what he supposed was a handsome pink-cheeked maiden standing in front of a dry-goods store, and said to himself: "There is a pair of lips for you. I will make those other fool bugs green with envy when I tell them what a soft snap I struck in the way of osculation." But when the kissing-bug lit on the lips of the figure and began to work his kissing apparatus, he was surprised to find the supposed female exhibited no interest in the performance, and the only effect was to batter and bruise his mug until he wasn't able to attend to business for a week. When he returned home and told his troubles to his parent, the old bug, who had some experience with wax figures himself, said, as he gave his descendant the bug-laugh: "My son, the inexperienced fool judges from appearances, but after awhile you will learn that you can't always bank on cherry lips and a beautiful complexion."

THE RHINOCEROS AND THE MOSQUITOES

A rhinoceros, who was traveling through Indiana in connection with an aggregation of wild beasts and other living wonders, was resting in his cage after the heat and burdens of the day, when a flock of mosquitoes from the Wabash bottoms flew that way, looking for business and amusement combined. And the leader of the flock, who carried a bill as long as the tine of a carving-fork, seeing the rhinoceros, said to its companions, "We will just light down on this lubberly beast and give him a taste of high life on the Wabash." The rhinoceros said not a word, but smiled as he used to smile in his native jungle when he saw a good thing in prospect, and rubbed his nose horn on the side of the cage as the mosquitoes tackled him. And when they had finally given up the thing as a bad job and flown away, each with a broken bill, the beast gave a grunt of satisfaction and remarked; "I wonder if there are any more chumps around here who would like to go up against this hide of mine? If there are any others who would like to have some fun with me, I am open for engagements."

MORAL.—The thick-skinned individual has considerable advantage in this world.

THE TOUGH SPRING CHICKEN

A boarder in a restaurant, who had ordered spring chicken, set up a roar when the piece of cooked fowl was set before him, saying to the waiter: "What do you mean by trying to palm this off on me for spring chicken? Why, I couldn't cut it with an ax." "Calm yourself, my excited friend," said the undisturbed waiter, as he carelessly picked a cockroach out of the milk pitcher; "that is spring chicken all right enough, just as represented, but it was raised in Kentucky, where toughness is no indication of age."

THE TIGER AND THE CAT

A house-cat, having heard that it belonged to the same family as the tiger, became puffed up on account of the supposed relationship, and went around the neighborhood blowing about his connection with royalty. Shortly afterward the swell-headed cat, seeing a royal Bengal tiger in the zoo, approached the lord of the jungle and with a bland smile remarked: "I am one of your near relatives, and thought I would step up and call on you." "Is that a fact?" asked the tiger, with a slight curl of the lip. "Well, come here, cousin, and allow me to embrace you." Then the fool cat, flattered by this reception, came up within reach of the tiger, who caught it between his jaws and squeezed the life out of it before a person of active speech could say Jack Robinson. And a companion, who had heard the boasting cat talk, said, as it viewed the dead feline lying in the bottom of the tiger's cage: "It occurs to me that I would rather be just a common Thomas-cat alive, and be able to sit on the back-yard fence and yowl, than the dead relative of a royal Bengal tiger."

THE CRICKET AND THE OPERA SINGER

A cricket who believed it could sing managed to get located in an opera-house where a noted prima donna had an engagement. And as the prima donna began to trill, the cricket began to chirp. When the noted trilleress had finished her trill, the crowd broke out in a storm of applause which lasted for several minutes. When finally the applause had subsided, the cricket turned to a companion, and, rubbing its feet together with great satisfaction, said: "There are a lot of ducks around here who think I can't sing, but I suppose you noticed the way I brought down that house."

MORAL.—Sometimes an individual supposes he is cutting a large amount of congealed moisture, when as a matter of fact nobody is paying any attention to him.

THE ANT AND THE ROBIN

A busy ant, who frequently lectured her offspring on the necessity of being up betimes in the morning, started off at the first streak of dawn in search of grub. But as the busy ant was hiking out in the direction of some food, she saw in the distance a robin, who was also out on a grub-hunting expedition. It flew down and took the busy ant in and carried it away to its nest. Then one of the young ants, who looked out of the front door of the ant-hill in time to see his mother carried away in the robin's bill, said to his brethren and sisters: "If mother had been content to lie abed a spell and take it easy, she wouldn't have been fed to one of those blamed young robins this morning."

Julia A. Moore

Julia A. Moore (1847–1920), a farm wife in Michigan, delighted incredulous newspaper critics when the inspiredly terrible dithyrambs of her THE SWEET SINGER OF MICHIGAN SALUTES THE PUBLIC *(1876) came to their attention. Taste for burlesque was strong and Julia was a godsend. Bill Nye had a lot of sport with her; Mark Twain is known to have been indebted to her for suggestions as to the obituary verses he uses in* TOM SAWYER *and* HUCKLEBERRY FINN. *Thanks to Walter Blair, who resurrected Julia with a fine flourish by publishing in 1929 a garland of her verses adorned by an appreciative introduction, she is still beguiling and instructing writers. Ogden Nash acknowledges that his concept of odd rhymes is directly descended from the "Sweet Singer," who blandly yoked "drachm" with "slang." The "Sweet Singer" at first was transported at what she took to be the most extravagant praise of her poetic genius, but by the time her second book was published, she began to smell a rat, and in this effort, entitled* A FEW CHOICE WORDS TO THE PUBLIC, WITH NEW AND ORIGINAL POEMS *(1878), she observed in a defensive appendix:*

"I wrote SOME *of those poems when quite young, and I had them published just as they were written. I wished for something different from all literary work, something to catch the public eye, and I think I have it in that little book. Its rare combination has caused a great many literary people to laugh at my ignorance, yet at the* SAME *time, some of them could not help thinking that the sentiments were good, although so rarely constructed in poetry."*

Little Libbie

One more little spirit to Heaven has flown
  To dwell in that mansion above,
Where dear little angels, together roam,
  In God's everlasting love.

One little flower has withered and died,
  A bud nearly ready to bloom,
Its life on earth is marked with pride;
  Oh, sad it should die so soon.

Sweet little Libbie, that precious flower
  Was a pride in her parents' home,
They miss their little girl *every* hour,
  Those friends that are left to mourn.

Her sweet silvery voice no more is heard
  In the home where she once roamed;
Her place is *vacant* around the hearth,
  Where her friends are mourning lone.

They are mourning the loss of a little girl,
  With black eyes and auburn hair,
She was a treasure to them in this world,
  This beautiful child so fair.

One morning in April a short time ago,
  Libbie was active and gay;
Her Saviour called her, she had to go,
  Ere the close of that pleasant day.

While eating dinner, this dear little child
  Was choked on a piece of beef.

Doctors came, tried their skill awhile,
  But none could give relief.

She was ten years of age, I am told,
  And in school stood very high.
Her little form now the earth enfolds,
  In her embrace it must ever lie.

Her friends and schoolmates will not forget
  Little Libbie that is no more;
She is waiting on the shining step
  To welcome friends home once more.

The Southern Scourge

The yellow fever was raging,
  Down in the sunny South;
And in many of the cities,
  There was death in every house.
This plague a war was raging,
  With the lives of people there;
The young and old were stricken down,
  And lay in sad despair.

No comfort, all was misery
  In many a southern home.
Where once was peace and quietness,
  Now in distress are thrown;
For death the house has visited,
  And caused the inmates to mourn
The loss of some dear loving friend,
  That on earth no more shall roam.

Some people in delirium,
  Have wandered from their home;
Have wandered to a vacant house,
  And there have died alone,
With no kind friend to care for them,
  Or close their dying eyes.
Oh, God! in horrid misery
  Hundreds of people died.

There were many whole families
  Taken down sick in a day;
With no one to care for them,
  In death they passed away.
Their spirits rose to God above,
  Where sickness is no more,
Where peace and comfort ever reign,
  On Heaven's blissful shore.

There is many a southern city
  To-day is filled with woe,
And many of the inhabitants
  Have wandered to and fro
To nurse the sick and dying—
  The dead for the grave prepare.
They tried to do their duty,
  With hearts filled with despair.

The Howard Association
  Have been doing all they can,
To keep the "plague" from raging
  Throughout the southern land;
They nursed the sick, they fed the poor,
  They work both night and day,
This brave band in the southern scourge
  Heroic courage display.

This noble band of charity
  Have went from house to house,

To ease the sad misery of
  The sufferers at the south;
Sad scenes of death and suffering
  Each day they must endure,
As in the daily rounds they went
  Among the afflicted poor.

The noble northern people
  Have helped them all they can,
In money, food and clothing
  Which they had at their command;
There is many a southern person
  That will bless this Howard band,
For their noble deeds of charity
  To the sufferers of their land.

Grand Rapids Cricket Club

In Grand Rapids is a handsome club,
  Of men that cricket play,
As fine a set of skillful men
  That can their skill display.
They are champions of the West,
  They think they are quite fine,
They've won a hundred honors well;
  It is their most cunning design.

Brave Kelso, he's considered great,
  Chief of the club he is found;
Great crowds he draws to see him bowl
  The ball upon the ground.
And Mr. Follet is very brave,
  A lighter player than the rest,
He got struck severe at the fair ground
  For which he took a rest.

When Mr. Dennis does well play,
  His courage is full great
And accidents to him occur,
  But not much, though, of late.
This ball play is a dangerous game,
  Brave knights to play it though.
Those boys would be the nation's pride,
  If they to war would go.

From Milwaukee their club did come,
  With thoughts of skill at play,
But beat they was, and then went home—
  Had nothing more to say.
Grand Rapids club that cricket play,
  Will soon be known afar,
Much prouder do the members stand,
  Like many a noble star.

Sketch of Lord Byron's Life

"Lord Byron" was an Englishman,
  A poet I believe,
His first works in old England
  Was poorly received.
Perhaps it was "Lord Byron's" fault
  And perhaps it was not.
His life was full of misfortunes,
  Ah, strange was his lot.

The character of "Lord Byron"
  Was of a low degree,
Caused by his reckless conduct,
  And bad company.

He sprung from an ancient house,
  Noble, but poor, indeed.
His career on earth, was marred
  By his own misdeeds.

Generous and tender hearted,
  Affectionate by extreme,
In temper he was wayward,
  A poor "Lord" without means;
Ah, he was a handsome fellow
  With great poetic skill,
His great intellectual powers
  He could use at his will.

He was a sad child of nature,
  Of fortune and of fame;
Also sad child to society,
  For nothing did he gain
But slander and ridicule,
  Throughout his native land.
Thus the "poet of the passions,"
  Lived, unappreciated, man.

Yet at the age of 24,
  "Lord Byron" then had gained
The highest, highest pinacle
  Of literary fame.
Ah, he had such violent passions
  They was beyond his control,
Yet the public with its justice,
  Sometimes would him extol.

Sometimes again "Lord Byron"
  Was censured by the press,
Such obloquy, he could not endure,
  So he done what was the best.
He left his native country,
  This great unhappy man;

The only wish he had, " 'tis said,"
    He might die, sword in hand.

He had joined the Grecian Army;
    This man of delicate frame;
And there he died in a distant land,
    And left on earth his fame.
"Lord Byron's" age was 36 years,
    Then closed the sad career,
Of the most celebrated "Englishman"
    Of the nineteenth century.

Petroleum V. Nasby

David Ross Locke (1833–1888), who wrote in the character of "Petroleum V. Nasby," a semi-illiterate, unscrupulous and viciously bigoted friend of the slavocracy during the Civil War, was born in New York State, but wandered west to Ohio as a journeyman printer. As was often the case, he progressed from printing to writing and began to gain recognition for his PETROLEUM V. NASBY *letters in the* FINDLAY JEFFERSONIAN. *Later Locke bought an interest in the Toledo* BLADE *and became its editor, so Nasby went along. Lincoln was fond of the rambunctious Copperhead, regarding him as being of tremendous left-handed assistance to the Union cause. Father Abraham, sometimes to the impatience of its members, read to his cabinet choice sayings of Nasby, using them to illuminate discussions. "The Fall of St. Vallandigum," printed here, refers to the 1863 Ohio election for governor. C. L. Vallandigham, a Copperhead, is opposed by John Brough, an old-line Democrat who is a Union candidate. The piece expresses Nasby's consternation upon hearing that Brough is winning the election. Vallandigham, venerated by Nasby as "St. Vallandigum," is the patron saint of his church.*

The Fall of St. Vallandigum

CHURCH UV ST. VALLANDIGUM,
October the 14th 1863.

I'M SAD—and sick. My hed is fountain uv teers, and mine eyes distil dilootid corn-joose. My hart is lead, and my sole is pot-bellied with greef. My lims ake with woe, my manly form is bowd, and my venrable lox is turned white. O, Vallandigum, thou hast gone to the grave, and in the same toom is berrid all my hopes. Adoo, vane world, adoo! I'll be a nunnery.

The fate uv the peeple uv Ohio is seeld. Vallandigum is not only a exile far away, but there is a cheerful prospek, wich is daily improvin, uv his continnerin in the exile biznis fer an indeffynit period uv time. A tyrannikle President hez taken our old habis corpusses from us, and persistently refuses to furnish us new wuns; and the people, hevin acquiest by their votes, we lay bound hand and foot. Men fleein from conskripshen, and sich, kin be seezed and dragged into slavery; cavalry, drest in odjus bloo, hez licence to hunt the pantin fugitive, who, after drawin his bounty and pay, changis his mind, and desires to return to the buzum uv his family and the shootin uv enrollin orfisers and tax assessors will now be considered a crime. Alas!

The news affectid me variously. I hed our township all fixt, hevin distribitid tikkits, and knowin none uv em cood skratch em, ez they don't rite enny, I reseevd the returns with a gratifide smile. "Bless you, my children! you hev done nobly," sez I. Presently a currier arrivd, bringin the disturbin intellygens that the northern countis give Bruff thirty thousand, and two minnits thereafter another arrivd, statin that the suthrin countis had got loonatik and given Bruff thirty-five thousand. With a hart-rendin and sole-tarin shreek, I fell a inannymait corps on the flore . . . I awoke. An odor uv suthin natrel filled the room, givin me life agin. It wuz whisky. The worthy woman at whose house I board, hed bin rubbin the soles uv my feet with a jug, and givin me small doses uv the restorer thro a funnel. Her exershens restord me to life again. I presume the fact uv my owin six months board did not nerve her frajile arm. It wuz revrence.

Despondent and weery uv life, I attempted sooiside. I mixt my licker fer a day; I red a entire number uv the *Crisis;* I peroozed "Cotton is King," "Pulpit Pollytiks," and "Vallandigum's Record," but all in vane. Ez a last desprit resource, I attemptid to pizon myself by drinkin water, but that failed me. My stumick rejected it—I vomited.

I am to much prosterated to offer either advice or consolashen to my Dimekratick friends. We air in a stait uv abgect cussitude. To see Waid, and Chase, and Oin Luvgoy, and that 3-ply Abolishnist, Horris Greely, feelin good, is prusic acid and stricknine to us. I shell seek releef from my sorrers in the floin bole.

PETROLEUM V. NASBY.

George W. Peck

George Wilbur Peck (1840–1916) had the astonishing distinction of being elected Governor of Wisconsin on the Democratic ticket back in 1890, when one of his party had about as much chance as does a Republican in present-day Mississippi. It was not for this feat, however, that Peck won a measure of immortality, but for a previous accomplishment—the creation of "Peck's Bad Boy," a mischievous and ingenious urchin who made life miserable for his father as well as the groceryman, who was compelled to keep his eye peeled constantly to guard against the lad's bold appropriation of such loose edibles as were found abundantly loose in boxes and barrels before the chainstores neatly packaged everything into standard parcels. Peck, whose newspaper PECK'S SUN *first published the "Bad Boy" sketches, sailed jauntily into the governor's office as a result of his popularity as a humorist, but was defeated for re-election by lion-maned "Fighting Bob" LaFollette. Peck wrote a number of books, including* THE ADVENTURES OF ONE TERENCE MC GRANT *(1871), featuring a Celtic spiritual ancestor of Finley Peter Dunne's Mr. Dooley who ventured caustic opinions on the errors of the Grant administration, but he is best remembered as the author of* PECK'S BAD BOY *and* PECK'S BAD BOY AND THE GROCERYMAN, *both published in 1883.*

His Pa Fights Hornets

"Go AWAY from here now," said the grocery man to the bad boy, as he came into the store and was going to draw some cider out of a barrel into a pint measure that had flies in it. "Get right out of this place, and don't let me see you around here until the health officer says your Pa has got over the small-pox. I saw him this morning and his face is all covered with postules, and they will have him in the pest house before night. You git," and he picked up a butter tryer and went for the boy, who took refuge behind a barrel of onions, and held up his hands as though Jesse James had drawn a bead on him.

"O, you go and chase yourself. That is not small-pox Pa has got. He had a fight with a nest of hornets," said the boy.

"Hornets! Well, I'll be cussed," remarked the grocery man, as he put up the butter tryer, and handed the boy a slice of rotten muskmelon. 'How in the world did he get into a nest of hornets? I hope you did not have anything to do with it."

The boy buried his face in the melon, until he looked as though a yellow gash had been cut from his mouth to his ears, and after swallowing the melon, he said, "Well, Pa says I was responsible, and he says that settles it, and I can go my way and he will go his. He said he was willing to overlook everything I had done to make his life unbearable, but steering him into a nest of hornets, and then getting drunk, was too much, and I can go."

"What, you haven't been drunk," says the grocery man. "Great heavens, that will kill your poor old father."

"Oh, I guess it won't kill him very much. He has been getting drunk for twenty years, and he says he is healthier today than he ever was, since his liver got to working again.

You see, Monday was a regular Indian summer day, and Pa said he would take me and my chum out in the woods to gather hickory nuts, if we would be good. I said I would, and my chum said he would, and we got a couple of bags and went away out to Wauwatosa, in the woods. We clubbed the trees and got more nuts than anybody, and had a lunch, and Pa was just enjoying his religion first rate. While Pa was taking a nap under a tree, my chum and me looked around and found a hornets' nest on the lower limb of the tree we were sitting under, and my chum said it would be a good joke to get a pole and run it into the hornets' nest and then run. Honest, I didn't think about Pa being under the tree, and I went into the field and got a hop pole, and we put the small end of it into the nest, and gouged the nest a couple of times, and when the boss hornet came out of the hole, and looked sassy, and then looked back in the hole and whistled to the other hornets to come out and have a circus and they began to come out, my chum and me run and climbed over a fence, and got behind a pile of hop poles that was stacked up. I guess the hornets saw my Pa just as quick as they got out of the nest, cause pretty soon we heard Pa call to 'Helen Damnation,' or some woman we didn't know, and then he took his coat, that he had been using for a pillow, and whipped around, and he slapped hisself on the shoulders, and then he picked up the lunch basket and pounded around like he was crazy, and bime-by he started on a run toward town, holding his pants up, cause his suspenders was hanging down on his hips, and I never see a man run so, and fan himself with a basket. We could hear him yell, 'come on boys. Hell is out for noon' and he went over a hill, and we didn't see him any more. We waited till near dark because we was afraid to go after the bags of nuts till the hornets had gone to bed, and then we came home. The bags were awful heavy, and I think it was real mean in Pa to go off and leave us, and not help carry the bags."

"I swan," says the grocery man, "You are too mean to live. But what about your getting drunk?"

"O, I was going to tell you. Pa had a bottle of liver medicine in his coat pocket, and when he was whipping his hornets the bottle dropped out, and I picked it up to carry it home to him. My chum wanted to smell the liver medicine, so he took out the cork and it smelled just like in front of a liquor store on East Water street, and my chum said his liver was bad, too, and he took a swaller, and he said he should think it was enough to cut a feller's liver up in slices, but it was good, and then I had a peculiar feeling in my liver, and my chum said his liver felt better after he took a swaller, and so I took a swaller, and it was the offulest liver remedy I ever tasted. It scorched my throat just like the diphtheria, but it beats the diphtheria, or sore throat, all to pieces, and my chum and me laughed we was so tickled. Did you ever take liver medicine? You know how it makes you feel as if your liver had got on top of your lights, and like you wanted to jump and holler. Well, sir, honest that liver medicine made me dance a jig on the viaduct bridge, and an old soldier from the soldier's home came along and asked us what was the matter, and we showed him the bottle, and he said he sposed he had the worst liver in the world, and said the doctors at the home couldn't cure him. It's a mean boy that won't help an old veteran cure his liver, so I told him to try Pa's liver remedy and he took a regular cow swaller, and said, 'here's to your livers, boys.' He must have a liver bigger nor a cow's, and I guess it is better now.

"Then my liver begun to feel curious again, and my chum said his liver was getting torpid some more, and we both of us took another dose, and started home and we got generous, and gave our nuts all away to some boys. Say, does liver medicine make a feller give away all he has got? We kept taking medicine every five blocks, and we locked arms and went down a back street and sung 'O it is a glorious thing to

be a pirut king,' and when we got home my head felt bigger
nor a washtub and I thought p'raps my liver had gone to my
head, and Pa came to the door with his face tied up in towels,
and some yellow stuff on the towels that smelled like anarchy,
and I slapped him on the shoulder and shouted, 'Hello, Gov.,
how's your liver,' and gave him the bottle, and it was empty,
and he asked if we had been drinking that medicine and he
said he was ruined, and I told him we could get some more
down to the saloon, and he took hold of my collar and I
lammed him in the ear, and he bounced me up the stairs, and
then I turned pale, and had cramps, and I didn't remember
any more till I woke up and the doctor was with me, and Pa
and Ma looked scared, and the Doc. had a tin thing like you
draw water out of a country cistern, only smaller, and Ma
said if it hadn't been for the stomach pump she wouldn't have
had any little boy, and I looked at the knobs on Pa's face and
I laffed and asked Pa if he got into the hornets, too. Then the
Doc. laffed, and Ma cried, and Pa swore, and I groaned, and
got sick again, and then they let me go to sleep again, and
this morning I had the offulest headache, and Pa's face looks
like he had fallen on a picket fence. When I got out I went
to my chum's house to see if they had got him pumped out,
and his Ma drove me out with a broom, and she says I will
ruin every boy in the neighborhood. Pa says I was drunk
and kicked him in the groin when he fired me up stairs, and
I asked him how I could be drunk just taking medicine for
my liver, and he said to go to the devil, and I came over here.
Say, give me a lemon to settle my stomach."

"But, look-a-here," says the grocery man, as he gave the
boy a little dried up lemon, about as big as a prune, and told
him he was a terror, "what is the matter with your eye winkers
and your hair? They seem to be burned off."

"O, thunder, didn't Pa tell you about the comet exploding
and burning us all? That was the worst thing since the flood,
when Noar run the excursion boat from Kalamazoo to

Mount Ararat. You see we had been reading about the comet, which is visible at four o'clock in the morning, and I heard Pa tell the hired girl to wake him and Ma up when she got up to set the pancakes and go to early mass so they could see the comet. The hired girl is a Cathlick, and she don't make no fuss about it, but she has got more good, square religion than a dozen like Pa. It makes a good deal of difference how religion affects different people, don't it? Now Pa's religion makes him wild, and he wants to kick my pants and pull my hair, but the hired girl's religion makes her want to hug me; if I am abused, and she puts anarchy on my bruises, and gives me pie. Pa wouldn't get up at four o'clock in the morning to go to early mass, unless he could take a fish pole along and some angle worms. The hired girl prays when nobody sees her but God, but Pa wants to get a church full of sisterin', and pray loud, as though he was an auctioneer selling tin razors. Say, it beats all what a difference liver medicine has on two people, too. Now that hickory nut day, when me and my chum got full of Pa's liver medicine, I felt so good natured I gave my hickory nuts away to the children, and wanted to give my coat and pants to a poor tramp, but my chum, who ain't no bigger'n me, got on his ear and wanted to kick the socks off a little girl who was going home from school. It's queer, ain't it? Well, about the comet. When I heard Pa tell the hired girl to wake him and Ma up, I told her to wake me up about half an hour before she waked Pa up, and then I got my chum to stay with me, and we made a comet to play on Pa. You see my room is right over Pa's room, and I got two lengths of stove pipe and covered them all over with phosphorus, so they looked just as bright as a comet. Then we got two Roman candles and a big sky rocket, and we were going to touch off the Roman candles and the sky rocket just as Pa and Ma got to looking at the comet. I didn't know that a skyrocket would kick back, did you? Well, you'd a dide to see that comet. We tied a piece of white rubber garden hose to the stove pipe for a tail and went to bed, and when the hired girl woke us up we laid for Pa and Ma. Pretty soon we heard Pa's window open, and I looked out, and Pa and Ma had their heads and half their bodies out of the window. They had their night shirts on and looked just like the picture of Millerites waiting for the world to come to an end. Pa looked and seed the stove pipe and he said:

"Hanner, for God's sake, look up there. That is the damnedest comet I ever see. It is as bright as day. See the tail of it. Now that is worth getting up to see."

Just then my chum lit the two Roman candles and I touched off the rocket, and that's where my eye winkers went. The rocket busted the joints of the stove pipe and they fell down on Pa, but Ma got her head inside before the comet struck, and wasn't hurt, but one length of the stove pipe struck Pa endways on the neck and almost cut a biscuit out of him, and the fire and sparks just poured down in his hair, and burned his night shirt. Pa was scart. He thought the world was coming to an end, and the window came down on his back and he began to sing, "Earth's but a desert drear, Heaven is my home." I see he was caught in the window, and I went down stairs to put out the fire on his night shirt, and put up the window to let him in, and he said: "My boy, your Ma and I are going to Heaven, but I fear you will go to the bad place," and I told him I would take my chances, and he better put on his pants if he was going anywhere where there would liable to be ladies present, and when he got his head in Ma told him the world was not coming to an end, but somebody had been setting off fireworks, and she said she guessed it was their dear little boy, and when I saw Pa feeling under the bed for a bed slat I got up the stairs pretty previous now, and don't you forget it, and Ma put cold cream on where the sparks burnt Pa's shirt, and Pa said another day wouldn't pass over his head before he had me in the Reform School. Well, if I go to Reform School, somebody's got to pay attention, you can bet your liver. A boy can't have fun these days without everybody thinks he is an heathen. What hurt did it do to play comet? It's a mean father that won't stand a little scorching in the interest of science."

The boy went out, scratching the place where his eye winkers were, and then the grocery man knew what it was that caused the fire engines to be out around at four o'clock in the morning, looking for a fire.

M. Quad

"M. Quad," Charles Bertrand Lewis (1842–1924), was born in Liverpool, Ohio. He was a buck private in the Union Army during the Civil War, and following a tradition for newspaper humorists of his day, was a printer as well as a writer. While en route to a newspaper job in Tennessee, he was blown up in a steamboat explosion on the Ohio, an all too common variety of accident at the time. In 1869 Lewis began his long association with the Detroit FREE PRESS, where many of his best-known humorous pieces were first published. One of his inventions was Brother Gardner, pompous Negro president of the Lime Kiln Club, an organization having many of the characteristics of "The Mystic Knights of the Sea" familiar to Amos and Andy's radio listeners. However, such caricature was then in the mode and Lewis' jibes were more gentle than many others. He also anticipated the ludicrous domestic tribulations of soap-opera comics with his "Mr. and Mrs. Bowser" stories, and poked fun at Western journalism in articles supposedly culled from the nonexistent Arizona KICKER. The selections herein are reprinted from QUAD'S ODDS (1875). Lewis explains in his dedicatory note that he had planned to inscribe the miscellany to some newspaperman, "but when nearly five hundred newspapers, each saying a kind word for the book, had reached his table, it was plain that such a dedication would be ruled out of order." Quad then decided in favor of the Pawnee Indians ". . . for many private reasons, and hoping to push the sale of the book among such tribes as love to sit down and read, and hold spelling-bees, in preference to hunting around for scalps . . ."

Up among the Splinters

I was going up to Maysville, Kentucky, to take a "sit" on the *Bulletin*, and of course I took the steamer *Magnolia*, after reaching Cincinnati, in preference to all others. She was a tidy-looking boat, and her head clerk wore a diamond pin. He was the first steamboat clerk I had ever seen fastened to a $600 diamond, and I was determined to go on that boat if it killed me.

A runner for a rival boat assured me that *Magnolia* would blow up, while his boat would slide up the river like grease, but the diamond pin decided me.

"Good-bye, my white-haired rural friend!" sorrowfully exclaimed the rival runner as he turned away, and I never saw him again. Our paths diverged right there. Mine went skyward, and he went off and fell down a hatchway and was killed.

After the steamer left the wharf-boat I sat down in the cabin and listened, with others, while a fat man from Illinois read four or five columns of the impeachment trial of Andy Johnson. Throwing the paper down he said:

"Gentlemen, it seems to me—"

He stopped right there. He couldn't go on. The boiler exploded just then and we had business aloft. I don't exactly remember who went up first, or how we got through the roof. I am a little absent-minded sometimes, and this was one of the times.

The boilers made a great deal more noise than there seemed any occasion for. The explosion would have been A-1 with half the whizzing, grinding and tearing. One of the men who came up behind me seemed to think that something or other was out of order, and he yelled out to me:

"Say! what's all this?"

I pointed to the fat man, who was about five feet ahead of me, and then I began to practice gymnastics. I went up a few feet right end up, then a few feet more wrong end up, and then I wasn't particular which way I went up. The golden eagle off the pilot-house sailed around our heads, and it was a fine chance for the fat man to get off a handsome eulogy on the proud bird of freedom. He didn't do it, however. One of his ears had been torn off, a leg broken, and flying timbers kept pegging him every minute. I wanted to ask him to finish the remark he commenced in the cabin, but he seemed so cast-down and discouraged that I hadn't the heart to speak.

We finally arrived there. It was a good ways up, and the route had several little inconveniences. It was a grand location from which to view the surrounding country, but we didn't stop to view it. We had business below, and our motto was business before pleasure.

Somehow, I got mixed up with the fat man, and we couldn't hardly tell which was which. He made no complaints, and I didn't care, and so we got along very well together until we struck the water. When we went down to look for bottom we let go of each other. He staid down there and I came up. A number of others also came up about that time. One man got hold of a door and warned us that he was a member of the Legislature, and must therefore be saved, but we held a mass convention and decided that the Constitution of the United States guaranteed equal rights to all men, and we crowded him along.

As the door wouldn't float over ten or twelve, a half-dozen of us got hold of brooms, foot-stools, dusters, and so forth, and compared notes. A six-footer from Missouri was rushing around with a boot-jack in one hand, a table-cloth in the

other, and a look of anxiety on his face. As he floated near me
he called out:

"Young man, where are we going?"

I called back that I was a stranger in that locality, and
couldn't say whether we'd bring up in New Orleans or Fort
Leavenworth.

I finally got hold of the dining table, to which a red-headed
woman from St. Louis was clinging. As I caught the table she
exclaimed:

"Go away, young man—go away!"

I replied that the state of her toilet needn't confuse her
in the least. Her dress-skirt had been blown off, her hair
singed, and part of her hoop-skirt was over her head, but I
warned her that it was about an even thing. The band of my
shirt was still buttoned around my neck, and I had one boot
on, and it was no time to be captious. I remarked to her that
her nose was broken and several of her teeth were gone, but
she fired up and said I'd better "look to home," as I had one
eye ruined, a hole in my head, and was cooked in a dozen
places.

Before I could learn much of her history we were drawn
to the bank and taken off. I called out for a breadth of rag
carpet to make me a toga of, but no one would bring it, and
I had to faint away to avoid hearing any criticisms from the
crowd.

When I came to, a dozen of us were piled up together, and
the captain of the boat was making a speech. He said it wasn't
his fault, and that we mustn't feel hard toward him. He had
lost a fine dog by the accident, and he couldn't bear any further burden just then. He said that boats often blew up without apparent reason, but if he could ever ascertain the reason
of this blow-up he would send us the particulars. He seemed
like an honest-hearted man, and we felt sorry over the loss
of his dog.

When we got down to Cincinnati a policeman asked me if it made any difference to me where I was buried, and they sent me to the hospital until I could make up my mind. The hole in my head got to aching about that time, and the last I remember was hearing a man with a coarse voice call out: "Tell Jim to get a box ready for this corpse!"

Sixteen days after that I got my senses back, and for the succeeding six weeks had a very easy time. The coroner dropped in once a day to see if I still persisted in living; six daily reporters included me in their round; the doctors worked at the hole in my head and at my burns by turns, and after three months they came to the conclusion that I would live. Such little side issues as pneumonia, blindness, proud flesh and fever were not supposed to have any bearing on the main question.

It isn't good to be blown up. There are better ways of ascending and descending. Such things interrupt traveling programmes, and are often the foundation of funeral processions. I met the red-headed woman about a year ago, and she was quite friendly, but the fat man hasn't been heard of since. I fear that some of the machinery of the boat got into his pockets and held him down.

A Particular Girl

WAY BACK in the pioneer days of Michigan, when log houses contained parlor, kitchen, bedroom and all in one large room, a couple of travelers put up for the night at a cabin on the Grand River plank road. The family consisted of three persons, father, mother and daughter, the latter being sixteen or seventeen years old. There were two beds in the room, and the old woman fixed up a "shake-down" for the travelers.

About ten o'clock conversation was exhausted, and after the family had held a whispered conversation in a corner the old man advanced to the travelers and said:

"It's time to tumble in, and I must ask ye to step out door until the gal and the old woman git under cover. I hain't modest, and the old woman don't care a skip, but the gal is a leetle pertickler, and if ye'll jist step out till I holler it'll be doin' her a powerful favor."

The travelers waited outside the door until the old man "hollered," and he further excused himself by remarking:

"Yes, Marier's gittin' mighty pertickler, and I'll bet it won't be three month afore she'll want shoes and stocking and a breast-pin!"

"I won't nuther!" answered the girl.

"Well, I hope not," sighed the old man. "Marier's a good girl, and it would just about use me'n the old woman up if she got so proud that she wanted soap every time she washed her hands, and ile for her ha'r whenever she heard a land-looker holler!"

The Mother's Friend

SOME five or six years ago Mr. Gregory, of the Rochester *Chronicle*, invented what he called "Gregory's Eureka Spanker," being an invention calculated to lessen the labor of fathers and mothers in enforcing family discipline. The principle was correct, but the machines were all failures, as they could not be constructed with power enough to answer the purpose designed. The children were lifted up, laid face down on a small platform, and the mother worked the spanking apparatus as one turns a coffee-mill. A series of fans were arranged to strike the child thirty times per minute, but owing to the lack of power the child was led to believe that some one was tickling him, and would laugh himself almost to death. Another bad feature of the machine was the fact that it took at least ten minutes to spank a child. Thus, in a family where there were seven or eight children, an hour and a half was consumed in getting around, and by the time the last child had been spanked the first had entirely forgotten that anything unusual had occurred that day.

I am happy to inform mothers that I have brought out a new machine, founded on more correct principles, scientifically constructed, and warranted to do three times as much as I claim for it. It is called "The Mother's Friend," and the fact that it fills a want long felt is shown by every mail. The first machine was put on trial only three months ago, and now I have orders from nearly every State in the Union, and employ two saw-mills and ninety-seven skilled mechanics in its manufacture.

The following are selected at random from among several millions of testimonials:

OFFICE OF THE "COMMERCIAL,"
Cincinnati, O., June 20, '74

M. Quad—*Sir*—I was present last evening at a trial of your patent "Friend," and it does me good to inform you that it proved itself a great success. Thirty-five children were spanked in twenty-eight minutes by one woman, without any effort, and each one was far better spanked than the stoutest mother could have done it with a boot-jack. The *Commercial* will stand by you in this section.

Very truly,
M. HALSTEAD.

And the following is from New York:

M. Quad—*Dear Sir*—Mrs. Bryant and myself have had the pleasure of attending a spanking *soiree*, given for the purpose of testing your patent apparatus. It worked so successfully that we are going to adopt a child and purchase a Spanker. I have seen thousands of inventions, but I never saw anything which could afford a family the fun which the "Friend" can.

WM. CULLEN BRYANT.

And the following is from Washington:

M. Quad—Your note of the 15th inst., asking me what I thought of your new invention, was duly received. In answer let me say that I am delighted. It saves time, does its work well, runs easily, is substantially constructed, and if I had a family of children I'd go bare-footed all winter but what I'd have a Spanker. Can I secure the agency for the District of Columbia? What commission do you allow? I think I can sell five hundred in this city alone.

Ever yours,   GIDEON WELLES.

And this is from the ex-editor of the Lapeer (Michigan) *Democrat*:

M. Quad—*Sir*—The Spanker was received last evening and immediately put to work, and I must say that I am astonished and gratified at its manner of working. Our children have been angels ever since passing through the machine. Formerly, my wife had to use up an hour's time and half a bunch of shingles every day to spank our darlings, and then they weren't half attended to. Now, by the aid of your Spanker, she can do the work in five minutes. Draw on me for $40.

Respectfully,

L. D. SALE.

Other testimonials can be seen at my office, where one of the Spankers is also on exhibition. The regular discount will be allowed editors and clergymen.

Opie Read

Opie Read (1852–1939), was born in Nashville. In Little Rock he launched his rambunctious ARKANSAS TRAVELER, *from which the following two sketches are reprinted. Read's frank critiques of Arkansas mores did not serve to endear him to more substantial members of the community and in 1891 he found it expedient to depart for Chicago. He published his magazine for some time thereafter, and became successful as a novelist. He was of the frontier-humorist breed, though he outlived all of them. "Pleased with the Chills" is a recurrent theme among the pioneers —hard times and ill health induced by a malevolent climate. "An Englishman's Night" is akin to the celebrated song and dialogue from which Read derived the name of his magazine. The effete greenhorn engages the rustic in repartee, and comes off second best, as frequently occurs in the works of John S. Robb, J. M. Field, Mark Twain, and others.*

An Englishman's Night

MR. GEORGE LANSING, brother of Lord Glencove, came to America some time ago with a party of capitalists, and joined in an enterprise to purchase large tracts of pine lands in Arkansaw. Mr. Lansing, before he met any of the squatters, wrote many amusing letters home concerning them, for, being an Englishman, he fancied that he knew much of these people, and did not think that personal contact with them would extend the already broad territory of his views. He wrote a number of dialogues, in which he always "wound the squatter up," but he is wiser now.

Several days ago he set out on an expedition to visit a tract of land lying among the hills in a part of the country which had not been viewed by the members of the company. It was suggested that Mr. Lansing should be accompanied by some one who knew the country, but he hooted at the idea, wise owl, and declared that a man who had held his own in the jungles of India was eminently able to take care of himself anywhere in a bloody American state.

One evening after Mr. Lansing had gained a rough and thinly populated district, he was overtaken by a rain storm. In vain he sought shelter. Darkness came on, and missing the road, which had narrowed down to a mere bridle-path, he wandered around in the woods, alternately choked by grape-vines and sawed by green-briars. The lightning illustrated the sulphurous imprecations which he called down upon the American government, and as he lost his hat and was struck on the forehead by his horse, who threw up his head to avoid a briar, he shook his damp hand at the blackness above, and in a loud oath, questioned the purity of our institutions. At last he saw a light glimmering faintly among the dripping trees and tangled underbrush. Slowly guiding his horse in the direction whence came the welcome gleam, he at last reached a low rail fence, surrounding a small log house. Mr. Lansing shouted.

"Hello, yerself!" exclaimed a voice, as a man poked his head from the door.

"Who lives here?"

"I do."

"Of course. What is your name?"

"What's your name?"

"George Lansing. Does Simon Butt live here?"

"Not at present."

"Where does he live?"

"Don't know."

"Did he ever live here?"

"No."

"Then, why do you say 'not at present?'"

"'Cause he don't live here at present."

"My friend, I am wet and—"

"Must 'uv been out in the rain?"

"Yes, I was in all of that heavy shower."

"No, yer wa'n't."

"I say I was."

"I say yer wa'n't. Some o' that shower fell here, an' I know yer wa'n't here when it fell. Good-night," closing the door.

"Say, there!" called the Englishman.

"Wall," opening the door.

"I say I am wet and—"

"Must 'uv been out in the rain."

"And I'm hungry."

"Didn't have nuthin' to eat, mebby."

"I'd like to stay here until morning."

"All right, help yourself," closing the door.

"Hello, there!" cried the Englishman.

"Hello, yerself!" again opening the door.

"What sort of a man are you?"

"Democrat. What's yer own pollyticks?"

"Confound your politics. I—"

"Confound yer pollyticks, stranger, an' mo'n that, dod blame yer religion."

"Look here, my good fellow."

"One o' the best fellers yer ever seed."

"Glad to hear it. I am wet—"

"Must 'uv been out in the rain."

"I don't want any of your blasted foolishness, you know. I want to come in."

"All right, never said yer couldn't."

The floor of the little room seemed to be covered with children, and from a bed in a corner a head with long hair protruded. The squatter raked the chunks together—those people always keep a fire, winter and summer—and the cheerful blaze, shooting up the spacious "stack" chimney, invited the stranger to take off his coat and hold his steaming hands out to feel the warmth.

"How far is it to Simon Butt's?"

"Young Simon or old Simon?"

"Either one, I suppose."

"Wall, they live about a mile apart. Old Simon lives on one hill an' young Simon on t'other."

"But how far from here?"

"Yer know whar the spout spring is?"

"No."

"Wall, that's bad, fur it's the best water in the curmunity."

"Does Mr. Butt live near the spring?"

"Who, old Simon?"

"Yes."

"Wall, he don't live as close to it as young Simon does."

"How can I find the spring?"

"By goin' to young Simon's."

"But how can I find young Simon's?"

"By goin' to the spring."

"See here, old man, I have fooled with you long enough."

"Thank the lord!" said the squatter's wife, nervously jerking her tangled hair. "Wish yer would git through with yer transacshun an' let a body git some sleep. Tildy, if yer don't keep them hoofs still I'll make yer think yer air pizened."

"Can I lie down here on the floor and sleep?"

"Don't know, podner. Yer oughter know whut yer ken do."

"May I, then?"

"Yes, yer may, then or now; it makes no difference."

The Englishman was soon asleep. Early in the morning he was awakened by a "splutter" of hot grease from the frying-pan.

"If yer don't want ter git burnt, stir 'round," said the old lady. He stirred around, and soon discovered that he was only a few hundred yards from his destination.

"Why didn't you tell me it was so near?" exclaimed Mr. Lansing.

"Why didn't yer ax?" replied the squatter. "Yer kep' on wantin' ter know how fur it was, but didn't ax how near. Sich folks as you oughter larn how to talk 'fore yer leave home. Wall, er good mornin'."

Pleased with the Chills

Down in certain sections of the Mississippi River bottoms there is such an air of unconcern that the first thought of a traveler is: "These people are too lazy to entertain a hope." It is, however, not wholly a condition of laziness that produces such an appearance of indolence. Laziness may play its part, and, moreover, may play it well, but it cannot hope to assume the leading role. What, then, is the principal actor? Chills. There are men in those bottoms who were born with a chill and who have never shaken it off.

Some time ago while riding through the Muscadine neighborhood, I came upon a man sitting on a log near the roadside. He was sallow and lean, with sharp knob cheek bones and with hair that looked like soiled cotton. The day was intensely hot, but he was sitting in the sun, although near him a tangled grapevine cast a most inviting shade.

"Good-morning," said I, reigning up my horse.

"Hi."

"You live here, I suppose."

"Jest about."

"Why don't you sit over there in the shade?"

"Will when the time comes."

"What do you mean by when the time comes?"

"When the fever comes on."

"Having chills, are you?"

"Sorter."

"How long have you had them?"

"Forty-odd year."

"How old are you?"

"Forty-odd year."

"Been shaking all your life, eh?"

"Only half my life; fever was on the other half."

"Why don't you move away from here?"

"Becaze I've lived here so long that I'm afeerd I might not have good health nowhar else."

"Gracious alive, do you mean to say that having chills all the time is good health?"

"Wall, health mout be wuss. Old Nat Sarver moved up in the hills some time ago, was tuck down putty soon with some new sort of disease and didn't live more'n a week. Don't b'lieve in swappin' off suthin' that I'm used to fur suthin' I don't know nothin' about. Old-fashioned, every-day chills air good enough for me. Some folks, when they git a little up in the world, mout want to put on airs with dyspepsia and bronkichus, and glanders and catarrh, but, as I 'lowed to my wife the other night, old chills and fever war high enough fur us yit awhile. A chill may have its drawbacks, but it has its enjoyments, too."

"I don't see how anything about a chill can be enjoyable."

"Jest owin' to how you air raised, as the feller says. When I have a chill it does me a power of good to stretch, and I tell you that a fust-rate stretch when a feller is in the humor ain't to be sneezed at. I'd leave watermilon most any time to have a good stretch. High-o-hoo!" He gasped, threw out his legs, threw back his arms and stretched himself across the log. "It's sorter like the itch," he went on. "The itch has its drawbacks, but what a power of good it does a man to scratch! Had a uncle who cotch the itch in the army and he lay thar and scratched and smiled and scratched agin. In order to keep up with the demand of the occasion he sprinkled a lot of sand in his bed and tuck off all his clothes, so that every time he turned he'd be scratched all over. He kep' this up till the itch killed him, but he died a-scratchin' and a-smilin' and I reckon he was about as happy a dead man as ever lived. Wall, my fever is comin' on now and I reckon I'll git up thar under the shade."

He moved into the shade and stretched himself again.

"How long will your fever last?" I asked.

"Wall, I don't know exackly; three hours, mebby."

"Then what?"

"Wall, I'll funter around awhile, chop up a little wood to git a bite to eat with, swap a hoss with some feller, mebby, and then fix myself for another chill."

"Have you much of a family?"

"Wife and grown son. He's about the ablest chiller in the

country; w'y, when he's got a rale good chill on he can take hold of a tree and shake off green persimmons. W'y, he wins all the money the niggers have got, shakin' dice. Wall, have you got to go?"

"Yes."

"Wait till my fever cools down a little, and I'll beat you outen that nag you're ridin'."

"No, I don't care to walk."

"Good-bye, then. When you git tired livin' up thar among them new-fangled diseases, come down here whar everthing is old-fashioned and honest."

James Whitcomb Riley

James Whitcomb Riley (1849–1916) was born in Greenfield, Indiana. After a turn as an itinerant painter of advertising signs on barns and a season or so as entertainer and pitchman with a medicine show he went to work for the Anderson DEMOCRAT. *Fired for perpetrating a hoax relating to a supposed manuscript of Edgar Allan Poe he had some difficulty in resuming his newspaper career before the Indianapolis* NEWS *took a chance on him. Here he began to write the Hoosier-flavored verses signed* BENJ. F. JOHNSON OF BOONE *published in 1883 as* THE OLD SWIMMIN' HOLE AND 'LEVEN OTHER POEMS. *It was the beginning of a long and successful tenure as a folksy and often saccharine poet and popular lecturer. On the platform he was frequently teamed with Bill Nye. "Mister Hop-Toad" is reprinted from* HOME FOLKS *(1900).*

Mister Hop-Toad

Howdy, Mister Hop-Toad! Glad to see you out!
Bin a month o' Sund'ys sence I seen you hereabout.
Kind o' bin a-layin' in, from the frost and snow?
Good to see you out ag'in, it's bin so long ago!
Plows like slicin' cheese, and sod's loppin' over even;
Loam's like gingerbread, and clod's softer'n deceivin'—
Mister Hop-Toad, honest-true—Springtime—don't you
      love it?
You old rusty rascal you, at the bottom of it!

          Oh, oh, oh!
          I grabs up my old hoe;
          But I sees *you*,
          And s' I, "Ooh-ooh!
    Howdy, Mister Hop-Toad! How-dee-do!"

Make yourse'f more cumfo'bler—square round at your
      ease—
Don't set saggin' slanchwise, with your nose below your
      knees.
Swell that fat old throat o' yourn and lemme see you
      swaller;
Straighten up and h'ist your head!—*You* don't owe a
      dollar!—
Hain't no mor'gage on your land—ner no taxes, nuther;
You don't haf to work no roads—even ef you'd ruther!
'F I was you, and *fixed* like you, I railly wouldn't keer
To swop fer life and hop right in the presidential cheer!

Oh, oh, oh!
I hauls back my old hoe;
But I sees *you*,
And s' I, "Ooh-ooh!
Howdy, Mister Hop-Toad! How-dee-do!"

Long about next Aprile, hoppin' down the furry,
Won't you mind I ast you what 'peared to be the hurry?—
Won't you mind I hooked my hoe and hauled you back and
      smiled?—
W'y, bless you, Mister Hop-Toad, I love you like a child!
S'pose I'd want to 'flict you any more'n what you air?—
S'pose I think you got no rights 'cept the warts you wear?
Hulk, sulk, and blink away, you old bloat-eyed rowdy!—
Hain't you got a word to say?—Won't you tell me "Howdy"?

Oh, oh, oh!
I swish round my old hoe ;
But I sees *you*,
And s' I, "Ooh-ooh!
Howdy, Mister Hop-Toad! How-dee-do!"

Mark Twain

Mark Twain, born Samuel Langhorne Clemens (1835–1910), traveled a long way upward from Florida, Missouri, the village of his birth. His boyhood in Hannibal may be re-created by reading THE ADVENTURES OF TOM SAWYER *(1876) and* THE ADVENTURES OF HUCKLEBERRY FINN *(1884).* LIFE ON THE MISSISSIPPI *(1883) recapitulates his experiences as a river pilot, a kingly job in that era. After a season in the Far West as a lackadaisical gold hunter and a slightly more enthusiastic newspaperman, he went abroad to write the impressions of an American who had a great deal of the "booster" spirit which is one of our inheritances from the frontier. The rude man of the West, even in his latter days of sedate respectability in Hartford, Connecticut, often ridiculed the folderol and bombast of Old World royalty and nobility, as in "Was Solomon Wise?" reprinted from* HUCKLEBERRY FINN. *It is one of the discussions of the runaways as their raft floats down the Mississippi.*

Was Solomon Wise?

I READ considerable to Jim about kings and dukes and earls and such, and how gaudy they dressed, and how much style they put on, and called each other your majesty, and your grace, and your lordship, and so on, 'stead of mister; and Jim's eyes bugged out, and he was interested. He says:

"I didn't know dey was so many un um. I hain't hearn 'bout none un um, skasely, but ole King Sollermun, onless you counts dem kings dat's in a pack er k'yards. How much do a king git?"

"Get?" I says; "why, they get a thousand dollars a month if they want it; they can have just as much as they want; everything belongs to them."

"*Ain'* dat gay? En what dey got to do, Huck?"

"*They* don't do nothing! Why, how you talk! They just set around."

"No; is dat so?"

"Of course it is. They just set around—except, maybe, when there's a war; then they go to the war. But other times they just lazy around; or go hawking—just hawking and sp—Sh!—d'you hear a noise?"

We skipped out and looked; but it warn't nothing but the flutter of a steamboat's wheel away down, coming around the point; so we come back.

"Yes," says I, "and other times, when things is dull, they fuss with the parlment; and if everybody don't go just so he whacks their heads off. But mostly they hang round the harem."

"Roun' de which?"

"Harem."

"What's de harem?"

"The place where he keeps his wives. Don't you know about the harem? Solomon had one; he had about a million wives."

"Why, yes, dat's so; I—I'd done forgot it. A harem's a bo'd'n-house, I reck'n. Mos' likely dey has rackety times in de nussery. En I reck'n de wives quarrels considable; en dat 'crease de racket. Yit dey say Sollermun de wises' man dat ever live'. I doan take no stock in dat. Bekase why: would a wise man want to live in de mis' er sich a blim-blammin' all de time? No—'deed he wouldn't. A wise man 'ud take en buil' a biler-factry; en den he could shet *down* de biler-factry when he wants to res'."

"Well, but he *was* the wisest man, anyway; because the widow she told me so, her own self."

"I doan' k'yer what de widder say, he *warn't* no wise man nuther. He had some er de dad-fetchedes' ways I ever see. Does you know 'bout dat chile dat he'uz gwyne to chop in two?"

"Yes, the widow told me all about it."

"*Well*, den! Warn' dat de beatenes' notion in de worl'? You jes' take en look at it a minute. Dah's de stump, dah—dat's one er de women; heah's you—dat's de yuther one; I's Sollermun; en dish yer dollar bill's de chile. Bofe un you claims it. What does I do? Does I shin aroun' mongs' de neighbors en fine out which un you de bill *do* b'long to, en han' it over to de right one, all safe en soun', de way dat anybody dat had any gumption would? No; I take en whack de bill in *two*, en give half un it to you, en de yuther half to de yuther woman. Dat's de way Sollermun was gwyne to do wid de chile. Now I want to ast you: what's de use er dat half a bill?—can't buy noth'n wid it. En what use is half a chile? I wouldn't give a dern for a million un um."

"But hang it, Jim, you've clean missed the point—blame it, you've missed it a thousand mile."

"Who? Me? Go 'long. Doan' talk to *me* 'bout yo' pints. I reck'n I knows sense when I see it; en dey ain' no sense in sich doin's as dat. De 'spute warn't 'bout half a chile, de 'spute was 'bout a whole chile; and de man dat think he kin settle a 'spute 'bout a whole chile wid a half a chile doan' know enough to come in out'n de rain. Doan' talk to me 'bout Sollermun, Huck, I knows him by de back."

"But I tell you you don't get the point."

"Blame de point! I reck'n I knows what I knows. En mine you, de *real* pint is down furder—it's down deeper. It lays in de way Sollermun was raised. You take a man dat's got on'y one or two chillen; is dat gwyne to be waseful o' chillen? No, he ain't; he can't 'ford it. *He* know how to value 'em. But you take a man dat's got 'bout five million chillen runnin' roun' de house, en it's diffunt. *He* as soon chop a chile in two as a cat. Dey's plenty mo'. A chile er two, mo' er less, warn't no consekens to Sollermun, dad fetch him!"

I never see such a nigger. If he got a notion in his head once, there warn't no getting it out again. He was the most down on Solomon of any nigger I ever see. So I went to talking about other kings, and let Solomon slide. I told about Louis Sixteenth that got his head cut off in France long time ago; and about his little boy the dolphin, that would 'a' been a king, but they took and shut him up in jail, and some say he died there.

"Po' little chap."

"But some says he got out and got away, and come to America."

"Dat's good! But he'll be pooty lonesome—dey ain' no kings here, is dey, Huck?"

"No."

"Den he cain't git no situation. What he gwyne to do?"

"Well, I don't know. Some of them gets on the police, and some of them learns people how to talk French."

"Why, Huck, doan' de French people talk de same way we does?"

"*No,* Jim; you couldn't understand a word they said—not a single word."

"Well, now, I be ding-busted! How do dat come?"

"*I* don't know; but it's so. I got some of their jabber out of a book. S'pose a man was to come to you and say Polly-voo-franzy—what would you think?"

"I wouldn' think nuffn; I'd take en bust him over de head —dat is, if he warn't white. I wouldn't 'low no nigger to call me dat."

"Shucks, it ain't calling you anything. It's only saying, do you know how to talk French?"

"Well, den, why couldn't he say it?"

"Why, *he* is a-saying it. That's a Frenchman's *way* of saying it."

"Well, it's a blame ridicklous way, en I doan' want to hear no mo' 'bout it. Dey ain't no sense in it."

"Looky here, Jim; does a cat talk like we do?"

"No, a cat don't."

"Well, does a cow?"

"No, a cow don't, nuther."

"Does a cat talk like a cow, or a cow talk like a cat?"

"No, dey don't."

"It's natural and right for 'em to talk different from each other, ain't it?"

"Course."

"And ain't it natural and right for a cat and a cow to talk different from *us?*"

"Why, mos' sholy it is."

"Well, then, why ain't it natural and right for a *Frenchman* to talk different from us? You answer me that."

"Is a cat a man, Huck?"

"No."

"Well, den, dey ain't no sense in a cat talkin' like a man. Is a cow a man?—er is a cow a cat?"

"No, she ain't either of them."

"Well, den, she ain't got no business to talk like either one er the yuther of 'em. Is a Frenchman a man?"

"Yes."

"*Well*, den! Dad blame it, why doan' he *talk* like a man? You answer me *dat!*"

Artemus Ward

Charles Farrar Browne (1834–1867), whose pen name was Artemus Ward, was born near Waterford, Maine. Forced to support his widowed mother, he hired out as a printer's apprentice. In 1852, while working in Boston, he contributed a piece called "The Surrender of Cornwallis" to P. B. Shillaber's CARPET-BAG, *the same issue containing the first efforts of Mark Twain and George Horatio Derby. As a journeyman printer, Browne saw a great deal of the Middle West before setling down with the Cleveland* PLAIN DEALER, *becoming city editor in 1857. A year later he began his "Artemus Ward" letters, purportedly from the proprietor of a traveling exhibit consisting of some mangy tame bears, a kangaroo, and some assorted "wax figgers" of various immortals. The grotesque misspelling and quaint drollery suited the public fancy and Browne took to the lecture platform with great success. On a tour of the West he met Mark Twain, and arranged for the publication of the "Jumping Frog" story. He duplicated his American platform triumphs in England, where he died of tuberculosis. Ward's "goaks" are not relished by many people nowadays. Lincoln esteemed them as much as he did those of Petroleum V. Nasby. Before reading the Emancipation Proclamation to his cabinet in that fateful meeting in September, 1862, the President read aloud and laughed over Ward's rueful account of the havoc wrought among his wax works by vandals in Utica.*

The Octoroon

It is with no ordernary feelins of Shagrin & indignashun that I rite you these here lines. Sum of the hiest and most purest feelins whitch actoate the humin hart has bin trampt onto. The Amerycan flag has bin outrajed. I've bin nussin a Adder in my Boozum. The fax in the kase is these here:

A few weeks ago I left Baldinsville to go to N. Y. fur to git out my flamin yeller hanbills fur the Summer kampane, & as I was peroosin a noospaper on the kars a middel aged man in speckterkuls kum & sot down beside onto me. He was drest in black close & was appeerently as fine a man as ever was.

"A fine day, Sir," he did unto me strateway say.

"Middlin," sez I, not wishin to kommit myself, tho he peered to be as fine a man as there was in the wurld—"It is a middlin fine day, Square," I obsarved.

Sez he, "How fares the Ship of State in yure regine of the country?"

Sez I, "We don't hav no ships in our State—the kanawl is our best holt."

He pawsed a minit and then sed, "Air yu aware, Sir, that the krisis is with us?"

"No," sez I, getting up and lookin under the seet, "Whare is she?"

"It's hear—it's everywhares," he sed.

Sez I, "Why how you tawk!" and I gut up again & lookt all round. "I must say, my fren," I continnered, as I re-soomed my seet, "that I kan't see nothin of no krisis myself." I felt sumwhat alarmed, & arose & in a stentoewrian voice obsarved that if any lady or gentleman in that there kar had a krisis consealed abowt their persons they'd better projuce it to onct or suffer the konsequences. Several individoouls snickered rite out, while a putty little damsell rite behind me in a pinc gown make the observashun, "He, he."

"Sit down, my fren," sed the man in black close, "yu miskomprehend me. I meen that the perlittercal ellermunts are orecast with black klouds, 4boden a friteful storm."

"Wall," replide I, "in regard to perlittercal ellerfunts I don't know as how but what they is as good as enny other kind of ellerfunts. But I maik bold to say thay is all a onery set & unpleasant to hav around. They air powerful hevy eaters & take up a right smart chans of room, & besides thay air as ugly and revenjeful, as a Cusscaroarus Injun, with 13 inches of corn whisky in his stummick." The man in black close seemed to be as fine a man as ever was in the wurld. He smilt & sed praps I was rite, tho it was ellermunts instid of ellerfunts that he was alludin to, & axed me what was my prinserpuls?

"I haint gut enny," sed I—"not a prinserpul. Ime in the show biznis." The man in black close, I will hear obsarve, seemed to be as fine a man as ever was in the wurld.

"But," sez he, "you hav feelins into you? You cimpathize with misfortunit, the loly & the hart-sick, don't you?" he bust into teers and axed me ef I saw that yung lady in the seet out yender, pintin to as slick a lookin gal as I ever seed.

Sed I, "2 be sure I see her—is she mutch sick?" The man in black close was appeerently as fine a man as ever was in the wurld ennywhares.

"Draw closter to me," sed the man in black close. "Let me git my mowth fernenst yure ear. Hush—SHESE A OCTOROON!"

"No!" sez I, gittin up in a exsited manner, "yu don't say so! How long has she bin in that way?"

"Frum her arliest infuncy," sed he.

"Wall, whot upon arth duz she doo it fur?" I inquired.

"She kan't help it," sed the man in black close. "It's the brand of Kane."

"Wall, she'd better stop drinkin Kane's brandy," I replide. "I sed the brand of Kane was upon her—not brandy, my fren. Yure very obtoose."

I was konsiderbul riled at this. Sez I, "My gentle Sir, Ime a nonresistanter as a ginral thing, & don't want to git up no rows with nobuddy, but I kin nevertheles kave in enny man's hed that calls me a obtoos," with whitch remarks I kommenst fur to pull orf my extry garmints. "Cum on," sez I—"Time! hear's the Beniki Boy fur ye!" & I darnced around like a poppit. He riz up in his seet & axed my pardin—sed it was all a mistake—that I was a good man, etsettery, & sow 4th, & we fixt it all up pleasant. I must say the man in black close seamed to be as fine a man as ever lived in the wurld. He sed a Octoroon was the 8th of a negrow. He likewise statid that the female he was travlin with was formurly a slave in Mississippy: that she'd purchist her freedim & now wantid to purchiss the freedim of her poor old muther, who (the man in black close obsarved) was between 87 years of age & had to do all the cookin & washin for 25 hired men, whitch it was rapidly breakin down her konstitushun. He sed he knowed the minit he gazed onto my klassic & beneverlunt fase that I'd donate librully & axed me to go over & see her, which I accordinly did. I sot down beside her and sed, "yure Sarvant, Marm! How do yer git along?"

She bust in 2 teers & said, "O sur, I'm so retchid—I'm a poor unfortunit Octoroon."

"So I larn. Yure rather more Roon than Octo, I take it," sed I, fur I never seed a puttier gal in the hull endoorin time of my life. She had on a More Antic Barsk & a Poplin Nubier with Berage trimmins onto it, while her Ise & kurls was enuff to make a man jump into a mill pond without biddin his relashuns good-by. I pittid the Octoroon from the inmost recusses of my hart & hawled out 50 dollars ker slap, & told her to buy her old muther as soon as posserbul. Sez she "kine sir mutch thanks." She then lade her hed over onto my showlder & sed I was "old rats." I was astonished to heer this obsarvation, which I knowd was never used in refined society & I perlitely but emfattercly shovd her hed away.

Sez I "Marm, I'm trooly sirprized."

Sez she, "git out. Yure the nicist old man Ive seen yit. Give us anuther 50!" Had a seleck assortment of the most tremenjious thunderbolts descended down onto me I couldn't hav bin more takin aback. I jumpt up, but she ceased my coat tales & in a wild voise cride, "No, Ile never desart you—let us fli together to a furrin shoor!"

Sez I, "not mutch we wont," and I made a powerful effort to get awa from her. "This is plade out," I sed, whereupon she jerkt me back into the seet. "Leggo my coat, you scandaluss female," I roared, when she set up the most unarthly yellin and hollerin you ever heerd. The passinjers & the gentlemunly konducter rusht to the spot, & I don't think I ever experiunsed sich a rumpus in the hull coarse of my natral dase. The man in black close rusht up to me & sed "How dair yu insult my neece, you horey heded vagabone. You base exhibbiter of low wax figgers—yu woolf in sheep's close," & sow 4th.

I was konfoozed. I was a loonytick fur the time bein, and offered $5 reward to enny gentleman of good morrul carracter who wood tell me whot my name was & what town I livd into. The konductor kum to me & sed the insultid parties wood settle for $50, which I immejitly hawled out, & agane implored sumbuddy to state whare I was prinsipully, & if I shood be thare a grate while myself ef things went on as they'd bin goin fur sum time back. I then axed if there was enny more Octoroons present, "becawz," sez I, "ef there is, let um cum along, fur Ime in the Octoroon bizniss." I then threw my specterculs out of the winder, smasht my hat wildly down over my ise, larfed highsterically & fell under a seet. I lay there sum time & fell asleep. I dreamt Mrs. Ward & the twins had bin carried orf by Ryenosserhosses & that

Baldinsville had bin captered by a army of Octoroons. When I awoked the lamps was a burnin dimly. Sum of the passinjers was snorein like pawpusses & the little damsell in the pinc gown was a singin "Oft in the Silly nite." The onprinsipuld Octoroon & the miserbul man in black close was gone, & all of a suddent it flasht ore my brane that I'de bin swindild.

Interview with President Lincoln

I HAV no politics. Not a one. I'm not in the bisness. If I was I spose I should holler versiffrusly in the streets at nite and go home to Betsy Jane smellin of coal ile and gin, in the mornin. I should go to the Poles arly. I should stay there all day. I should see to it that my nabers was thar. I should git carriges to take the kripples, the infirm and the indignant thar. I should be on guard agin frauds and sich. I should be on the look out for the infamus lise of the enemy, got up jest be4 elecshun for perlitical effeck. When all was over and my candydate was elected, I should move heving & erth—so to speak—until I got orfice, which if I didn't git a orfice I should turn round and abooze the Administration with all my mite and maine. But I'm not in the bizniss. I'm in a far more respectful bizniss nor what pollertics is. I wouldn't giv two cents to be a Congresser. The wuss insult I ever received was when sertin citizens of Baldinsville axed me to run fur the Legislator. Sez I, "My friends, dostest think I'd stoop to that there?" They turned as white as a sheet. I spoke in my most orfullest tones & they knowed I wasn't to be trifled with. They slunked out of site to onct.

There4, havin no politics, I made bold to visit Old Abe at his humstid in Springfield. I found the old feller in his parler,

surrounded by a perfeck swarm of orfice seekers. Knowin he
had been capting of a flat boat on the roarin Mississippy I
thought I'd address him sailor lingo, so sez I, "Old Abe, ahoy!
Let out yer main-suls, reef hum the forecastle & throw yer
jib-poop over-board! Shiver my timbers, my harty!" (N.B.
This is ginuine mariner langwidge. I know, becawz I've seen
sailor plays acted out by them New York theater fellers) Old
Abe lookt up quite cross & sez, "Send in yer petition by &
by. I can't possibly look at it now. Indeed, I can't. It's onpossible, sir!"

"Mr. Linkin, who do you spect I air?" sed I.

"A orfice-seeker, to be sure," sed he.

"Wall, sir," sed I, "you's never more mistaken in your life.
You hain't gut a orfiss I'd take under no circumstances. I'm
A. Ward. Wax figgers is my perfeshun. I'm the father of
Twins, and they look like me—*both of them*. I cum to pay
a friendly visit to the President eleck of the United States.
If so be you wants to see me, say so, if not, say so & I'm orf
like a jug handle."

"Mr. Ward, sit down. I am glad to see you, Sir."

"Repose in Abraham's Buzzum!" sed one of the orfice
seekers, his idee bein to git orf a goak at my expense.

"Wall," sez I, "ef all you fellers repose in that there Buzzum thar'll be mity poor nussin for sum of you!" whereupon
Old Abe buttoned his weskit clear up and blusht like a maidin
of sweet 16. Jest at this pint of the conversation another
swarm of orfice-seekers arrove & cum pilin into the parler.
Sum wanted post orfices, sum wanted collectorships, sum
wantid furrin missions, and all wanted sumthin. I thought Old
Abe would go crazy. He hadn't more than had time to shake
hands with 'em, before another tremenjis crowd cum porein
onto his premises. His house and dooryard was now perfeckly
overflowed with orfice seekers, all clameruss for a immejit
interview with Old Abe. One man from Ohio, who had about
seven inches of corn whisky into him, mistook me for Old

Abe and addrest me as "The Pra-hayrie Flower of the West!" Thinks I *you* want a offiss putty bad. Another man with a gold-heded cane and a red nose told Old Abe he was "a seckind Washington & the Pride of the Boundliss West."

Sez I, "Square, you wouldn't take a small post-offiss if you could git it, would you?"

Sez he, "A patrit is abuv them things, sir!"

"There's a putty big crop of patrits this season, ain't there, Squire?" sez I, when *another* crowd of offiss seekers pored in. The house, dooryard, barns, woodshed was now all full, and when *another* crowd cum I told 'em not to go away for want of room as the hog-pen was still empty. One patrit from a small town in Michygan went up on top of the house, got into the chimney and slid into the parler where Old Abe was endeverin to keep the hungry pack of orfice-seekers from chawin him up alive without benefit of clergy. The minit he reached the fireplace he jumpt up, brusht the soot out of his eyes, and yelled: "Don't make eny pintment at the Spunkville postoffiss till you've read my papers. All the respectful men in our town is signers to that there dockyment!"

"Good God!" cried Old Abe, "They cum upon me from the skize—down the chimneys, and from the bowels of the yerth!" He hadn't morn' got them words out of his delikit mouth before two fat offiss-seekers from Winconsin, in endeverin to crawl atween his legs for the purpuss of applyin for the tollgateship at Milwawky, upsot the President eleck, & he would hev gone sprawlin into the fireplace if I hadn't caught him in these arms. But I hadn't more'n stood him up strate before another man cum crashing down the chimney, his head strikin me viliently again the inards and prostratin my voluptoous form onto the floor. "Mr. Linkin," shoutid the infatooated being, "my papers is signed by every clergyman in our town, and likewise the skoolmaster!"

Sez I, "You egrejis ass," gittin up & brushin the dust from my eyes, "I'll sign your papers with this bunch of bones, if

you don't be a little more keerful how you make my bread
basket a depot in the futur. How do you like that air per-
fumery?" sez I, shuving my fist under his nose. "Them's the
kind of papers I'll giv you! Them's the papers *you* want!"

"But I workt hard for the ticket; I toiled night and day!
The patrit should be rewarded!"

"Virtoo," sed I holdin' the infatooated man by the coat-
collar, "virtoo, sir, is its own reward. Look at me!, He did
look at me, and qualed be4 my gase. "The fact is," I continued, lookin' round on the hungry crowd, "there is scacely
a offiss for every ile lamp carrid round durin' this campane.
I wish thare was. I wish thare was furrin missions to be filled
on varis lonely Islands where eprydemics rage incessantly, and
if I was in Old Abe's place I'd send every mother's son of you
to them. What air you here for?" I continnered, warmin up
considerable, "can't you giv Abe a minit's peace? Don't you
see he's worrid most to death? Go home, you miserable men,
go home & till the sile! Go to peddlin tinware—go to choppin
wood—go to bilin' sope—stuff sassengers—black boots—git a
clerkship on sum respectable manure cart—go round as original Swiss Bell Ringers—becum 'origenal and only' Campbell
Minstrels—go to lecturin at 50 dollars a nite—imbark in the
peanut bizniss—*write for the Ledger*—saw off your legs and
go round givin concerts, with tuchin appeals to a charitable
public, printed on your handbills—anything for a honest living, but don't come round here drivin Old Abe crazy by your
outrajis cuttings up! Go home. Stand not upon the order of
your goin', but go to onct! Ef in five minits from this time,"
sez I, pullin' out my new sixteen dollar huntin cased watch
and brandishin' it before their eyes, "Ef in five minits from
this time a single sole of you remains on these here premises,
I'll go out to my cage near by, and let my Boy Constructor
loose! & ef he gits amung you, you'll think old Solferino has
cum again and no mistake!" You ought to hev seen them
scamper, Mr. Fair. They run of as tho Satun hisself was arter

them with a red hot ten pronged pitchfork. In five minits the premises was clear.

"How kin I ever repay you, Mr. Ward, for your kindness?" sed Old Abe, advancin and shakin me warmly by the hand. "How kin I ever repay you, sir?"

"By givin the whole country a good, sound administration. By poerin' ile upon the troubled waturs, North and South. By pursooin' a patriotic, firm, and just course, and then if any State wants to secede, let 'em Sesesh!"

"How 'bout my Cabinit, Mister Ward?" sed Abe.

"Fill it up with Showmen, sir! Showmen, is devoid of politics. They hain't got any principles. They know how to cater for the public. They know what the public wants, North & South. Showmen, sir, is honest men. Ef you doubt their literary ability, look at their posters, and see small bills! Ef you want a Cabinit as is a Cabinit fill it up with showmen, but don't call on me. The moral wax figger perfeshun musn't be permitted to go down while there's a drop of blood in these vains! A. Linkin, I wish you well! Ef Powers or Walcutt wus to pick out a model for a beautiful man, I scarcely think they'd sculp you; but ef you do the fair thing by your country you'll make as putty a angel as any of us! A. Linkin, use the talents which Nature has put into you judishusly and firmly, and all will be well! A. Linkin, adoo!"

He shook me cordyully by the hand—we exchanged picters, so we could gaze upon each others' liniments when far away from one another—he at the hellum of the ship of State, and I at the hellum of the show bizniss—admittance only 15 cents.

Ten Eyck White

Ten Eyck White conducted during the late 1870's and early 1880's a popular column in the Chicago TRIBUNE called "Lakeside Musings" gathered into a volume of the same name in 1884. One of White's favorite characters is the cynical "horse reporter," who usually manages to intercept naive or annoying visitors intent upon getting the ear of the editor. "Myrtle's Reward" illustrates the tendency of newspaper satirists of that day to jeer at the social pretensions of the bumptious NOUVEAU RICHE and their imitators in the future capital of pork and steel, as well as at the elegant embroideries of popular romantic fiction.

How to Regain Him

"Is THE hymeneal-happenings editor in?"

A very pretty young lady stood in the doorway and glanced in an appealing way at the occupants of the room.

"Hymeneal means something about getting married, doesn't it?" said the horse reporter.

"Yes, sir," replied the young lady, "but I don't want to marry. . . ."

"Oh, no; I know you don't," said the friend of Maud S. "Girls never do. They spend most of their time trying to escape from the dreadful abyss of matrimony into which countless young men are endeavoring to plunge them."

"The object of my visit," said the young lady, "is to see some editor in regard to a poem, and it occurred to me that perhaps the gentleman for whom I asked might be the person having such matters in charge. I have met with a sad disappointment, and have written this poem in commemoration of the event."

"I'm sorry he got away," said the horse reporter, "but perhaps you were lucky to lose him. There isn't anything in the poem about the brown mantle of October resting lightly on the hills, is there? or the deep green of the pines being reflected against the turquoise bloom of the autumn sky? Because if there is, we can't take it. There is more brown mantle-of-October poetry stowed away here than a window cleaner can use in a year. If you've got anything about the white messengers of heaven drifting silently through the keen air, or the gaunt outlines of the leafless oaks standing haggard against an unpitying sky, we might do business with you. Our stock of November poetry is rather light this season. If you could ring in something about a boot-black dying on the steps of a banker's residence Christmas eve, while inside the house the wassail bowl was going round, it would be a daisy."

"I'm afraid my poem will hardly meet the requirements you suggest," said the young lady, "because the theme is a sad one, and the treatment is naturally in accord with this fact. I can read it to you, however."

"Nothing about 'Put away his little rattle' in it, is there?"

"No, sir."

"Nor 'The beautiful Summer is dead, alas'?"

"Certainly not."

"Well, then, you may read it;" and the horse reporter settled himself in a critical attitude.

The young lady produced a roll of manuscript and read as follows:

> And this is the end of all, Ernest; the end of our happy
>   dreams;
> A walk to the quiet graveyard where the snowy marble
>   gleams;
> Tablets of blighted hopes, and broken hearts that moan
> For their buried loves, and the weary years that must be
>   lived alone.
>
> You go back to the world, Ernest—men's hearts so sel-
>   dom break—
> And go under new stars, in new skies set, soon others
>   ties will make;
> But I go back to a desolate life—no man can ever be,
> Though I roam the wide world over, what once you
>   were to me.
>
> And this is the end of all. Good-bye. Perhaps it had
>   caused less pain
> To have gone our separate ways without seeing each
>   other again.

For want of one little word, Ernest, lives often drift
apart;
You spoke that word, but it came too late; it only broke
my heart.

"Nice, ain't it?" remarked the horse reporter when the reading was finished. "Are you the girl that's been up to the graveyard and taken a look at the tablets of blighted hopes?"

"Yes, sir."

"Ernest is going back to the world, is he? What has he been doing in St. Louis all this time?"

"I hardly think you appreciate the circumstances under which the poem was written," said the young lady.

"Oh, yes I do. Ernest is your young man, and you have quarreled with him because he only called you his tootsy-wootsy eighteen times instead of twenty, as you had figured on. You think your heart is broken, and you want to get even by breaking other people's hearts with your poetry. That's wrong. Just now the world seems desolate, and the horizon of your life is o'er cast with leaden colors. But time heals all wounds, and in about a month from now, when some other young man mentions oysters, the chances are you will beat the record getting your sealskin jacket off the hat-rack."

"You are very much mistaken, sir," said the young lady. "My love is no ephemeral passion."

"Do you still want Ernest?"

"Yes, sir."

"Well, I can tell you how to get him."

"Oh, can you?" asked the girl enthusiastically. "I shall be so thankful if you will."

"You take this poem," said the horse reporter, "and send it to him. Then drop him a line saying the papers have agreed to print it for you. If he doesn't weaken when it comes to having his name mixed up with a lot of graveyards, blighted hopes, broken hearts and a desolate life, I shall miss my guess."

"Do you really think so?" asked the girl.

"Yes; really and truly."

"And I will tell you whether or not your plan succeeds," she continued.

"Never mind that part of it," replied the compiler of the 2:30 list. "The scheme will work, all right. Come around again after you are married, and I will give you a pointer on how to keep Ernest at home nights."

Myrtle's Reward

AT SUNSET on a beautiful day in June a solitary horsecar might have been seen ascending the brow of a hill. As the dappled palfrey which drew it bravely on reached the crest of the eminence and paused for an instant before beginning the downward journey, the intelligent beast gave a snort of terror, and sprang so suddenly to one side that the helmeted knight in whose womanly-white hands were gathered the reins was yanked violently over the brake, and most of the air knocked out of his system ere he could regain his position abaft the dashboard, and again head the terrified charger in the direction of Western avenue.

"By my halidom!" quoth the knight. "St. Julien must have seen an oat."

It was true. Some roystering son of Blue Island avenue, going home with many a flagon of bock beer beneath his corselet, had with wasteful hand thrown by the roadside no less than several oats, at the sight of which the neighing steed which so gallantly breasted the brow of the hill at the opening of this chapter, was stricken with the terror that always comes to beasts when that which they have ne'er before beheld comes suddenly within the vista of their gaze.

"Curses on the horse! he has broken my suspender!" exclaimed Roderigo O'Rourke, eighth Duke of Wexford, as he wound the lines around the brake and spliced his pants with a string.

In a corner of the car sits Myrtle Hathaway, her pure, passionless face with wine-red lips pressed closely to the window. She is pure as the driven snow, and chaste as an ice-wagon. Two years ago she was the petted idol of doting parents—the pampered child of luxury and unlimited confectionery—but one soft, sensuous day in summer, when the fields were laughing in the golden glory of an ample harvest, her father came home and said to her in tear-choked tones: "We must sleep in the woodshed to-night; this house is no longer mine. All that I possessed has been lost forever."

Myrtle did not question him, did not seek to intrude upon the sacred precints of his grief, but went silently away and blew in her last quarter for ice-cream.

George W. Hathaway did not long survive the horse-race that swept away his fortune, and in the fall they buried him in the sun-kissed cemetery beyond the beer garden, away from the noise and turmoil of the great city. But Myrtle, although accustomed to every luxury that credit could purchase, was possessed of a brave heart and large feet, and had gone forth to battle with the world and earn her own living. "I will gain my daily bread," she said; but after learning that making seventeen shirts for eight cents was the most lucrative operation open to her, she had concluded to change her subscription to the tri-weekly.

On the opposite seat of the car from Myrtle sat Bertha Redingote. The girls had moved in the same social circle in the days when Myrtle lolled idly in the lap of luxury, but now that she sat on one knee Bertha did not recognize her. But Myrtle cared not for this. "Let Bertha flaunt her pros-

perity and grenadine polonaise in my face, if she will," she
had said, "the time may come when I shall again be heading
the procession, and if it does, I shall have a pool or two on
myself."

"Leavitt street," said the conductor, his voice arousing
Myrtle from the reverie into which she had fallen. Both girls
left the car. On the corner, his choke-me-to-death collar looking weirdly white beneath the fitful glare of the West Side
gas, stood Ethelbert de Courcey—"Good-bye, John," the
boys called him, because they said that name was easier to
remember, and had a Cook county tinge to it. He was a good
young man—almost too good to be true—and very rich. His
wealth made him the object of maneuvering on the part of
designing mothers with marriageable daughters, but thus far
he had escaped unscathed. Both girls knew him. Bertha advanced with a witching Ogden avenue smile on her face, as
if to claim his company in her homeward walk; but he heeded
her not. Advancing quickly to Myrtle's side, he said:

"May I see you home, Miss Hathaway?"

"Yes," replied the girl, the pink suffusion of a blush hustling
rapidly over her cheek as she took his arm.

On the way to the humble pie-foundry where she fought
the bedbugs, they talked upon the current topics of the day
—the cable-cars, how Maud S. would drive to the pole, Mr.
Beecher's indigestion, etc; but presently Ethelbert's voice sank
lower, his tones became more tender, and he told the blushing
girl the story of his love—of how he fain would make her his
West Washington street bride. When he had finished, Myrtle
looked up into his eyes—those eyes so tender and true—and,
with a little happy sob, called his bluff.

PART THREE

YESTERDAY AND TODAY

*Modern Voices, Some of Them Recapturing
the Past*

George Ade

George Ade (1866–1944) was born in Kentland, Indiana. Graduating from Purdue University, he worked for a while on a small town paper in Indiana before he invaded Chicago—the big town by the big lake—in 1890. For several years he contributed odd bits and sketches, jingles, burlesques of grand opera, parodies of dime novels, and other divertissements to the RECORD *under the general classification of "Stories of the Streets and of the Town." He is better known for his series of "Fables in Slang" beginning in 1899 and continuing for many years in a number of volumes. The uninhibited style and lingual innovations of the* FABLES *seemed as bizarre to traditionalists of their day as does the "jive" talk of our era. Ade also wrote several more than ordinarily popular plays, including "The Sultan of Sulu" (1902) and "The College Widow" (1904). "Il Janitoro" is one of the "Stories of the Streets and of the Town."*

Il Janitoro

MR. TYLER paid $7 for two opera tickets.

Although he slept through one duet he felt fully repaid for going, because Mrs. Tyler raved over the opera and wasted all her superlatives on it. The music was "heavenly," the prima donna "superb" and the tenor "magnificent."

There is nothing so irritates a real enthusiasm as the presence of calm scorn.

"Don't you like it?" asked Mrs. Tyler, as she settled back after the eighth recall of the motherly woman who had been singing the part of a 16-year-old maiden.

"Oh, yes; it's all right," replied Mr. Tyler, as if he were conceding something.

"All right! Oh, you iceberg! I don't believe you'd become enthusiastic over anything in the world."

"I like the music, my dear, but grand opera drags so. Then the situations are so preposterous they always appeal to my sense of humor. I can't help it. When I see Romeo and Juliet die, both singing away as if they enjoyed it, I have to laugh."

"The idea!"

"You take it in this last act. Those two fellows came out with the soldiers and announced that they were conspiring and didn't want to be heard by the people in the house, and then they shouted in chorus until they could have been heard two miles away."

"Oh, you are prejudiced."

"Not at all. I'll tell you, a grand opera's the funniest kind of a show if you only take the right view of it."

Thus they argued, and even after they arrived home she taunted him and told him he could not appreciate the dignity of the situations.

It was this nagging which induced Mr. Tyler to write an act of grand opera. He chose for his subject an alarm of fire in an apartment house. He wanted something modern and up-to-date, but in his method of treatment he resolved to reverently follow all the traditions of grand opera. The act, hitherto unpublished, and written solely for the benefit of Mrs. Tyler, is here appended:

(Mr and Mrs. Taylor are seated in their apartment on the fifth floor of the Bohemoth residential-flat building. Mrs. Taylor arises, places her hand on her heart, and moves to the center of the room. Mr. Taylor follows her, with his right arm extended.)

MRS. TAYLOR: I think I smell smoke.

MR. TAYLOR: She thinks she smells smoke.

MRS. TAYLOR: I think I smell smoke.

MR. TAYLOR: Oh. What is it? She says she thinks she smells smoke.

MRS. TAYLOR: What does it mean, what does it mean?
This smell of smoke may indicate,
That we'll be burned—oh-h-h, awful fate!

MR. TAYLOR: Behold the smell grows stronger yet,
The house is burning, I'd regret
To perish in the curling flames;
Oh, horror! horror!! horror!!!

MR. AND MRS. TAYLOR: Oh, sad is our lot, sad is our lot,
To perish in the flames so hot,
To curl and writhe and fry and sizz,
Oh, what a dreadful thing it is
To think of such a thing!

MRS. TAYLOR: We must escape!

MR. TAYLOR: Yes, yes, we must escape!

MRS. TAYLOR: We have no time to lose.

MR. TAYLOR: Ah, bitter truth, ah, bitter truth,
We have no time to lose.

MR. AND MRS. TAYLOR: Sad is our lot, sad is our lot,
                               To perish in the flames so hot.
MR. TAYLOR: Hark, what is it?
MRS. TAYLOR: Hark, what is it?
MR. TAYLOR: It is the dread alarm of fire.
MRS. TAYLOR: Ah, yes, ah, yes, it is the dread alarm.
MR. TAYLOR: The dread alarm strikes on the ear
                 And chills me with an awful fear.
                 The house will burn, oh, can it be
                 That I must die in misery,
                 That I must die in misery,
                 The house will burn, oh, can it be
                 That I must die in misery?
MRS. TAYLOR: Come, let us fly!
MR. TAYLOR: 'Tis well. 'Tis well! We'll fly at once.
          (*Enter all the other residents of the fifth floor.*)
MR. TAYLOR: Kind friends, I have some news to tell.
                 This house is burning, it were well
                 That we should haste ourselves away
                 And save our lives without delay.
CHORUS: What is this he tells us?
            It must be so;
            The building is on fire
            And we must go.
            Oh, hasten, oh, hasten, oh, hasten away.
            Our terror we should not conceal,
            And language fails to express the alarm
            That in our hearts we feel.
MR. AND MRS. TAYLOR: Oh, language fails to express the
                              alarm
                   That in their hearts they feel.
              (*Enter the Janitor*)
JANITOR: Hold, I am here.
MR. TAYLOR: Ah, it is the Janitoro.

MRS. TAYLOR: Can I believe my senses,
                Or am I going mad?
                It is the Janitoro,
                It is indeed the Janitoro.

JANITOR: Such news I have to tell.

MR. TAYLOR: Ah, I might have known
                He has such news to tell.
                Speak and break the awful suspense.

MRS. TAYLOR: Yes, speak.

JANITOR: I come to inform you
                That you must quickly fly.
                The fearful blaze is spreading,
                To tarry is to die.
                The floors underneath you
                Are completely burned away.
                They cannot save the building,
                So now escape I pray.

MRS. TAYLOR: Oh, awful message,
                How it chills my heart.

JANITOR: The flames are roaring loudly,
                Oh, what a fearful sound!
                You can hear the people shrieking
                As they jump and strike the ground.
                Oh, horror overtakes me,
                And I merely pause to say
                That the building's doomed for certain.
                Oh, haste, oh, haste away.

MRS. TAYLOR: Oh, awful message.
                How it chills my heart.
                Yet we will sing a few more arias
                Before we start.

MR. TAYLOR: Yes, a few more arias and then away.

CHORUS: Oh, hasten, oh, hasten, oh, hasten away.

MRS. TAYLOR: Now, ere I retreat,
                Lest death o'ertakes me

> I'll speak of the fear
> That convulses and shakes me,
> I sicken to think what may befall,
> Oh, horror! horror!! horror!!!

MR. TAYLOR: The woman speaks the truth,
And there can be no doubt
That we will perish soon
Unless we all clear out.

CHORUS: Oh, hasten, oh, hasten, oh, hasten away.

(But why go further? The supposition is that they continued the dilatory tactics of grand opera and perished in the flames.)

Nelson Algren

Nelson Algren (1909–   ) was born in Detroit, but moved to Chicago as a small boy. Several work-hunting expeditions which took him to various parts of the United States by boxcar and hitchhiking gave him as an invaluable byproduct of his travels both the material for some of his subsequent stories of underdogs and his sympathetic and comprehending attitude toward them. His early short stories appeared in THE ANVIL, STORY, THE AMERI-CAN MERCURY, *and in a great many of the "little" magazines. He published two novels,* SOMEBODY IN BOOTS *(1935) and* NEVER COME MORNING *(1942), before he saw some rugged action in France and Germany during the closing days of World War II. "The Heroes" is from* THE NEON WILDERNESS.

The Heroes

CORPORAL HARDHEART wasn't much of an Indian, even to look at. He didn't like to hike, he hated living in tents, he was afraid of horses, and he was blind as a bat in the woods after dark. I'd spent one night on bivouac with him back in the States, and the little joker had gotten lost three times before morning. He couldn't even start a fire with matches, far less with flint. But he liked firewater fine: that's why we sometimes called him Chief Boozeheart.

He was mostly Mex, with a touch of Osage in the eyes, but liked to pretend he was full-blooded. He had the deadpan Indian look when he wanted to put it on, and he loved putting it on. Standing with arms folded across his mess kit at the head of the chow line, wearing a fatigue cap as jauntily as a crow feather, he'd maintain a stolid silence until he saw there was nothing but warmed-over C-ration or cold Argentine corned beef again.

"There are better ways to die than to starve, Paleface," he'd announce solemnly to Mess Sergeant Infantino, who was twice as dark as himself. "White man kills the red man's buffalo. Red man must have buffalo: the meat to eat and the hide to keep him warm." He'd go on in that vein until the mess officer came in to see what was holding up chow. "I have spoken," Chief would conclude with dignity then—and grab a double portion of everything, whooping and hollering like a fool; then dash off to Special Service to find out when they were going to start showing movies.

Chief had gotten his education at movies. He hadn't missed anything with Yellow-Hand, Geronimo, or Sitting Bull in it for fifteen years and knew most of their lines by heart. The

most moving sequence he'd ever witnessed was from *Western
Union*, wherein Yellow-Hand plants an arrow directly between the shoulder blades of a telegraph lineman. Chief liked
to lie back on his cot, with a half-empty cognac bottle in his
hand, and reflect nostalgically on Yellow-Hand's accuracy.

"The beauty part was," he'd explain, "where he come down
head over heels 'n that arrer stickin' out so far in front you
could've tied a ribbon on it." Outside of the mess line he
didn't talk much like an M-G-M Indian. But he knew how to
corral cognac.

My cot was next to his, and we started buddying up, though
not because of the proximity of the cots. He didn't want any
Paleface buddy, he said: he was a lone wolf, being both the
only Indian and the only volunteer, Regular Army, in the outfit. But I pleased him, accidentally, one morning in southern
Germany, when he had to get out the guard, by reciting for
him:

> By the shores of Gitche Gumee,
> By the shining Big-Sea-Water,
> Stood the wigwam of Chief Hardheart,
> Sergeant of the Guard, Chief Hardheart.
> Ewa-yea! my little owlet!

"Say more, Lineman," he asked. But that was all I could
remember or invent. I'd hooked an oversized German pocket-
knife in my belt, the way I'd seen infantry linemen do, and
it had reminded Chief of the lineman of *Western Union*.

That was the basis of our friendship; it was that sort of
friendship. He was constantly suggesting that I climb up
something: if no telephone pole were handy he'd jerk his
thumb toward the flagpole in front of the receiving tent.

"You ought to learn to shinny up that thing like a *real*
lineman," he'd insist. "Then you'd be the real thing and could
get transferred to the infantry."

"Maybe you could learn to fly and get transferred to the paratroops," I'd tell him. He didn't want any part of that, of course. He didn't want to fly any more than he wanted to climb. In fact, it was all he could do to climb into his cot half the time. It always seemed four or five feet high to him when he got stiff, for some reason.

And I would have to admit that Custer had been more of a terrorist than a soldier. "He'd of been court-martialed if he'd lived to go back to Washington," I'd concede.

"It's a lead-pipe cinch he *should* have been," Chief would assert, and would add seriously, "Custer never should have gone West that time in the first place."

"Why not?"

"Because who'd want to leave Olivia De Havilland to all those Washington wolves?" And he'd whoop and holler his bucktoothed laughter. He was like that all the time: when he was most serious he was joking and when he was joking he was most in earnest.

One night we put on our medic armbands, for protection against snipers, to hunt for cognac. The armband was the best protection a medic had. It said in the book. Some protection. Chief shoved his .45 into his raincoat pocket and handed me a British .22. Some Indian.

"White man is soft," he assured me, loading the .45 with the barrel pointed at my toes. "Paleface need red man for guide. Red man protect Paleface from evil forest spirits."

"You got most of the evil spirits in Germany inside you already," I told him. It was after two in the morning and he already smelled so I was afraid the odor might waken the guards. The guards could sleep through gunfire, but would sit bolt upright at the faintest hint of schnapps in the wind. In front of the receiving tent Witzel, a little Pennsylvania weasel, private of the guard, was sleeping one off. His rifle had been jabbed, barrel down, into the mud a dozen yards away and he was sleeping hunched up against the flap of the tent. Holding down that flap was the first work I'd ever seen him do.

He had turned me in once, at Camp Twenty Grand, when I was cooking up K-rations in my tent instead of remaining on duty guarding the officers' latrine in the rain. The enlisted men had developed an outrageous habit there of using it, instead of their own, during the night; although their own was a perfectly good one only half a mile out in the woods, which were mined. I'd wanted to even up on Witzel for the week of detail he'd gotten me that time, so I grabbed the rifle and showed it under my coat, intending to drop it down the first convenient sump, but Chief had an even better idea.

"We'll get schnapps out of some Kraut farmer for it," he decided. "Then in the morning we'll turn the Kraut in for possession of firearms 'n we'll both be heroes." We got out of bounds talking like that, and it was so dark all I could see was the fall and rise of the Chief's hunched shoulders in front of me.

"Red man has eyes in the dark. He speaks the tongue of the forest creatures," he told me.

"You walk into a couple combat MPs you won't need your damn eyes," I told him. "They'll show you the way." And he dropped the Hollywood Indian line for a while. Funny recalling it now, and we worried about Special Guards and Hospital Guards and MPs and officers and noncoms—everything but Krauts.

Once a plane came over and we paused long enough to be able to tell, by the break in the motor, that it was German. But there were so many more immediate dangers, from our own buddies, that the Kraut stuff always seemed sort of remote, so long as you didn't see anything but the distant flare of guns or the hum of a motor in the darkness overhead. Our war was with the second lieutenants, the MPs, and the cooks.

Whenever I'd get hungry I'd think of the breakfast they'd be planning, about this hour, to poison us with, and I wouldn't feel hungry for a while. Our cooks could have messed up the Lord's Supper.

I'll never know whether my little owlet found the house by accident or design—but they'd left a tiny kerosene lamp burning and we caught its glint through a rent in the blackout curtain and shoved in. They tumbled back against the wall like frightened rabbits and there wasn't a man among them.

A grandmother, a middle-aged daughter, a couple middle-aged *hausfraus,* a girl of seventeen, and half a dozen Kraut sprouts between five and twelve. They just huddled up, the women in front of the sprouts, waiting for us to mow them down. Chief turned off the lamp and played his flashlight along their faces, lingering a moment on the seventeen-year-old's. *"Foy-yer verboten!"* he scolded, as though by shouting he could make himself better understood, and the grandmother began throwing water into the stove.

"Nein," I said, *"licht verboten,"* and pointed at the darkened lamp. So it was all right to keep their stove burning and there I was with another man's rifle, holding half a dozen helpless women at bay while Chief began prowling around for firewater. He turned out a couple drawers, threw some papers on the floor, then retrieved one and returned to me with it. It bore a swastika in one corner and looked like some sort of diploma. All I could make out of it, by flashlight, was that it certified some *fraulein* to belong to the local Kampfire girls.

We wouldn't have known that we had a good thing, but the seventeen-year-old came forward, her face rigid with genuine fright.

"Mine," she acknowledged heroically, and added, *"Me nichts Nazi."* She tried to convince us then that she wasn't an international spy because she belonged to the Kampfire girls, but we weren't having any. We knew better.

"You Mata Hari," Chief told her with dead-pan conviction. He'd seen that one too.

"*Nein*. Harry *gefangene*," she asserted. Harry must have been her boy friend, for she crossed her wrists to indicate a prisoner of war. I wavered when she went down on her knees then, to beg the damning indictment back, but Chief was adamant.

"Paleface squaw must not fear her red brother," he told her, and Muni himself couldn't have looked more immovable when he said it.

"*Trinken*," I told her, to shorten her anguish, "*wir wollen schnapps.*"

Without further pleading the girl rose and left the house quietly, wearing a sort of shawl to protect her from the rain. We weren't too sure where she'd gone, what she'd gone after, or what she'd come back with. They weren't supposed to be out after dark any more than we. But we sat down to wait, well clear of the windows.

She must have crawled along hedgerows to get wherever she had gone, because she brought it back in about twenty minutes. It was almost a full bottle, too. Chief passed it around: Everybody had to drink, even the little ones had to have their lips wetted with it. It wasn't until that had been accomplished that Chief returned the diploma to the girl and there was still enough left in the bottle for one good snort apiece. Then the party was over and I made the girl kiss Chief goodby and he made me kiss the grandmother.

The *hausfraus* shook their heads disapprovingly at this crazy stuff, really offended that we weren't going to take them seriously after such a promising beginning.

It had stopped raining, and a sweet wet light was blowing hard through the trees and we didn't have to stand reveille. But we did have to be on litter duty at seven, so we ditched the rifle and at chow I told Witzel where he could find it if he still wanted it. He didn't seem to get mad, although he was usually an explosive little rat. And when we got into the mess hall Sergeant Infantino remarked that Germany had capitu-

lated sometime in the night and I thought that's fine, maybe
the war'll be over one of these days.

It didn't feel like it was over. Witzel turned us both in for
stealing his rifle and Chief lost his stripes the same afternoon.
They couldn't break me down to anything but a yardbird,
which I was most of the time anyhow, and Chief came out
to watch me haul buckets of dirt out of one hole in order to
fill in another. After a while he took off his shirt and got a
bucket of his own. Then I'd empty the dirt into his bucket
and he'd cart it back to the hole I'd dug it out of, and I'd dig
it out and carry it back to his bucket. This simplified the detail, as we could alternate in resting while the other hauled,
and half a dozen Kraut PWs came up to watch us with
solemn envy. They envied anybody who was working at any
methodical task, and wanted to help us at first. But we
wouldn't let them because they'd just lost the war, and after
a while their solemn envy turned to solemn wonder, because
they couldn't figure out what we were trying to build. Just
stood watching the crazy Americans working up a sweat hauling dirt from one hole to another until their wonder became
annoyance and they muttered gutturally, looking around for
someone with bars on, as though they'd like to turn us in too.
There was quite a hard feeling rising, especially when we
began barking orders at each other and their heads would
turn from one to the other and they couldn't tell who was the
superior. They didn't see anything funny in it and the colonel
didn't either.

He felt the Chief had mocked the assignment I'd been
given, so he took me off and Chief had to carry a full field
pack up and down in front of the orderly room from reveille
to retreat the next day. It was a lucky thing that he'd filled it
with empty cardboard ration boxes, to make it look like he
had his equipment in it, because everything he owned was
concealed in my duffel bag; so there wasn't anything to the
detail except walking up and down.

By night he was so drunk, from the cognac that sympathetic buddies had given him to sustain him in his long ordeal, that he became convinced he really was a paratrooper and wanted to jump off the bulletin board, pack and all. Only he couldn't climb that high, and I refused to boost him. So he ordered me to recite *Hiawatha* over the public-address system, and when I refused he threatened to have me transferred to the infantry first thing in the morning, and I told him that Custer could have licked Sitting Bull in a man-to-man fight, and he started getting sick. He wanted to heave and he couldn't, so I put a finger down his throat to help him and he damned near bit it off. I think I hit him eight or ten times before he let loose, and there was quite a row and I thought we were in for it again.

But it was all right because the colonel wasn't around, he was sleeping off a drunk in the nurses' quarters and it looked like he'd stay that way three or four days anyhow. He usually did, and put it down on the schedule as classes in orientation. But everybody liked him better oriented that way anyhow, as that was the only time he talked like he might be related to the human race.

Chief sobered up and behaved himself nobly for a week, but we weren't on friendly terms any more as his face was still swollen and my finger still bandaged, and after a week I guess he had enough of good conduct, because he went off to look for the house where we'd corralled the cognac by himself.

He went off sober, while it was still light, and took the same path we'd stumbled along in the dark, but he would have been better off to have left drunk and by darkness. A hundred yards from the house he stepped on a Teller mine, and we didn't get to him for almost an hour, when the *fraulein* came running up and told us they had him in the house.

They brought him in on a litter looking like he'd been dug

out of a coal mine, with both feet blown off at the ankles and even his dog tags blackened.

When they got him onto the table he was still conscious and spoke to the doc, looking down at where his feet had been. "Well," I heard him say, "I can still sleep with the *frauleins* anyhow."

He might still have been able to manage that, at that, except that he'd been left lying across that path too long.

It was rough enough, but it wasn't too bad because when the chaplain arrived in his jeep, to hold services, he was stone sober, and he brought a T/5 and a Pfc to help him and they were sober as anybody, and everybody was really sober.

All, that is, but the colonel. He was still conducting Orientation up in the nurses' quarters and was putting in for a Purple Heart. He thought he'd been wounded when a champagne cork had popped into the wall above his head.

Jack Balch

Jack Balch was born in London and spent part of his boyhood in Russia and in Constantinople. He came to Saint Louis as a youth, and has remained there ever since. His short stories have appeared in THE ANVIL, AMERICAN STUFF *(1937), an anthology of material by members of the Federal Writers' Project, and elsewhere. He was Assistant State Director of the Missouri Writers' Project, and has worked for the Saint Louis* POST-DISPATCH *as book reviewer, dramatic critic, and feature writer. He has written and directed two plays produced in Saint Louis,* ME, THE SLEEPER *and* WITH CHALK ON THE SIDEWALKS. LAMPS AT HIGH NOON, *the novel from which "Momma Gest and the Irisher" is reprinted, is the story of Morris Gest, free-lance writer of Saint Louis, wafted into comparative affluence when he lands a job as a federal writer on the local project. His determination to make things a little easier for his workhorse mother precipitates the situation described here.*

Momma Gest and the Irisher

SHE HAD never had a servant before. What *does* one with a servant? Is it as if she, Mrs. Gest (let the truth be told!), is a *pritza*, to the manner born—a—a *government?* How, then, does one instruct a servant? If addressed too abruptly, would she not feel insulted? And, really, now, is she not after all a person, a living woman? How can you take a *living woman* and say, as to one's own, "Do this, do that!"

And another thing (resentfully, she marshaled reasons), so accustomed was she herself simply to do whatever was to be done, to drag herself methodically and unthinkingly from one job to another through the day, which never is long enough for all that is to be done, that she simply did not know how you make a beginning. And from where.

Besides (the thought filled her with anger at Charlie), who knows how this woman did her work? Plainly, from the looks of her, an *Irisher,* she was not to be trusted. Suppose she scrubbed too hard here, a little not enough there, that would be fine, would it not! And to let her "monki uhruhnd" with the food, what a thought too! Mrs. Gest had heard stories (don't ask her where, she had heard them) of these people. A sprinkle of poison dropped into the soup, a spit into the coffee —what then, is the Jew loved? A vision of Janice writhing on her back, poisoned, rose before her mind.

"Mother," Janice moaned. "You have killed me!"

She was filled with horror.

"God should only watch over us," she muttered.

Meanwhile the woman had taken off her coat. She had looked around the kitchen. A quick thrust of satisfaction in the proud breast of Mrs. Gest as she perceived, with woman's intuition and the instinctive knowledge of other women that transcends race, that Mrs. Johnson approved of what she saw. A house clean as a pin! A sink you could sleep on, so it shines! A quick one-act fantasy, one of those little plays that no playwright can match for utter and triumphant blending of the qualities of beauty and the ideal, was conceived, written and produced, witnessed and applauded in the fastidious theater of her mind, in a second, Mrs. Johnson, her face transfigured, stands in a circle of her friends in some unknown setting. They hang on her every word. And Mrs. Johnson talks.

"I'll tell you the God's honest truth," says Mrs. Johnson, "a house such as Mrs. Gest keeps I have never seen. So nice, so clean, it's a pleasure! I mean it. A pleasure! You would think," says Mrs. Johnson (not that the audience has objected on this score; far from it; for their faces beam and they murmur appreciatively among themselves), "you would think that she could not do it. After all, is Mrs. Gest a rich woman?"

"How does she do it?" say all the Irishers. "How does she manage?"

"It's the God's own miracle," says Mrs. Johnson helplessly. "She does it, that is all I know. *How*, don't ask me!"

Flash! The play had run its course. But Mrs. Gest had been warmed by it. Mrs. Johnson, after all—a woman, like herself— a woman—it was plain—who has worked so hard. And to have to go out to strangers! Tears filled her eyes. Later, she would modestly narrate to Nussim, to the Widow Cohen, to Charlie even, what Mrs. Johnson had said about her household. She would tell it as though Don't think this is my opinion, it is what Mrs. Johnson said. Nor would she be conscious of guile.

She warmed by the second to her visitor. It was nice to have somebody in the house with you through the long day. Actually, she could hardly think of her "visitor" as a servant. With a sudden burst of energy, she set about bustling.

"A cup of coffee," she mumbled. "How can one go without a cup of coffee?"

Mrs. Johnson hung her coat over a chair.

"Yes, Ma'am," she said. "It's cold outside. I sure could do with a cup of coffee."

Before even Mrs. Gest could see the pattern of her motions, she had put coffee, bread, butter on the table. A lunge into the icebox produced her prize, the big jar that she kept carefully wrapped in a paper bag and toward the back of the lowest shelf for fear somebody would see it—a jar of herring and onions. A piece of cold garlic sausage came next, a little plate of tomatoes and black olives.

"Eat, eat," she urged. "For work one must have strength. . . . All right," she argued and conceded to herself, "I too will have a little something."

She looked searchingly at the other woman:

"Mrs. Johnson. *Please*. The herring and onions. You should not tell nobody. My family, they don't want me to have nothing. Only to know that there is herring in the house, Charlie would make noise to change the night into day. It's a disgrace for the neighbors."

She took a piece of herring in her fingers; quickly, with eager haste, she stripped it of as many bones as she could find, first ripping it deftly in two in order to get at the bones, and with a sigh put it between two slices of black pumpernickel bread, heavily buttered to exasperate the onions and bring out the full power of their flavor. Then, delicately, waiting until Mrs. Johnson too was ready for the assault, she put it to her mouth, one finger in the air, and took a huge slow long bite.

"Oh," she said, "how good that is!"

Mrs. Johnson, surprised at first by the nature of this beginning of her employment with Mrs. Gest, soon adapted herself. She ate what was placed before her, drank the contents of her cup as fast as it was filled (several times by the shy Mrs. Gest), and—in fact—began to gorge herself with an avidity even greater than her hostess'. The two looked at

each other occasionally with the flushed gleeful expression of
conspirators. Finally, with a large sigh of repletion, they sat
back. Mrs. Gest relieved the gas on her stomach by belching.
Mrs. Johnson, who had been keeping it in out of a notion of
refinement, belched. They looked at each other, both now at
ease.

"Now you just sit there," Mrs. Johnson suddenly said,
fussily, "I'll get the dishes cleaned before you know it."

Mrs. Gest, whose head was ringing from the effects of her
totally unexpected and savage descent on the forbidden food-
stuffs, allowed her to do this. She felt that she could do no
other. Watching her, she saw that the job Mrs. Johnson was
doing was a good job. The woman evidently knew how to
wash dishes. She allowed herself the luxury of sitting a minute
longer. Then, with a grunt, she got to her feet.

She went heavily toward the middle room. There, increas-
ingly conscious that she had eaten too much, she began to
make the beds. Why was it that the things she liked should
be so fraught with poison for her! The herring, which had
lain wistful in the icebox for days, haunting her disturbed and
lustful dreams as a young maiden haunts the blood of aged
monarchs, had, now that she had abandoned fear and eaten of
it, begun to punish her. She could feel the little tell-tale lumps
forming in the softest, the most tender parts of her stomach
and breasts, the lumps that soon would be damning the blood-
stream in its course, forcing the tributary torrents into her
head where soon they would hammer, hammer. She bent over
the pillows, shaking them, afraid to bend too far, for fear
dizziness would assail her. And (she was immensely surprised,
for she had forgotten that she was now a "boss") Mrs. Johnson had come to the other side of the bed.

"I'll do that," Mrs. Johnson said.

"Yes," she agreed weakly. "Thank you very much."

She found that she would have to sit down. Just for a moment. Yes, she had eaten too much herring, but even now she

refused to believe that she should not have eaten it. All her days were full of the memory of what a strong capable woman she had always been (*always*), and she refused to admit how sick she was. Also, she did not know that she had eaten the herring as a way of telling Charlie that she did not need help, no matter how often she had asked for it. In fact, she blamed Charlie for her present debacle. *Nu*, suppose she complained, she kicked, it was her business. The way they stormed at her, you would think—you would think—she didn't know what you would think—

To hide her weakness, which would pass, which would have to pass, which had always passed, she invented the pretext of going into the kitchen to heat up some water for the wash to follow.

"You finish the beds, please, Mrs. Johnson," she said, "I will go put on the water."

She went into the next room and began to put on the water. She filled a bucket full from the faucet. As she lifted it, she got dizzy. She put it down gently on the floor, and moved to the table. She sat down. All this as quietly as she could, an immense concentration of will-power. She sat there and waited for the dizziness to pass. She just closed her eyes and endured the malignant passage of her beloved enemy, the herring. She opened her eyes, not able to stand being closed in with the thumping in her head. The huge empty jar stood before her, the mute symbol of the feast that had been here. She stared at it with no anger. Rather with puzzlement and pain that she should be so fond of it, and it so false to her. And suddenly, from the other room, where she had left Mrs. Johnson and could hear her moving about, she heard a heavy crash.

"My God!" she said, and came to her feet.

She rushed into the room.

Mrs. Johnson had fallen across the bed and from there had fallen to the floor. She lay there now, face down, moving her arms and legs feebly, like a fish that has been on land for some time but still moves itself in hope that, miracle of miracles, water will be its reward. And from Mrs. Johnson's throat came queer gasps, as though she were trying to cough and could not.

Horrified, Mrs. Gest went down on her knees beside her.

"Mrs. Johnson! For God's sake, pull yourself together. What is the matter, Mrs. Johnson! What is wrong with you!"

With infinite care, she put her hand on Mrs. Johnson's forehead. It was cold, covered with sweat. "God save us all," she muttered, and turned her over, putting a pillow under her head. She went to the sink, poured a glass of water, brought it back.

"Drink this," she urged.

Mrs. Johnson, her head lifted up level with the rim of the glass, opened her mouth. She drank a few sips. Her eyes returned to life.

"Lift me up," she breathed hoarsely.

This was easier asked than done. Mrs. Gest was no featherweight, but neither was Mrs. Johnson. Strange to think of two such women as fragile, to be handled with care. But, with a gentleness and patience that the sick know the sick require, she tried, shifting first her weight, then Mrs. Johnson's, engaging an arm here, a mass of flesh there, securing first this leverage, that fulcrum, until finally, after an apparent eternity of effort, the major part of Mrs. Johnson, the *decisive* part of her weight, had fallen across the bed, and a swing of the feet accomplished the rest of her. She lay, breathing heavily. And Mrs. Gest, her legs suddenly and completely faint and powerless with the effort, lay down beside her. . . .

So they lay, a quiet, even a peaceful sight, the two large women. And after a while the edge of the terrific thumping in Mrs. Gest's head wore off. The line of peril receded from her heart. Time beat again, and with the awakening of interest and vitality, a sense of the ridiculousness of the situation came upon her too.

She had a vivid picture, of a sudden, of Charlie's standing by the side of the bed looking at them speechlessly, the expression of his face.

"I laugh," she said aloud, between spasms of mirth, "but what is funny, let my enemies tell me!"

Mrs. Johnson groaned at hearing words, and tried struggling to a sitting position. Her "boss" rose.

"Sch, *shuh*," she said, as though she were addressing a child, "lay still. You must lay still. You mustn't move, Mrs. Johnson. It aint good for you."

"I aint et much for two days," Mrs. Johnson said, shamefaced and penitent. "I guess you give me too much to eat."

"Woe is me!" Mrs. Gest exclaimed.

"Just let me lay here a while. I gets spells like this ever now and then."

Mrs. Gest, overawed and contrite at the thought that she had helped bring on Mrs. Johnson's illness, got up and walked weakly into the kitchen. There she contrived, to put the water onto the stove, as she had started to do, and lit the fire. She pulled out the tub, the washboard, and the chairs for the wash and got all in readiness. Then she sat down to wait for the water to heat. Hearing Mrs. Johnson begin to groan again, she realized how frightened she was.

"How you feel?" she asked, panic-stricken.

"I don't feel good," Mrs. Johnson said, in a plaintive voice. "I ate too much of that herring. I got a condition. I aint supposed to eat that kind of stuff. . . . I aint et nothing but bread and coffee for two days."

She closed her eyes and lay still, lines of suffering on her face. Mrs. Gest ran to the wall on the other side of which dwelt the Widow.

"Mrs. Cohen," she shouted. "Mrs. Cohen!"

No answer. When you didn't want the Widow to hear anything, she was there and heard all.

She went out on the "summer" porch and called Mrs. Seller to her window.

"Mrs. Seller, please, I beg you! do me a favor. Tell your boy he should make a telephone call for me."

"What's the matter, Mrs. Gest. Are you sick again, may it not be so?"

"It's a mad world, Mrs. Seller. When they say 'mad,' they should be believed. Not *I* am sick, it is my servant. My son, Charlie, the *philosopher*, he got me a servant. She gasps and goes out like a light!"

"One of ours?"

"A *goya*! But God is my witness, a *goya* is also, unfortunate person, a human being. What contains life can also suffer, Mrs. Seller."

"I will call my boy, if only he will deign to come."

But when the boy came to the window, Mrs. Gest discovered that she did not know where Charlie worked.

"It is for the Government," was all she could tell him. "He *writes*. He makes with a pencil. The Government pays him and he writes."

"Don't you know the name? Woddaya want *me* to do!"

"W.P.A.!" shrieked Mrs. Gest, seized with an inspiration. "He writes books for the Government."

Mrs. Seller suddenly drew back a large fist and slapped her son across the head.

"Ask her no questions, go telephone."

"Don't hit me, Ma. You think it don't hurt?"

"Hit him not, Mrs. Seller. An angel is he, not a boy!"

"Angel, go telephone! May the Devil, the Unmentionable One, seeing you, have mercy, and depart still alone!"

* * *

His mother having Adolph call up to say that somebody

else was sick, not she, was too novel not to have a touch of questionable mystery attached to it. Softly, for some reason, Charlie came up the stairs. Softly, without knocking, he opened the door. The first thing he saw was his mother standing over the washtub and scrubbing away as hard as she could. There was a scared and anxious expression on her face, but also (as she looked up and saw him) an unmistakable air of having her own way after all, chalk-white though this air was. In her excitement, however, she had forgot to wash and get rid of the herring-jar and he smelled it. She smelled it at the same time he did, but at once—considering Mrs. Johnson's illness to prove that there were weaker ones than she in this wide world—determined to brazen it through. He could almost see her defenses forming, obstinate, gloating (just now) cat-like little instruments of war.

"What did you do?" he asked. "Knock her out?"

She spoke with scorn.

"A helper he got me. Three times already she has vomited on the floor."

"And you? How many times did you vomit?"

"None of your business."

He went in to take a look at Mrs. Johnson. His mother had drawn the shade in that room, and the sick woman lay in the darkness, only the glint on her dry lips and the open teeth showing. He went back into the kitchen.

"She looks pretty sick. What happened?"

Mrs. Gest tried to look as though her good offices had been exhausted in vain. "She ate too much, that is all. I said, 'Please, Mrs. Johnson, don't eat so much.' "

"And the herring—all gone between the two of you, huh?"

She burst into tears. "Nothing he lets me eat. Bread, vegetables, who can live on bread and vegetables. Who *wants* to live on bread and vegetables! No meat, no herring, no nothing. This is too rich, this has got too much I don't know what, this hasn't got enough, my troubles alone can understand them. And don't go to the show, it is bad for your eyes, it draws the blood, it makes your head hurt, and when your head hurts, you are in danger. And a blood vessel you will burst maybe. Don't worry, don't laugh, don't, don't, don't! And wash not, the doctor tells me. Ten years ago he tells me and all the time I keep on washing. Now my son gets a job. Two months he has a job. Stop everything, he says. And brings me a cadaver, she falls from her feet!"

Her crying had the quality in it that distressed him more than any other form of weeping or displeasure she possessed (and after half a lifetime of practice, she was a virtuoso). It was that of a child, a forlorn child (he always imagined), sitting in a corner and watching the other kids play. There was in it none of that artifice he could at any other time expect from her.

"Don't cry, Ma," he said gently. "That isn't what I meant."

He walked to and fro in front of her, wishing he could touch her, say something. Alas, years of the extremes of experience build up a seeming hardness that is difficult to break through and the expression of which is never conventional. People who seldom suffer can, in moments of grief or need, fly to each other. To an outside observer, to the God of churches perhaps, such immediate and complete demonstration may seem the height of true affection, but affection (like courage) is easy to exercise when no great drains on it are required, and for this reason the greatest shows of affection are invariably shown (so it would seem) among the untroubled. Soldiers watching each other die try to say all that they can no longer say—or even imagine—with the apparently irrelevant proffer of a cigarette.

"Ma," he said with difficulty, "I got nothing against you eating herring. If I could fix it, I would make you eat a ton of herring a day. But—" A gesture completed what he could not find words for. "You're awfully pale, Ma. Why don't you go lie down." Feeling that it might bring a laugh, he added, "The boss and her helper. What a boss! . . . I'll do the wash."

It did. "The *boss*," she said. "Has anybody in all the history seen such a boss!"

Groaning and laughing, she made her way to the bed.

"Mrs. Johnson," he heard her say, "I will keep you company."

He heard her lie down.

"Oh," from the Jewish woman.

"Oh," from the Irish.

Gwendolyn Brooks

Gwendolyn Brooks was born in Topeka, Kansas, but moved to Chicago as a child. She attended classes at Englewood High School and Wilson Junior College and began to express her impressions of Chicago's South Side Negro district in verse published in HARPER'S POETRY, COMMON GROUND, *and other periodicals. In 1947 she was awarded a Guggenheim Fellowship. The following poems are reprinted from* A STREET IN BRONZEVILLE.

When Mrs. Martin's Booker T.

When Mrs. Martin's Booker T.
Ruined Rosa Brown
Mrs. Martin moved away
To the low west side of town.
"Don't care if I never see that boy
Again to the end of my days.
He wrung my heart like a chicken neck.
And he made me a disgrace.
Don't come to tell me he's dyin'.
Don't come to tell me he's dead.
But tell me if'n he take that gal
And get her decent wed."

At the Hairdresser's

Gimme an upsweep, Minnie,
With humpteen baby curls.
'Bout time I got some glamour.
I'll show them girls.

Think they so fly a-struttin'
With they wool a-blowin' 'round.
Wait'll they see my upsweep.
That'll jop 'em back on the ground.

Got Madam C. J. Walker's first.
Got Poro Grower next.

Ain't none of 'em worked with me, Min.
But I ain't vexed.

Long hair's out of style anyhow, ain't it?
Now it's tie it up high with curls.
So gimme an upsweep, Minnie.
I'll show them girls.

The Date

If she don't hurry up and let me out of here.
Keeps pilin' up stuff for me to do.
I ain't goin' to finish that ironin'.
She got another think comin'. Hey, you.
Watcha mean talkin' about cleanin' silver?
It's eight o'clock now, you fool.
I'm leavin'. Got somethin' interestin' on my mind.
Don't mean night school.

Jack Conroy

"The Sissy from the Hardscrabble Rock Quarries" is one of a group of stories I collected in the course of an involuntary tour of the country as a migratory worker. Its genre is familiar—a variant of the frontier brag. Children of the Midwest (and probably in other sections of the country) have a comic boast: "I live on Tough Street. The farther down the street you go, the tougher it gets. I live in the last house." The "sissy" who is too tough for the people of the surrounding area but too delicate for his associates is a folk figure who persists in popping up everywhere in the United States when tall tales are being swapped. Stewart Holbrook says that he knows him as a native of the Northwest, where he's called "The Sissy from Anaconda." "The Sissy from the Hardscrabble Rock Quarries" is part of a manuscript collection CHICAGO INDUSTRIAL FOLKLORE, *compiled by the Federal Writers' Project of the Works Project Administration for the State of Illinois. It appeared in* A TREASURY OF AMERICAN FOLKLORE, *edited by Benjamin A. Botkin.*

The Sissy from the Hardscrabble County Rock Quarries

THE MEN that work in the rock quarries of Hardscrabble County are so tough they crack big rocks just by spitting on them. The farther you go west in the county the tougher the men get, and the rock quarries are right on the western boundary line. When they set off a blast, those bullies are right out there with ten-year-old white oaks in their hands batting those big boulders around, or else they're playing catch without any gloves.

When they get constipated in the rock quarry camp they never use anything but blasting powder, and they whip their children with barb wire until the kids get to be ten years old and then they thrash their parents.

Strangers almost never travel into the rock country, because no man, woman, beast or child that dared to try it ever returned to tell about it no more than any soul ever fetched back a report from hell.

When the quarrymen leave their camp, everybody but invalids, little children, and cripples take to the hills till the danger's past. It's lucky that they usually come in a drove, and you can see their dust for miles away and hear their fearsome blackguarding and whooping for a good hour and a half before they strike the city limits.

Gentlemen, it's no lie nor fairy tale when I tell you that those Hardscrabble County quarrymen are enough to plague a saint. They use them in the farm villages to scare little children and make them behave, but the grownups are even scareder than the young ones.

One day a lone wolf got right into town before anybody knew he was on the way. He came riding two snapping, snarling panthers, straddling them with a foot on each, and he was lashing them into a lather with a whip made of three six-foot rattlesnakes knotted together.

This fellow was a sight to behold, and everybody knew in a minute that he was a quarryman. He stood a good eight feet without tiptoeing, and not enough fat on him to grease a one-egg skillet. That man was muscled like a draft mule, and he moved around like a bolt of lightning on its holiday.

First thing off he went to the shoe store and bought him a pair of brogans. Then he got a nickel's worth of stout roofing nails from the hardware store and asked for the loan of a hammer. He drove these roofing nails right through the soles and heels of the shoes and put the shoes back on his feet. He wore a size fifteen, broad last.

"That's the way I like it," he said. "It gives you a good grip and all you got to do when your foot itches is to wiggle it around a little."

"I want to get prettied up a little," the quarryman said, and went into the barber shop. The barber took the edge off his shears when he tried to cut his hair.

"Ain't you got no tinsmiths in this town?" asked the quarryman. "Get a pair of tinsnips, extra large. And fetch a blowtorch from the plumber's. I ain't had a decent shave for a month of Sundays."

He dropped in the Blue Moon Saloon then and asked for a good stiff drink, talking as polite as chips. The bartender planked down a bottle of his strongest brand of fortyrod. Some of it sloshed over and ate a spot of varnish off the bar the size of a five-dollar bill. The quarryman lost his temper then, and snorted and fumed fit to kill.

"None of that bellywash for me! I'd as soon have a pinky, sticky ice cream sody with a cherry on it."

"What sort of a charge do you crave, stranger?" asked the bartender, his false choppers almost shaking out of his mouth.

"Gimme a prussic acid cocktail with a little sulphuric for

a chaser," ordered the quarryman, "and see that you don't go diluting it with no carbolic, either. What are you, anyway? One of them temperance cranks? You must think I'm a plumb teetotaler!"

The bartender dashed out the back way and hotfooted it to the drug store and got the stuff for the drinks. The quarryman got in a little better humor then, and began passing the time away by spitting on the floor and burning holes right through to the ground underneath.

"Not bad!" he said. "A little weak. Only trouble with this tipple is that it's hell on underwear. Every time you break wind it burns a hole in them."

"I guess you aim to get back to the quarries before night-fall, don't you, stranger?" said the bartender, hoping to God it was so.

"No, no!" answered the quarryman, shaking his head kind of sad. "I don't reckon I'll ever go back."

He grabbed a can of tomatoes off the shelf behind the bar and gulped it down without chewing it open.

"Don't it lay heavy on your stomach, stranger?" asked the bartender, terribly put out that the quarryman wasn't leaving that night.

"Not long," answered the quarryman. "I soon digest the can from around the tomatoes. It's easy. A doorknob is harder, but I can do it easy as pie when I set my head to it."

"You aim to make your home in our little Magic City?" asked the bartender, still hoping he had heard wrong.

"Hell's fire and damnation no, man!" said the quarryman, so riled he bit a foot long chunk out of the mahogany bar and spat it right in the bartender's face. "I wouldn't live here for love nor money. I wouldn't be caught dead here."

"Well, then," said the bartender, getting a little bolder, "why did you leave the quarries?"

"Aw, I didn't *want* to," answered the quarryman. "I had to."

"You had to? Why? Get in a fight or some kind of trouble there?"

"A fight? Are you plumb stark, staring looney, man? Whoever heard of a man getting into trouble over fighting in the Hardscrabble County rock quarries?"

"Why did you have to leave then?"

"Well," said the quarryman, looking like a sheepkilling dog. "They chased me out because they said I was a sissy."

Frank Marshall Davis

Frank Marshall Davis (1905–   ) was born in Arkansas City, Kansas. Graduating from Kansas State University, he came to Chicago in 1927. He is editor of the Associated Negro Press and executive editor of the Chicago STAR. *"Robert Whitmore" is from* BLACK MAN'S VERSE *(1938) and "Two Women" is from* I AM THE AMERICAN NEGRO *(1937).*

Robert Whitmore

Having attained success in business
possessing three cars
one wife and two mistresses
a home and furniture
talked of by the town
and thrice ruler of the local Elks
Robert Whitmore
died of apoplexy
when a stranger from Georgia
mistook him
for a former Macon waiter.

Two Women

As maid for Mrs. Harold Billingsworth
Dahlia Green
supplemented the Petite Beauty Salon
by curling her mistress' straight hair
several times weekly.
Paydays
Dahlia went straightway
to the Afro Beauty College
to have her own moss unkinked.
At sixty both women
from efforts to imitate
the natural appearance of each
above the ears
were forced to buy wigs
from the salons.
Yet this was a triumph for civilization
And American progress—
Think how they aided
the entire hair industry!

Peter De Vries

Peter De Vries (1910–   ) was born in Chicago. Graduating from Calvin College, Grand Rapids, in 1931 with an A.B. degree, he spent the summer of that year studying at Northwestern University. Then he edited a community newspaper, contributed stories to several "little" magazines, and in 1938 joined the editorial staff of POETRY: A MAGAZINE OF VERSE, *going to the* NEW YORKER *in a similar capacity in 1944. His books include* BUT WHO WAKES THE BUGLER? *(1940),* THE HANDSOME HEART *(1943), and* ANGELS CAN'T DO BETTER *(1944). "Different Cultural Levels Eat Here" appeared originally in the* NEW YORKER, *November 16, 1946. A dramatized version was used as a curtain raiser for an Actors' Laboratory production of Sean O'Casey's* JUNO AND THE PAYCOCK *staged in Hollywood.*

Different Cultural Levels Eat Here

WHEN the counterman glanced up from the grill on which he was frying himself a hamburger and saw the two couples come in the door, he sized them up automatically as people who had spent the evening at the theatre or the Horse Show or something like that, judging from their clothes. They were all about the same age—in their early forties, he decided, as they sat down on the stools at the counter. Except for them, the place was empty. At least, the front was. Al Spain, the proprietor, was sitting out in the kitchen working on a ledger.

The counterman drew four glasses of water, stopping once to adjust the limp handkerchief around his neck. He had been whistling softly and without continuity when they entered, and he kept it up as he set the water glasses down.

"Well, what's yours?" he asked, wiping his hands on his apron and beginning with the man on the end.

"Hamburger."

"Mit or mitout?"

The man paused in the act of fishing a cigarette out of a package and glanced up. He was a rather good-looking fellow with dark circles under his eyes that, together with the general aspect of his face, gave him a sort of charred look. "Mit," he said at length.

The counterman moved down. "And yours?" he asked the woman who was next.

"I'll have a hamburger, too."

"Mit or mitout?"

The second woman, who had a gardenia pinned in her hair, leaned to her escort and started to whisper something about

"a character," audibly, it happened, for the counterman paused
and turned to look at her. Her escort jogged her with the
side of his knee, and then she noticed the counterman watching her and stopped, smiling uneasily. The counterman looked
at her a moment longer, then turned back to the other woman.
"I'm sorry I didn't get that," he said. "Was that mit or mitout?"

She coughed into her fist and moved her bag pointlessly on
the counter. "Mit," she said.

"That's two mits," the counterman said, and moved on
down to the next one, the woman with the gardenia. "And
yours?"

She folded her fingers on the counter and leaned toward
him. "And what would we come here for except a hamburger?" She smiled sociably, showing a set of long, brilliant
teeth.

"Mit or mitout?" he asked flatly.

She wriggled forward on the stool and smiled again. "May
I ask a question?"

"Sure."

"Why do you say 'mit or mitout'?" Her escort jogged her
again with his knee, this time more sharply.

The counterman turned around and picked up a lighted
cigarette he had left lying on the ledge of the pastry case.
He took a deep inhale, ground the butt out underfoot, and
blew out the smoke. "To find out the customer's wish," he
said. "And now, how did you want it?"

"I think mitout," she said. "I like onions, but they don't
like me."

"And yours?" he asked the last one, the second man.

"I'll have a hamburger, too," the man said. He fixed his
eyes on a box of matches in his hands, as though steeling himself.

"Mit or mitout?"

The man fished studiously in the matchbox. "Mitout."

The four watched the counterman in complete silence as he took the hamburger patties from a refrigerator and set them to frying on the grill. They all wanted coffee, and he served it now. After slicing open four buns, he turned to his own sandwich. He put the meat in a bun and folded it closed, the others watching him as though witnessing an act of legerdemain. Conscious of their collective gaze, he turned his head, and scattered their looks in various directions. Just then the phone rang. The counterman set his sandwich down and walked past the four customers to answer it. He paused with his hand on the receiver a moment, finished chewing, swallowed, and picked up the phone.

"Al's," he announced, his elbows on the cigarette counter. "Oh, hello, Charlie," he said brightening, and straightened up. "How many? . . . Well, that's a little steep right now. I can let you have half of that is all. . . . O.K., shoot. . . . That's nine mits and three mitouts, right? . . . Check. . . . That'll be O.K." He consulted the clock overhead. "Send the kid over then. So long."

He hung up and was on his way back to the grill when he became aware that the woman with the gardenia was whispering to her escort again. He stopped and stood in front of her with his hands on his hips. "I beg your pardon, but what was that remark, lady?"

"Nothing."

"You passed a remark about me, if I'm not mistaken. What was it?"

"I just said you were wonderful."

"I was what?"

"Wonderful."

"That's what I thought." He went back to the hamburgers, which needed attention.

As he turned them in silence, the woman regarded him doubtfully. "What's the matter?" she asked at last, ignoring the nudging from her friends on either side.

The counterman's attention remained stonily fixed on his work.

"Is something wrong?" the woman asked.

The counterman lowered the flame, stooping to check it, and straightened up. "Maybe," he said, not looking at her.

She looked at her friends with a gesture of appeal. "But what?"

"Maybe I'm sore."

"What are you sore about?" the woman's escort asked. "She only said you were wonderful."

"I know what that means in her book."

"What?"

The counterman turned around and faced them. "We have a woman comes in here," he said, "who everything's wonderful to, too. She's got a dog she clips. When she hits a cab driver without teeth who doesn't know any streets and you got to show him how to get to where you want to go, he's wonderful. Fellow with a cap with earlaps come in here with some kind of a bird in his pocket one night when she was here. He had a coat on but no shirt and he sung tunes. *He* was wonderful. Everything is wonderful, till I can't stand to hear her talk to whoever she's with any more. This lady reminds me a lot of her. I got a picture of *her* all right going home and telling somebody I'm wonderful."

"But by wonderful she means to pay you a—"

"I know what wonderful means. You don't have to tell me. Saloons full of all old junk, they're wonderful, old guys that stick cigar butts in their pipe—"

"The lady didn't mean any harm."

"Well . . ."

There was a moment of silence, and the charred-looking man signalled the others to let well enough—or bad enough, whichever it was—alone, but the other man was impelled to complete the conciliation. "I see perfectly well what you mean," he said. "But she meant not all of us stand out with a sort of—well, trademark."

The counterman seemed to bristle. "Meaning what?"

"Why, the way you say 'mit or mitout,' I guess," the man said looking for confirmation to the woman, who nodded brightly.

The counterman squinted at him. "What about it?"

"Nothing, nothing at all. I just say I suppose it's sort of your trademark."

"Now, cut it out," the counterman said, taking a step closer. "Or you'll have a trademark. And when you get up tomorrow morning, you'll look a darn site more wonderful than anybody *she* ever saw."

The charred-looking man brought his hand down on the counter. "Oh, for God's sake, let's cut this out! Let's eat if we're going to eat, and get out of here."

"That suits me, bud," said the counterman.

The commotion brought Al Spain from the kitchen. "What seems to be trouble?" he asked, stepping around to the customer's side of the counter.

"She said I was wonderful," the counterman said, pointing. "And I don't see that I have to take it from people just because they're customers, Al. I may fry hamburgers for a living, but I'm no freak."

"Maybe she didn't mean any harm by it," the proprietor said.

"It's the way she said it. The way that type says it. I know. You know. We get 'em in here. You know what they think's wonderful, don't you?"

"Well," Al said, scratching his head and looking at the floor.

"Cabbies that recite poems they wrote while they cart you, saloons full of old—"

"Oh, Jesus, are we going through that again?" the charred-looking man broke in. He stood up. "Let's just go," he said to his friends.

"We'll go into this quietly," Al said, and removed a toothpick from his mouth and dropped it on the floor. "We're intelligent human beings," he continued, with an edge of interrogation, looking at the others, who gave little nods of agreement. He sat down on one of the stools. "Now, the thing is this. This man is fine." He waved at the counterman, who stood looking modestly down at the grill. "He's a great fellow. But he's sensitive. By that, I mean he gets along fine with the public—people who come in here from day to day, you understand. Has a pleasant way of passing the time of day, and a nice line of gab, *but*—different cultural levels eat here, and he doesn't like people that he thinks they're coming in here with the idea they're slumming. Now don't get me wrong," he went on when the woman with the gardenia started to say something. "I like all types of people and I'm tickled to death to have them come in here, you understand. I'm just saying that's his attitude. Some things set his back up, because he's like I say, sensitive." He crossed his legs. "Let's go into this thing like intelligent human beings a little farther. What prompted you to pass the remark—namely, he's wonderful?"

The charred-looking man groaned. "Oh, Christ, let's get—"

"Shut up, Paul," the woman with the gardenia said. She returned her attention to the proprietor. "It was just—oh, it all starts to sound so silly. I mean it was a perfectly insignificant remark. It's the way he says 'mit or mitout.' "

Al was silent a moment. "Is that all?" he asked, regarding her curiously.

"Yes."

"It's just a habit of his. A way he's got." Al looked from her to the counterman and back again.

"You see," she said, "it's making something out of nothing. It's the way he says it. It's so—so offhand-like and—well, the offhand way he evidently keeps saying it. It's so—marvellous."

"I see. Well, it's just a sort of habit of his." Al was studying her with increasing interest.

"Of course, we're sorry if we've offended him," said the woman's escort.

"We'll let it go that way," the counterman said.

"Fine! We'll say no more about it," Al said, gesturing covertly to the counterman to serve up the sandwiches. "Come again anytime," he added, and went back to the kitchen.

The two couples composed themselves and ate. The counterman went and leaned on the cigarette case, over a newspaper. The door opened and a small man in a tight gray suit came in and sat down, pushed his hat back, drew a newspaper out of his pocket, and spread it on the counter. The counterman dropped his, drew a glass of water, and set it before the customer.

"What'll it be?"

"Two hamburgers."

The two couples stopped eating and looked up, and there was complete silence for a moment. Then they bent over their food, eating busily and stirring their coffee with an excessive clatter of spoons. Suddenly the clink of cutlery subsided and there was dead silence again. The counterman wiped his hands on his apron, turned, and walked to the refrigerator. He opened it, took out two patties, set them on the grill, and peeled off the paper on them. He sliced the buns and set them in readiness on a plate. Standing there waiting for the meat to fry, he cleared his throat and said, looking out the window at something in the street, "Onion with these?"

"No. Plain," the customer said, without raising his head from the paper.

The two couples hurried through their sandwiches and coffee, crumpled their paper napkins, and rose together. One of the men paid, left a half dollar tip on the counter, turned, and herded the others through the door, following them him-

self and closing the door rapidly and quietly. The counterman shoved the cash register shut and went back to the grill
without looking at them or glancing through the window as
they unlocked their car at the curb, got in, and drove off. He
served the man his sandwiches. Then he came around the
counter and sat on a stool with the paper.

Suddenly the door opened and a big fellow in a bright
checkered shirt came in, grinning. "Hello, paesan!" the newcomer said. "Loafing as usual, eh?"

The counterman jumped off the stool and held out his
hand. "Louie! When did you get back?"

"For God's sake!" The counterman went back behind the
counter. "Glad to see you."

"Glad to see you, too, you lazy bastard."

"How many, Louie?"

"I'm starved. Fry me up three."

"Mit or mitout?"

"Mit."

Leonard Dubkin

Leonard Dubkin (1904–   ) was born in Chicago, but rambled around quite a bit before returning to settle down as editor and proprietor of the RADIO TALENT GUIDE, *a job to Dubkin's taste because it enables him to lock up shop whenever he feels like it. He has been a newspaperman in Chicago, New Orleans, Omaha, and New York. Having learned about the unglamorous hoarse-voiced, and bedraggled birds of Chicago's streets and parks, he speaks for them in* THE MURMUR OF WINGS *(1945) from which "A Hawk in the Loop" is reprinted.* ENCHANTED STREETS: THE UN-LIKELY ADVENTURES OF AN URBAN NATURE LOVER, *much of which had appeared serially in the* ATLANTIC MONTHLY, *was published in 1947.*

A Hawk in the Loop

A LETTER was published in the readers department of our paper one day which raised a great hue and cry in the city and faced us all with a grave possibility. The letter appeared at a time when there was no war in Europe, there had not been a scandal in our municipal government in almost three months, there was a lull in gangster murders, and we had become bored with the depression. It therefore hit us right between the eyes.

According to this letter, our downtown pigeon population was being decimated by a terrible scourge. While walking down Michigan Boulevard one afternoon "Bird Lover" had stopped for a minute to watch the pigeons in the grass beside the Art Institute. Suddenly he saw a large hawk swoop down on the unsuspecting birds, seize one of them in his claws, and fly off with it. None but a native of our city could appreciate the consternation this letter aroused, the feeling of horror it called up in the breast of every loyal citizen. To think that we were harboring in our city a murderous hawk that preyed on our beloved pigeons and, if its depredations were not stopped, would continue eating them until not one was left, or until the few survivors left us for some less hawk-infested locality, was too horrible to contemplate.

The thousands of pigeons in the Loop are our especial pride; we feed them, protect them, and recognize them in our laws. Restaurant owners and shopkeepers throw out food for them every day; a little old woman comes to Grant Park at three o'clock daily with a sackful of stale bread which she scatters on the grass for them; thousands of "L" riders feed them peanuts out of their hands while waiting for trains; and an old man makes an honest living by selling bags of cracked corn to those who would feed the pigeons beside the Art Institute. We do not hold against them the fact that their unsightly nests protrude from under the eaves of the Art Institute, the Public Library, and many otherwise beautiful buildings, or that these collections of twigs, string, paper, straw, and feathers, when placed as they often are under the "L" platforms, catch fire from stray sparks as the trains go by and form a serious fire hazard. Nor do we boil over with rage, as we have every right to do, when, as we walk along Michigan Boulevard passing the Public Library, or at some other place in the Loop, we feel a slight plop overhead and take off our hat to find it splashed with pigeon droppings.

But why, you will ask, do we put up with these annoyances and continue to offer our hospitality to these ungrateful birds? Well, because we like them; they gratify our aesthetic feeling for beauty. We like to watch five or six hundred of them walking about in the grass beside the Art Institute, a few males cooing and puffing out their chests and strutting about in circles, some preening their feathers, others, with head under wing, fast asleep in the sun. It thrills us to watch the whole flock suddenly hop into the air, as though in response to some invisible signal, and clap their wings together loudly as though applauding, then spiral upward and go around and around swiftly in a great circle over Grant Park and the tops of the cars on Michigan Boulevard, between the high walls of the great skyscrapers. It amuses us to watch them nimbly dodging people's legs and the wheels of cars and horses' hooves as they walk about in the streets of the Loop, looking for some stray crumb or courting a prospective mate. There may also be psychological reasons; perhaps the inhabitants of our city have rather well-developed inferiority complexes, and acting as guardians for all these defenseless pigeons bolsters our egos and reminds us that there are, after all, weaker creatures on this planet than we humans, creatures whom we have subjugated and who depend upon us for their living. But why should we have to rationalize our fondness for pigeons? Why should we puzzle our brains to explain logically an emotion as elemental as the love of parents for their children? We love our pigeons because we love them, and that should be sufficient explanation.

Until the letter by "Bird Lover" appeared in the paper no one had ever seen a hawk in our city, but now almost everyone began to see it. Every day two or three letters from people who had also seen the hawk were published. Some had merely seen him wheeling in the sky in search of pigeons, others saw him swoop on a pigeon and fly away carrying the poor bird in his claws, and one man wrote that he had been watching the marauder for three days through the window of his downtown hotel room and had seen him capture twenty-two pigeons. This would have made an average of more than seven pigeons a day, which seemed quite a lot for one hawk. But we were prepared to believe almost anything of that terrible bird of prey.

At first all discussions of the hawk were confined to the columns in the paper devoted to letters from readers, but it was inevitable that sooner or later he would invade the news columns. This happened when a traffic accident occurred on Michigan Boulevard as a result of the curiosity of a motorist who, as he was passing the Art Institute where the pigeons were congregated, stuck his head out of the car window to see if the hawk was about. Soon after that there was a news item about a woman who had fainted on the steps of the Public Library, and when she was taken to a doctor explained that she had been sitting there all day, without food or drink, in the hope of seeing the bird of prey. After that the lid was off, and no edition was complete without a news story pertaining to the hawk on page one or two, either some eyewitness account of a raid on the pigeon colony or an interview with a professional ornithologist regarding the habits and customs of various species of hawks.

But authority meant nothing in the matter of identifying

the hawk, for everyone seemed to have his own opinion in the matter of the species to which this particular hawk belonged. Some claimed it was the common hen hawk, but others said it was too small for a hen hawk and that it was most certainly a sparrow hawk. Still others thought it might be a Cooper's hawk or a sharp-shinned hawk. An ornithologist who was interviewed at the railroad depot where he changed trains on his way to New York from Los Angeles, said that since he had not seen the bird he could not, of course, be certain of its identity, but he thought it might possibly be a red-shouldered hawk, *Buteo lineatus*, which was notoriously fond of pigeons. After this interview appeared in print a great many letters were sent by indignant people who resented the interference of an outside ornithologist in our personal affairs, but the indignation subsided when someone pointed out that the red-shouldered hawk, *Buteo lineatus*, was the common or hen hawk.

It was certainly exciting while it lasted, and it gave us all a new topic of conversation. When you met some acquaintance on the street, instead of saying, "Looks like rain, doesn't it?" or "How's the missus?" you said, "Have you seen it yet?" The answer might be, "No, have you?" or "Yes, I think I did, yesterday afternoon about two-thirty, over by the Stadium." People waiting for their bus on Michigan Boulevard stood with their hands shading their eyes, gazing eagerly into the sky, and all during the day stenographers and clerks and office boys kept poking their heads out of office windows in the Loop, hoping for a quick glance at the hawk. Many young fellows brought air rifles down to the office, and during their lunch hour sat on window ledges, clutching their guns and praying for just one shot at it. And well they might pray, too, for the slaying of that bird would mean local fame, with pictures in the papers and a possible vaudeville contract.

The pigeons in the Loop went about their business, if one can call eating and sleeping and making love a business, as

though they were unaware of all the excitement and the solicitude in their favor. As a matter of fact they were probably
better fed during this period than at any time in the past, for
many people who had never before thought of feeding them
now threw bread crumbs out in the street or bought a nickel's
worth of corn for them from the old man who made an honest
living selling it. If the pigeons had hired a press agent he could
not have thought of a better publicity stunt to arouse interest
in them and make the people of our city pigeon-conscious.
But of course it couldn't have been a publicity stunt; too many
people had actually seen the hawk.

Yes, many people had seen the hawk, but they were never
sure of it; they always added, "Of course I could have been
mistaken; it may have been only a piece of paper in the wind
or some other harmless bird." Some had seen the hawk capture
a pigeon and fly away with it, but you never met those; they
were always a friend of the one you were talking to or "a
fellow I met the other day" or "a fellow my brother knows."
When one of the papers offered a reward of fifty dollars to
anyone who could show conclusive proof that there was a
hawk in the Loop, that is, bring its recently killed body or a
photograph of it to their office, no one took the offer seriously. By that time we were tired of the hawk; it had had a
long run, but now we wanted a change. So when a respectable
married man, president of a bottling concern, was found dead
in the apartment of a night-club hostess the papers threw out
any type still standing in the composing rooms that dealt
with hawks or pigeons or any other feathered creatures, and
birds became a dead issue in our city.

Was there actually a hawk preying on the pigeons in the
Loop? I do not know, nor does anyone else except "a brother
of a fellow who works in Field's" and "a man who delivers
ice to the Congress and told a friend of mine who works
there" and "a girl who told our maid that her boy friend shot
at it with a .22."

C. L. Edson

C. L. Edson (1881–   ) was born in Wilber, Nebraska. "At that time," he says, "Willa Cather was an 8-year old girl from Virginia in Wilber, a Bohemian center." Edson graduated from the University of Kansas in 1904 and went to work as a columnist on the Kansas City STAR. *He left in 1912 to do a two-year stretch on the New York* EVENING MAIL, *conducting a column called "An Arkansas Man on Broadway." He has written two books,* THE GENTLE ART OF COLUMNING, A TREATISE ON NEWSPAPER HUMOR *(1922) and* THE GREAT AMERICAN ASS *(1926), the latter published anonymously. He now lives in Topeka. "Ballad of Kansas City" appeared originally in the Kansas City* STAR.

Ballad of Kansas City

Grain built Babylon, war raised Rome.
Films built Hollywood, as gold built Nome.
Hogs made Chicago with their dying squeal;
Up popped Pittsburgh with the birth of steel.
Come, Kansas City, make your story brief:
"Here stands a city built o' bread and beef."

The streamlined *Hummer* with its ears pinned back,
Races through the city on the Belt Line track,
Sees the Union Station, and the brakes buck down,
And we tarry twenty minutes in the Big Beef town.

The Pioneer Yankees who had nine lives
Built this City where the race survives.
The sod-corn planter, when the world was new—
And the herders and the traders and the stock yards crew;
They planted Kansas City, and the darn thing grew.
A Mid-West Main Street with cow-town capers
Is hidden from the eye by the high skyscrapers.

The planters and the hunters from the buffalo chase
Had to have a city for a market place.
The bear-cat killers and the Dan Boone clan,
The boys who taught the panther his respect for man,
Had planted Kansas City where the bull trails ran.

The log cabin builder found himself "Out West;"
He built a soddy dug-out like a ground squirrel's nest.
The ax, and the chopper, and his woods were done;
He had to shed his ax and get a buffalo gun.
The Dan Boone tribe then traipsed across the grass,

Eating buffalo beef but nary garden sass!
The St. Louis steamboats stopped at this land,
Their nozzles high and dry in the Kaw River sand.
Kansas City "landing" was a plainsman's retreat
That grew into a Capital of Beef-and-Wheat!

Where is Westport Landing and its bull and harness trade?
Where is Leesport Landing and the local fuss it made?
The Port of Independence and the Port of Wyandotte?
They are rusted, they are busted, they are buried and forgot;
And the locomotive whistle goes a-roaring o'er the spot.
The river was the sponsor of those towns upon the shore,
The river was their wet nurse, but it suckles them no more;
Their landings all have languished where the weeds and willows
      wave,
Their dream of catfish commerce is a ghost within a grave;
The river towns are dust upon the Kansas City pave.
The Iron Mare is mother of an epoch here begun,
And the city, Kansas City, is the railroad's son.
Little Kansas City, when its bones were green as gristle,
Swapped a catfish sea port for a locomotive whistle.
"It is cute; it's a beaut! Can't you hear that whistle toot?"
It cost our river birthright, and some voted bonds to boot.

The youngster Bennie Franklin had bought a whistle, too: "Don't
pay too much for whistles," is the moral that he drew.
Did Kansas City weep when the harvest was to reap?
That town of bone-and-gristle bought its whistle plenty cheap.

Here is the Harvey House; that's a lucky break;
We'll tarry twenty minutes for a Kansas City steak.
Stroll through the Station where the tribe trails meet,
The clans from the cotton, the hordes from the wheat;
See the West in action, from a grand stand seat.
Six sheep shearers out of old Cheyenne,
Ten tie hackers from the Ozark hills,
An oil king and cotton king from Texarkan',
An Arkansas hill-billy, skeered of other bills.

A rich Swede farmer in a ten-cent collar,
A tall, tanned Texan in a wide-brimmed hat,
A dude ranch tourist who has never earned a dollar,

A Wind River "booster" with his pockets flat. . . .
Squaw-men, con men, half-breeds and rotten men,
Wheat kings, cattle kings, corn, wool, and cotton men,
Seethe through the station where the gates are down
In the Great Gate City and the big trade town.

HISTORY OF KANSAS CITY

"I shot a deer—put a bullet through his brain,"
The Old Settler said, "where it's now Sixth and Main.

"I whacked bulls—me and twenty wagon hands,
Teaming up the holler where the Junction stands.

"In the old stone building where they later had the *Star*,
Shot a blanket Indian in a fracas at a bar."

Thirty years later the Settler's son said:
"I saw Adam God paint the town red.

"This *Star* reporter sure flopped, face down,
While Adam God's fanatics were shooting up the town."

Back in 1900 I also recall
Bryan's nomination in Convention Hall.

Ninety days before that meet of Demercratic men,
Down burned Convention Hall—we built it up again.

FIVE-STAR FINAL

Here stands a city built of bread-and-beef.
Rome had a short life, Athens' was brief;
Hollywood rose up like a rocket-glare,

Airplane factories put Wichita there.
Michigan's Detroit has the Gasoline Horse,
Berlin had Germany's *military force!*
Mussolini's Rome had a chesty fool,
Washington is buttressed by political drool;
Topeka had "elections" and is going strong
As a chorus for the Atchison-Topeka song.
But Salt Lake City has sugar beets,
Chicago has hogs and assorted meats;
And Kansas City, as is truly said,
Is built upon the basis of both meat and bread.

The *California Hummer*, with its ears pinned back,
Is gliding from the Station on the Belt Line track,
And the tourist in the diner has a beef steak brown,
As a high life reminder of a corn-fed town.

Jake Falstaff

Jake Falstaff was the pseudonym of Herman Fetzer (1899–1935), who was born on an Ohio farm and returned to it in memory for material he used in JACOBY'S CORNERS *and* COME BACK TO WAYNE COUNTY. *A newspaperman in Akron and Cleveland, and for a short time in New York, Fetzer conducted his "Pippins and Cheese" column with wit and audacity.* BULLS OF SPRING *(1937) is a collection of his poems. "Alice in Justice-Land," originally published in the New York* WORLD *in 1929, was reprinted as a pamphlet by the American Civil Liberties Union in 1935. I am indebted to Hazel Fetzer for the use of this material and for the privilege of using the poems selected from a forthcoming collection of Jake Falstaff's miscellaneous work.*

Alice in Justice-land

"WHO ARE these poor unfortunates in this miserable bull-pen?" asked Alice, a sympathetic tear in her eye.

"They are guilty of free speech," said the White Knight.

"Please don't tease me," said Alice. "Persons cannot be charged with free speech."

"Who said anything about charging them with free speech?" demanded the White Knight. "They aren't charged with anything of the sort. Free speech is only what they're guilty of."

"Well, then, what is the charge against them?"

"They are charged with being vagrants."

"But they aren't vagrants."

"Certainly not. But you can't deny that they *are* guilty of free speech."

"I thought that the only person who could be charged with vagrancy was a tramp."

"What a primitive notion! Tramps are *never* charged with vagrancy."

"What are they charged with then?"

"With burglary."

"But they aren't necessarily guilty of burglary."

"No, perhaps not. But they are guilty of vagrancy. And if you treat them exactly in the right way, they'll plead guilty to burglary. I have you there."

"Well, then," said Alice, "am I to understand that if you are guilty of one thing you are always accused of being guilty of something else?"

"I beg pardon," said the Knight, haughtily. "I am not guilty of anything."

"I used the word 'you' only because one gets so confused if one uses 'one' in one's sentences."

"Objection overruled," said the White Knight. "Answer Yes or No."

"Answer Yes or No to what?"

"To the charge."

"But I'm not charged with anything."

"Perhaps not. But you will be."

"Why?"

"Because you are kind-hearted."

"Being kind-hearted is no crime."

"Not a crime, exactly, perhaps, but it can be an official inconvenience."

* * *

"I hope you will not be impatient with me," said Alice. "I'm really quite interested in this system, and I would like to know more about it."

"Please choose your words more carefully. You sound like a spy, and if I thought you were, I would be compelled—on my conscience as a citizen—to have you arrested on a charge of resisting arrest."

"But I haven't resisted arrest."

"If a policeman tried to arrest you on a charge of resisting arrest, wouldn't you resist?"

"Of course."

"You see, you're guilty already."

* * *

"Oh," said Alice, just a little exasperated, "let's change the subject. Who is that man sitting in the solitary confinement cell?"

"That," said the White Knight, "is a Dangerous Criminal."

"Oh, a murderer."

"Certainly not. More dangerous than a murderer. He is a Thinker."

"It's no crime to think."

"You don't seem to get the idea at all. It *is* a crime to obstruct the traffic."

"How did he obstruct traffic?"

"He didn't. But he declared that it was ridiculous for a judge to drive in an intoxicated condition to the court and sentence men to jail for driving while intoxicated."

"I don't see what that has to do with obstructing traffic."

"That's exactly the beauty of it—it has nothing to do with it. That makes it so much easier to prove."

*   *   *

"The whole system," said Alice, "is silly."

"Nothing of the kind," said the White Knight. "It's very sane and very human. If you hate your neighbor as you love yourself, you don't charge him with being a hateful person. You call up the police and tell them that his automobile is parked without a tail light. That's our system exactly. Only we carry it a step farther. Our system has been made so perfect that the tail light doesn't have to be out. It can be proved that it *might* go out—that it's *potentially* out.

"By the same token, you see, people *might* gather in groups to discuss the opinions of the man who says a drunken judge oughtn't sentence drunks. And that *might* obstruct traffic."

"The whole system seems to be predicated on the word 'might,' " said Alice.

"Might," said the White Knight, solemnly, "makes right. The whole thing in a nutshell is this:

"It's much easier to convict a man of something he didn't do than it is to prove that what he really was doing was a crime.

"So if a man is guilty of passing tracts, we charge him with littering the streets. If he is picketing, we charge him with loitering. If he writes a book which doesn't agree with our economic notions, we have him arrested on a charge of obscenity. If he thinks the workingman has as much right to drink as the executive, we apprehend him on a charge of violating the Mann act.

"If the charge doesn't stick, we try another.

"If he appeals, we charge him with something else. There's the beauty of the system. If you charge a man with the crime he really committed, your prosecution is limited to one count. But if you charge him with something else, you have the whole book of statutes to choose from.

"If a man gets free on four or five various charges, we commit him to an insane asylum."

"Doesn't it happen sometimes that a man gets free of everything?" Alice asked.

"Oh, certainly. But the system provides even for that. By that time he has spent all his money on litigation, his reputation is ruined, and he has spent as much time in jail as he would have spent on the original charge anyhow."

"Then," said Alice, in sad bewilderment, "am I to understand that most of the people in jail are innocent?"

"Every one," said the White Knight tolerantly but wearily, "every one in the world, my dear child, is innocent of something."

Ballad of a Bull-Fiddle that Loved a Tailor's Goose

It was a big bull-fiddle
    And he loved a tailor's goose
And he wasted away in the middle
    Cause she said it was no use.

In dulcet diapason
    He wooed to beat the band.
She said, "Go chew a raisin,
    I've pressing work at hand."

And the big bull-fiddle suffered,
    As who, indeed, has not
When love beholds him buffered
    'Twixt plot and counterplot?

He suffered for an hour,
    He suffered through to dawn,
And his reason lost its power—
    His strength was almost gone.

The big bull-fiddle's master
    Was smit with sudden dread
For he heard the pulse go faster
    Within the viol's head.

The big bull-fiddle shuddered
    When he thought of his married life
With a young cow-fiddle, uddered
    With clarinet and fife.

He stretched his mighty thorax;
  His thewy neck grew red;
From fire-kit he tore ax
  And spit the fiddler's head!

"By God," he swore to heaven,
  And crunched a violin,
"I'll eat me fiddlers seven
  And spit 'em out ag'in!"

Lay back, lay back, good people,
  The big bull-fiddle's loose,
He has climbed the Baptist steeple
  For love of the tailor's goose!

He has chewed away the spire
  And kicked the belfry down.
Go spread the word of his ire
  From town to frightened town!

The big bull-fiddle's mother
  Is tugging at his sleeve.
He has left her there to smother
  Who clothed him yestereve!

He has ranted out of the city;
  He is out upon the earth—
Now, gods of fate, have pity
  On folk of foreign birth!

He has smashed the tailor's doorway,
  And played the very deuce.
He is sailing off to Norway
  With the kidnapped tailor's goose!

He breasts the bold Atlantic—
  Both ship and captain he.
The tailor's goose is frantic.
  She cannot walk the sea.

He has taken her off to Sweden
   To be his blushing bride.
Oh, gods that plotted Eden,
   'Twere better she had died!

In the darkened playhouse middle
   Between the stage and stands
A smitten heifer-fiddle
   Is wringing her tragic hands.

Couplet

When lovely woman stoops to folly,
Golly!

Poem by Petey, the Stenographer

OUTWARD SIGNS

The nicest man I ever knew
Said "Hello" like this: "Hooloo!"

I've had big necking from a mate
Who waited till the eighteenth date.

My best-remembered long romance
Was with a guy that couldn't dance.

Mark this down and mark it well;
By outward signs you cannot tell.

There even may be good in heels
Who wear their mufflers at their meals.

Amos R. Harlin

Amos R. Harlin spent his early childhood in Gainesville, Missouri, a sequestered village of the Ozark hinterlands, and moved to West Plains in the same state when he was eight years old. West Plains, where his father was mayor for 32 years, was ". . . just another hill town with just a few more people, dust-laden trails called streets, open cisterns, mosquitoes, and a school system that had its inspiration in the Spanish Inquisition." When Harlin left the hills to attend college, he grew resentful of the supercilious and stereotyped conception of the hill-billy fostered by such vehicles of expression as the radio and screen. FOR HERE IS MY FORTUNE *(1946), from which "Plainsville's First Hossless Kerridge" is reprinted, is the author's attempt to counteract some of the current false impressions about people of the Ozark country.*

Plainsville's First Hossless Kerridge

THE FIRST mistake in judgment father ever made was, in the light of his usual foresight, the most incredible mistake he could have possibly made.

Father was a successful businessman. Which is another way of saying he possessed a talent for assimilating facts, seeing those facts in their true perspective and thus reaching a correct reckoning of things to come.

Yet when he saw the invention which was to give Plainsville more than all else, more than his own efforts, and the efforts of those like him, more than the railroad would ever give, he could not foresee its future.

By the first law of economics the railroad could bring Plainsville little more than it took away. Plainsville could only send away what it took from its trade territory, and vast as was that territory, this was very little. This territory extended back through miles and miles of hills, but what strength it had was dissipated through a hundred crossroads stores with but comparatively little reaching Plainsville. A good team could lug no more than half a load over the existing mountain wagon trails, so the farmer produced but little more than he used, usually no more than enough to cover his staples. This surplus he would not haul a mile further than necessary.

The invention which was to change all this was to encourage the farmer and stock man to produce enough not only for his needs, but also for luxuries and a comfortable bank account. That which was to bring all this surplus flowing into Plainsville and give it a degree of wealth, stability and security, stood before Father's eyes.

Yet Father, like all the businessmen of the town, with the exception of Jess Erickson, who saw it in the light of advertising value, found this worker of miracles only very amusing. And it was funny that day. There had been few days when we had known such hilarious fun.

They unloaded this new wonder onto the railroad freight platform one morning in early spring. Two men came from the factory to demonstrate it to Jess Erickson with the hope he would add it to the line of buggies, wagons and farm machinery he carried in his big hardware store.

Standing black and shiny on the freight platform, it might have been a rather heavily built rubber-tired hack, without a top, shafts, or a tongue. Otherwise it was a high-wheeled hack, complete to patent leather dashboard and mud guards. As Stub Fletcher said, being a little on the happy side again:

"Be thet all of hit? 'Pears a mite bobtailed, lookin' from yhere."

The factory men worked over the machine, stopping to look inside, squatting to peer underneath, followed by every boy who could duck school. We pushed and shoved to look just where they had looked, squatting to peer up underneath, following their gaze, just as if we knew what we were looking at. Businessmen and town loafers alike stood about the platform, lounged on packing boxes and freight trucks, wearing all-wise expressions of tolerant amusement. They smoked a lot, chewed and spit a lot and talked loud and knowingly. Beyond the fact that it was an "auteemobile" or, what was more easily said, a "hossless kerridge," they knew no more of what they were looking at than we boys, but they had no doubt as to its future.

"They'll niver git hit to the squarr," said Ned Hill.

Cousin Lew Conway spat bravely off the platform and called out, "Mought jist as well load her back on the kivvered kyars, fellers; thim featherbed tars won't last out halfway up river hill."

"Gawd a'mighty," said Will Sterling, "I opine I'd hafta

hawg-tie, blindfold and back my woman and our young'uns into thet thang."

The factory men gave no attention to these remarks other than to grin when the men laughed loudly at what they considered a good one. Finally they brought out a crank and inserted one end in a hole on the right side of the machine just under the front seat. One man climbed into the seat and arranged himself under a bar which, when he was seated, was within easy reach of his hands when held about a foot above his lap. He pushed the bar away, then drew it toward him and the front wheels moved slightly from right to left. We kids drew back and the town men fell silent.

The man in the seat braced himself, adjusted a small lever on the bar and called, "Watch your arm, Fred. All right, twist her tail."

Fred heaved on the crank. There was a clicking sound. The body of the machine rocked a trifle on its springs, then jerked back into place. Fred repeated his twist a dozen times. Sweat trickled down into his eyes. He wiped it away and threw off his coat and said, "Sure your spark's retarded, Harry? I'll spin her."

He grasped the crank in both hands, set his feet wide apart and heaved the crank around and around. The machine trembled under the force of his efforts.

Suddenly there was a loud pop. The machine leaped upward like a spurred horse and a cloud of sooty smoke was exploded from the back end. Then silence.

The man in the seat jiggled the little lever.

"Try her again, Fred. She'll go this time."

Fred spun the crank. There was a loud pop, then, pop-pop-pop. The machine, its four wheels planted firmly on the platform, shook its body exactly as a dog coming out of water stops, plants his feet and shakes his body . . . then, silence.

Fred spat, flipped off the sweat, adjusted his galluses and spun again.

The pops came in rapid staccato. The machine shook vio-

lently, jiggled the man in the seat up and down like a man on
a wagon seat with his team in a dead run down a rocky hill-
side. After a moment the man adjusted the little lever and the
pop and clatter softened to a somewhat regular put-put-put.

The four wheels settled firmly on the platform but the
body of the machine continued to undulate back and forth,
from side to side, in a tremulous rhythmic swing.

Stub Fletcher began to shout in time with the rhythm and
wriggle his hips. "Tata-tah-tah-tah-tee-dee-ah-tah-tah-tah-tah-
tah. There, fellers," he yelled, "is a hootchy-kootchy fer ye."

Uncle Johnnie became the barker for Stub and the undulat-
ing hossless kerridge. He held a length of white pine for a
cane and his hat tipped over one eye at a rakish angle. His
voice low, his tones persuasive, he chanted:

"See Zubelda. See her dance. You have seen your mother
make jelly . . . you have seen it quivvah . . . see Zubelda . . .
how she dances . . . how she quivvahs."

The factory men were surprised and a bit puzzled by these
monkeyshines but they laughed with everybody else. Then
Fred shouted, "You ready, Harry? Run her down the ramp."

Everybody stepped back a step or two. Fred cleared the
way to the ramp. Harry pulled down the little lever, the popping became louder and the sway of the body increased to
a bounding jiggle. His foot pressed a pedal and the chains
tightened on the sprockets inside the back wheels. The machine jerked, leaped forward, settled back on the wheels then
rolled down the ramp. Harry brought it to a stop in the
middle of the street.

The crowd rushed down to gather round. Until they had
seen with their own eyes, none could believe it would move
under its own power. Talk was rapid and excited. We stood
looking up in awe at Harry on the high seat. How did a man
learn to control such power?

Fred called to Jess Erickson, "Come on, Mr. Erickson,
climb in."

Jess Erickson hesitated, not because he was afraid of the machine, but he dreaded being conspicuous as he would be up there in the back seat with all eyes upon him. He searched the crowd until he spotted Uncle Johnnie.

"Come on, Johnnie," he called, "what ye say?"

Uncle Johnnie, who would have mounted a loco mustang in front of the crowned heads of Europe if it promised to be fun, climbed in, tipped hat, white pine stick and all. Jess Erickson followed him.

Fred climbed into the front seat beside Harry. There were shouts of caution and advice, and with a steady pop-popping they rolled forward up Ozark Avenue.

Kids whooped, dogs barked and everybody trotted along beside the machine.

Somebody called to mind the town's favorite story of Newt Riley and his brother Phil trying to ride a wild colt in the barn lot and there came shouts of:

"Hold her, Newt, she's a-rarin'."—And from across the street—"Hold her, hold her! She's a-headin' fer the barn. Circle her, Newt, circle her—she'll kill us both!"

Up the street, farmers were battling teams and wagons into alleys and side streets while women, children and old men risked life and limb to scramble out between wheels and over tail gates to run back to the street and stand bug-eyed along the curb.

As the street made a gradual climb, the speed was never more than a comfortable trot, so where the grade became steeper as it neared the square, men ran ahead to free horses from the hitching rack around the courthouse fence. Even so, two horses snapped their reins, galloped to the far side of the square where they stood, heads and tails high, snorting defiance at this weird hossless hack that rolled uphill, popping and shooting smoke out of its tail as it came.

With a gay put-putting the machine rounded the square gathering an ever-increasing crowd, and turned into South

Street to come to a triumphant stop before Erickson's Hardware and Farm Implements Store. The men stepped down to
go into the store.

Jess Erickson called to Moon, telling him to get into the
seat and not let anybody climb over the machine. Moon made
the seat in a single leap and motioned me to follow. He then
told Jug and Pook-eye to get in the back seat, as "it looked
like hit was goin' to take a heap of watchin'."

At first folks kept their distance, but gradually came closer
until they were touching the wheels, crouching down to peer
up underneath, testing the slickness of the patent leather mud
guards and dashboard.

Moon discovered a large rubber bulb fastened to the side of
the seat. Inserted in the bulb was the end of a brass horn,
the bell pointing to the ground. He gave the bulb a quick
squeeze. The resultant honk produced four bruised heads,
started babies crying and dogs barking. Thereafter we waited
until a group of newcomers had gathered around; we even
urged them to get down low and view the wonders underneath, then we took turns blowing the horn. Everybody had
a fine time.

By evening it was known that Jess Erickson had agreed to
buy the machine providing it climbed to his house, high on
the side of Hobart's Hill, under its own power. As no such
important news could be kept secret, every detail was dis-
cussed by young and old. The factory men had agreed not
only to drive up to Jess's house, but to back the machine all
the way up the steep climb. As everybody knew how difficult
it was to back a wagon up even a slight slope, all agreed that
Jess's money would stay right where it was in the bank. The
trial was set for the next morning.

South Street, leaving the square, climbs a gentle slope for
a block or two, then drops sharply to cross a deep wash on
a high fill before starting its long steep climb to the top of
Hobart's Hill. The road is level on the fill, so Fred and Harry

turned the machine around here and made their preparations for backing up the hill.

The footbridge crossing the wash was crowded to the breaking point but not a person went more than a block up the hill. All said that outsiders just didn't know Ozark Hills. Why, a good team had to stop as many as ten times dragging any kind of load up Hobart's Hill.

Jess Erickson stood alone, far up the hill where he had drawn a line across the street in front of his house. He held an Erickson Hardware and Farm Implement Company check in his hand. Everyone knew when a wheel crossed that line the check was Harry's and it was a closed deal.

Father sat on a rail of the bridge. He spoke low to Cousin Matt.

"Jess sure knows how to play to the grandstand. It's good business even if he gets the damned thing. Everybody in the country is talking Erickson's hardware. But a contraption like that will never get anywhere in this country."   .

On the fill the machine stood shimmying in rhythm with a soft put-put from the pipe sticking out of the back. Fred and Harry took a last look around and climbed into the front seat. The put-put increased its tempo to a vicious popping and the machine started backing. It moved slowly but steadily upward.

There were no shouts, no calls. Folks walked slowly, in silence, keeping pace with the machine. There was something awe-inspiring, something unbelievable in the sight of that bobtailed hack backing steadily up the steep grade. The steering bar jerked frantically back and forth in Harry's hands as the wheels dropped into a rut or fell off a rock, but the machine continued to climb.

A freckle-faced boy walking in his sock feet beside me, carrying a pair of new store-bought shoes in his hands, said, "Hit'll stop whar thet shelf of rock goes antegogglin' acrost the road."

But the machine twisted over the six-inch shelf of rock and went on. Folks were looking from one to the other now, and measuring by eye the narrowing distance between the machine and Jess Erickson.

Strange how people will shout over small things yet in the face of a real wonder remain silent. There was hardly a word spoken, only the heavy breathing as they, straining forward, hurried to keep abreast of the machine. All eyes were on Jess Erickson, standing on the line, holding aloft the check.

A wheel crossed the line and Harry reached out a hand and gathered in the check. He waved it high above his head. There was an awed cheer, then those who still had wind enough started to run, for it was evident that the machine was going on to try for the crest of the hill.

The grade lessened above Jess Erickson's line until it was nearly flat on the crest where earth had been cut away to make the fill at the bottom of the hill. The machine gathered some speed and was rolling backward over the comparative level with a gay triumphant popping when, with the hilltop a scant ten yards away, Monk Watson's mule team came over the crest.

Monk was bringing a load of stove wood to town; his woman, kids and grandpap were strung out, sitting on the wood behind him. His team, half-blind with age and weary after pulling a load up the far side of the hill, would not have noticed a lesser apparition; but a shiny hack backing at them, shooting as it came, was too much for even a pair of aged mules.

They reared straight into the air, whirled around until a front wheel cramped against the wagon. The wagon groaned, reeled, and threatened to come apart, but slid around and went bumping away behind the mules as they galloped down the far side of the hill.

The mules were too stiff-jointed to attain any speed, even down hill, and all would have been well had not Grandpap attempted to stand upright to shout, "Gawd damn hit, hit's a thang—tain't man ner beast!"

He had a wooden leg so he stood none too firm on the stacked wood. A roll of the wagon sent him head first over a back wheel, but by some miracle of agility he landed upright. His wooden leg, which supplied the missing member from the knee down, plunged into soft earth and snapped off half its length.

Grandpap lay flat on his back, waving the remmant of his wooden leg in the air, while his shouts called upon the Lord to witness that he had "met the workin's of the Devil plumb squarr in the middle of the big road; and hit warr all the fault of Mattie [his oldest grandchild!] who warr a-runnin' the brash with thet Gawd-defyin' Homer Hawkins."

But his tune changed when Monk brought his team to a stop, turned around and came back to pick him up. Monk believed lawin' beat work any day. A few words in Grandpap's ear, and by the time they lifted him back onto the wagon he had discovered pains from the top of his head to the bottom of his one foot. Come evening, Jess Erickson owned an automobile complete with suit for damages and attachment.

The factory men were in town for two days teaching Ed Hawks, who assembled plows and wagons for Erickson's Hardware, to operate the machine. They didn't try Hobart's Hill again. When they had gone Ed practiced a few days, keeping to fairly level ground. Then he and Jess tried for a solid week to get up the hill, but they never got more than a quarter of the way. A month passed before Ed Hawks' brother, who worked in an automobile plant in Detroit, came home for a visit and solved the mystery. He explained how the machine, being geared so much lower in reverse, would of course climb a much steeper hill backward than it would forward.

Jess Erickson didn't care. He laughed more at himself than anybody dared laugh at him. The machine was polished and set just inside the big window of his warehouse where his wagons and farm implements were on display. Few there were who came to town without dropping in to see the hoss-less kerridge. In turn they looked at the new wagons and plows. Far more new wagons appeared on the roads, far more new plows broke the earth than ever before. You had to get up early in the morning to beat Jess Erickson.

So it was that our first automobile, standing bright and shiny in the window, though it never saw a hundred miles of road, brought its own change, as if predicting the vast changes its descendants would one day bring even to the farthest hills.

Sydney J. Harris

*Sydney J. Harris (1916–   ), born in London, came to Chicago
as a small child. He began with the* DAILY NEWS *as copy boy and,
after an interlude during which he published and edited* THE
BEACON, *a militantly liberal journal of opinion, rose to the eminence of dramatic critic and columnist. His somewhat astringent
"Strictly Personal" column attracts a great number of letters, pro
and con. Harris is also a member of the faculty of the University
of Chicago College. The following selections are reprinted from
Harris' column in the Chicago* DAILY NEWS.

Author's Prefaces

SOME DAY I hope to find a truly honest Author's Preface to a book. I don't ask that the book be profound or even entertaining. All I want to see is an honest preface.

Pick up a serious tome on philosophy or sociology, and you run head-first into the same preface all the time. Maybe the authors buy them ready-made from a preface factory. I can quote them by heart already:

"I wish to express my gratitude to my colleague, Prof. Bumbleshoot, for assisting me in deciphering the Assyrian holograph on page 271. Also I am grateful for the invaluable assistance in correcting grammatical errors given by Prof. Solecism, who placed a subordinate clause in the subjunctive preterit on page 296.

"My thanks also to Miss Zomby, who compiled the index, A to M, and Miss Scabies, who compiled the index, N to Z. Also to Mrs. Doppelhanger, who placed the carbon paper in my typing sheets, Prof. Fizzle for providing me with a new ribbon, and Mr. Glandhaufen for numbering the galley proofs.

"My deepest appreciation, however, goes to my dear wife, Hezpazia, and my darling children, Donder, Blitzen, and Prancer, who constantly encouraged me throughout my labors."

None of the authors (or professors, either) that I have known ever felt this way during the throes of preparing a book. A much more candid, and realistic, preface would run this way:

"A murrain upon all my stupid, pettifogging colleagues who keep interrupting my work with their ridiculously inept

suggestions! My secretary is a lardhead who can't tell a meta-
phor from a metatarsal, and the three librarians who tried to
help me with research belong in a home for defective children.

"An ancient Gaelic curse on all typesetters, proofreaders,
binders, and publishers, who have jointly conspired to make
my book resemble a head of lettuce that has been gnawed by
a pack of prairie dogs. This goes double for my indexers, who
must have been using the Phoenician alphabet.

"As for my wife and kiddies, all I can say is it's a wonder
I ever finished the book at all. Half the time my study looks
like a millinery shop, and the rest of the time it resembles the
Indianapolis Speedway. Then there was the case of the Four
Missing Chapters that were found months later, lining the
pantry shelves. God only knows how this book got published."

Is there an honest author in the house?

Hats Off to These Lovelies

SOME YEARS ago, a national magazine published a list of "The
10 Greatest Women in History," which included a couple of
Queens, Joan of Arc, Mme. Curie and a few other famous
females.

Frankly, I could compile a better list myself, and have been
engaged in the task over the last six months. So, without further fuss, here is my personal Gallery of Great Women:

Mrs. Abner Strongforth of the Bronx. One morning at the
breakfast table, she asked her husband: "Abner, what shall we
have for dinner tonight?" Instead of answering something un-
decipherable, like "Mmnnph," as he had for 17 years, Abner

replied: "Shrimp cocktail, beef broth, Long Island duckling, sweet potatoes, baked Alaska and tea."

When he got home that night, Mrs. Strongforth had prepared exactly what he asked for. He immediately called in three neighbors to witness this rare phenomenon. I have their signed affidavits in my possession.

Mrs. Bette Lou Schmalhausen of Weetoken, N.J. One morning last August, she walked into a grocery store, ordered a dozen eggs, and when the clerk brought them over, she didn't ask: "Are these eggs fresh?" The clerk promptly fainted from shock, but the manager, with fine presence of mind, legally recorded the incident.

Miss Clarabelle Clavier of Minneapolis. On Oct. 19, 1945, Miss Clavier boarded a streetcar to visit her sister's house. The second she stepped on the streetcar, she had the exact fare in her hand, and gave it to the conductor, who was surrounded by a dozen other females who had been burrowing in their purses for 10 minutes and could find only five dollar bills.

Miss Clavier was presented with the Order of the Strap by the Minneapolis Transit Co., and the conductor, after years of backsliding, has become a regular churchgoer. "I now believe in miracles," he told his pastor.

Mrs. Sydney J. Harris of Chicago. On April 5, 1947, Mrs. Harris attended the opening of a new play with her husband and another couple. When they got home four hours later, Mrs. H. still had *both of her gloves.*

Mr. Harris immediately telephoned all the newspapers and asked them to send out photographers to take pictures of this unprecedented occurrence. But despite the presence of the other couple, who swore to the fact, all the picture editors refused to believe that a married woman could return home from an evening at the theater with both her gloves still in her possession.

Even Mme. Curie never did, I'll bet!

Ernest Hemingway

Ernest Hemingway (1898–   ), was born in Oak Park, Ill., a suburb of Chicago. His father, a physician, often sought relaxation in hunting and fishing trips to the Michigan wilds with young Ernest as a companion. A great many of Hemingway's earliest and best short stories betray the impact of these excursions. "The Light of the World" is reprinted from THE FIFTH COLUMN AND THE FIRST FORTY-NINE STORIES *(1938).*

The Light of the World

WHEN he saw us come in the door the bartender looked up and then reached over and put the glass covers on the two free-lunch bowls.

"Give me a beer," I said. He drew it, cut the top off with the spatula and then held the glass in his hand. I put the nickel on the wood and he slid the beer toward me.

"What's yours?" he said to Tom.

"Beer."

He drew the beer and cut it off and when he saw the money he pushed the beer across to Tom.

"What's the matter?" Tom asked.

The bartender didn't answer him. He just looked over our heads and said, "What's yours?" to a man who'd come in.

"Rye," the man said. The bartender put out the bottle and glass and a glass of water.

Tom reached over and took the glass off the free-lunch bowl. It was a bowl of pickled pig's feet and there was a wooden thing that worked like a scissors, with two wooden forks at the end to pick them up with.

"No," said the bartender and put the glass cover back on the bowl. Tom held the wooden scissors fork in his hand. "Put it back," said the bartender.

"You know where," said Tom.

The bartender reached a hand forward under the bar, watching us both. I put fifty cents on the wood and he straightened up.

"What was yours?" he said.

"Beer," I said, and before he drew the beer he uncovered both the bowls.

"Your goddam pig's feet stink," Tom said, and spit what he had in his mouth on the floor. The bartender didn't say anything. The man who had drunk the rye paid and went out without looking back.

"You stink yourself," the bartender said. "All you punks stink."

"He says we're punks," Tommy said to me.

"Listen," I said. "Let's get out."

"You punks clear the hell out of here," the bartender said.

"I said we were going out," I said. "It wasn't your idea."

"We'll be back," Tommy said.

"No you won't," the bartender told him.

"Tell him how wrong he is," Tom turned to me.

"Come on," I said.

Outside it was good and dark.

"What the hell kind of place is this?" Tommy said.

"I don't know," I said. "Let's go down to the station."

We'd come in the town at one end and we were going out the other. It smelled of hides and tan bark and the big piles of sawdust. It was getting dark as we came in, and now that it was dark it was cold and the puddles of water in the roads were freezing at the edges.

Down at the station there were five whores waiting for the train to come in, and six white men and four Indians. It was crowded and hot from the stove and full of stale smoke. As we came in nobody was talking, and the ticket window was down.

"Shut the door, can't you?" somebody said.

I looked to see who said it. It was one of the white men. He wore stagged trousers and lumbermen's rubbers and a mackinaw shirt like the others, but he had no cap and his face was white and his hands were white and thin.

"Aren't you going to shut it?"

"Sure," I said, and shut it.

"Thank you," he said. One of the other men snickered.

"Ever interfere with a cook?" he said to me.

"No."

"You can interfere with this one," he looked at the cook. "He likes it."

The cook looked away from him, holding his lips tight together.

"He puts lemon juice on his hands," the man said. "He wouldn't get them in dishwater for anything. Look how white they are."

One of the whores laughed out loud. She was the biggest whore I ever saw in my life and the biggest woman. And she had on one of those silk dresses that change colors. There were two other whores that were nearly as big but the big one must have weighed three hundred and fifty pounds. You couldn't believe she was real when you looked at her. All three had those changeable silk dresses. They sat side by side on the bench. They were huge. The other two were just ordinary looking whores, peroxide blondes.

"Look at his hands," the man said and nodded his head at the cook. The whore laughed again and shook all over.

The cook turned and said to her quickly, "You big disgusting mountain of flesh."

She just kept on laughing and shaking.

"Oh, my Christ," she said. She had a nice voice. "Oh, my sweet Christ."

The other whores, the big ones, acted very quiet and placid as though they didn't have much sense, but they were big, nearly as big as the biggest one. They'd have both gone well over two hundred and fifty pounds. The other two were dignified.

Of the men, besides the cook and the one who talked, there were two other lumberjacks, one that listened, interested but bashful, and the other that seemed getting ready to say something, and two Swedes. Two Indians were sitting down at the end of the bench and one standing up against the wall.

The man who was getting ready to say something spoke to me very low, "Must be like getting on top of a hay mow."

I laughed and said it to Tommy.

"I swear to Christ I've never been anywhere like this," he said. "Look at the three of them." Then the cook spoke up.

"How old are you boys?"

"I'm ninety-six and he's sixty-nine," Tommy said.

"Ho! Ho! Ho!" the big whore shook with laughing. She had a really pretty voice. The other whores didn't smile.

"Oh, can't you be decent?" the cook said. "I just asked to be friendly."

"We're seventeen and nineteen," I said.

"What's the matter with you?" Tommy turned to me.

"You can call me Alice," the big whore said and then she began to shake again.

"Is that your name?" Tommy asked.

"Sure," she said. "Alice. Isn't it?" She turned to the man who sat by the cook.

"Alice. That's right."

"That's the sort of name you'd have," the cook said.

"It's my real name," Alice said.

"What's the other girls' names?" Tom asked.

"Hazel and Ethel," Alice said. Hazel and Ethel smiled. They weren't very bright.

"What's your name?" I said to one of the blondes.

"Frances," she said.

"Frances what?"

"Frances Wilson. What's it to you?"

"What's yours?" I asked the other one.

"Oh, don't be fresh," she said.

"He just wants us all to be friends," the man who talked said. "Don't you want to be friends?"

"No," the peroxide one said. "Not with you."

"She's just a spitfire," the man said. "A regular little spitfire."

The one blonde looked at the other and shook her head. "Goddamned mossbacks," she said.

Alice commenced to laugh again and to shake all over.

"There's nothing funny," the cook said. "You all laugh but there's nothing funny. You two young lads; where are you bound for?"

"Where are you going yourself?" Tom asked him.

"I want to go to Cadillac," the cook said. "Have you ever been there? My sister lives there."

"He's a sister himself," the man in the stagged trousers said.

"Can't you stop that sort of thing?" the cook asked. "Can't we speak decently?"

"Cadillac is where Steve Ketchel came from and where Ad Wolgast is from," the shy man said.

"Steve Ketchel," one of the blondes said in a high voice as though the name had pulled a trigger in her. "His own father shot and killed him. Yes, by Christ, his own father. There aren't any more men like Steve Ketchel."

"Wasn't his name Stanley Ketchel?" asked the cook.

"Oh, shut up," said the blonde. "What do you know about Steve? Stanley. He was no Stanley. Steve Ketchel was the finest and most beautiful man that ever lived. I never saw a man as clean and as white as Steve Ketchel. There never was a man like that. He moved like a tiger and he was the finest, free-est, spender that ever lived."

"Did you know him?" one of the men asked.

"Did I know him? Did I know him? Did I love him? You ask me that? I knew him like you know nobody in the world and I loved him like you love God. He was the greatest, finest, whitest, most beautiful man that ever lived, Steve Ketchel, and his own father shot him down like a dog."

"Were you out on the coast with him?"

"No. I knew him before that. He was the only man I ever loved."

Every one was very respectful to the peroxide blonde, who

said all this in a high stagey way, but Alice was beginning to shake again. I felt it sitting by her.

"You should have married him," the cook said.

"I wouldn't hurt his career," the peroxide blonde said. "I wouldn't be a drawback to him. A wife wasn't what he needed. Oh, my God, what a man he was."

"That was a fine way to look at it," the cook said. "Didn't Jack Johnson knock him out though?"

"It was a trick," Peroxide said. "That big dinge took him by surprise. He'd just knocked Jack Johnson down, the big black bastard. That nigger beat him by a fluke."

The ticket window went up and the three Indians went over to it.

"Steve knocked him down," Peroxide said. "He turned to smile at me."

"I thought you said you weren't on the coast," some one said.

"I went out just for that fight. Steve turned to smile at me and that black son of a bitch from hell jumped up and hit him by surprise. Steve could lick a hundred like that black bastard."

"He was a great fighter," the lumberjack said.

"I hope to God he was," Peroxide said. "I hope to God they don't have fighters like that now. He was like a god, he was. So white and clean and beautiful and smooth and fast and like a tiger or like lightning."

"I saw him in the moving pictures of the fight," Tom said. We were all very moved. Alice was shaking all over and I looked and saw she was crying. The Indians had gone outside on the platform.

"He was more than any husband could ever be," Peroxide said. "We were married in the eyes of God and I belong to him right now and always will and all of me is his. I don't care about my body. They can take my body. My soul belongs to Steve Ketchel. By God, he was a man."

Everybody felt terribly. It was sad and embarrassing. Then Alice, who was still shaking, spoke. "You're a dirty liar," she said in that low voice. "You never layed Steve Ketchel in your life and you know it."

"How can you say that?" Peroxide said proudly.

"I say it because it's true," Alice said. "I'm the only one here that ever knew Steve Ketchel and I come from Mancelona and I knew him there and it's true and you know it's true and God can strike me dead if it isn't true."

"He can strike me too," Peroxide said.

"This is true, true, true, and you know it. Not just made up and I know exactly what he said to me."

"What did he say?" Peroxide said complacently.

Alice was crying so she could hardly speak from shaking so "He said 'You're a lovely piece, Alice.' That's exactly what he said."

"It's a lie," Peroxide said.

"It's true," Alice said. "That's truly what he said."

"It's a lie," Peroxide said proudly.

"No, it's true, true, true, to Jesus and Mary true."

"Steve couldn't have said that. It wasn't the way he talked," Peroxide said happily.

"It's true," said Alice in her nice voice. "And it doesn't make any difference to me whether you believe it or not." She wasn't crying any more and she was calm.

"It would be impossible for Steve to have said that," Peroxide declared.

"He said it," Alice said and smiled. "And I remember when he said it and I *was* a lovely piece then exactly as he said, and right now I'm a better piece than you, you dried up old hot-water bottle."

"You can't insult me," said Peroxide. "You big mountain of pus. I have my memories."

"No," said Alice in that sweet lovely voice, "you haven't any real memories except having your tubes out and when you started C. and M. Everything else you read in the papers. I'm clean and you know it and men like me, even though I'm big, and you know it, and I never lie and you know it."

"Leave me with my memories," Peroxide said. "With my true, wonderful memories."

Alice looked at her and then at us and her face lost that hurt look and she smiled and she had about the prettiest face I ever saw. She had a pretty face and a nice smooth skin and a lovely voice and she was nice all right and really friendly. But my God she was big. She was as big as three women. Tom saw me looking at her and he said, "Come on. Let's go."

"Good-bye," said Alice. She certainly had a nice voice.

"Good-bye," I said.

"Which way are you boys going?" asked the cook.

"The other way from you," Tom told him.

Kin Hubbard

Kin Hubbard (1868–1930), born Frank McKinney Hubbard and better known as the creator of "Abe Martin," set out from his birthplace, Bellefontaine, Ohio, in 1891 to join the staff of the Indianapolis NEWS. *He had had some initial training as all-around man on his father's paper the Bellefontaine* WEEKLY EXAMINER. *Equally versatile in Indianapolis, he was staff cartoonist as well as reporter. In 1904 he began writing the text and drawing the pictures for a column expressing the opinions of an attenuated rustic, "Abe Martin, Brown County, Indiana." Other regular characters, such as Miss Fawn Lippincutt, Lester Moots, Ike Lark, and Miss Tawney Apple appeared, and as the years went by the sly, salty wisdom of the one-panel comic with picture above and short aphorism below won it an immense following. Annual compilations of Abe Martin's sayings were published, with only a few years missed, from 1906 until Hubbard's death.*

Namin' Children

By Mrs. Leghorn Tharp

THER's been quite a lot written in regard t' th' namin' o' children, an' a lot more should be written considerin' th' seriousness o' the subject. Too many children are sent out int' th' world with names out o' all proportion t' ther looks an' ther abilities an' ther physiques—boys an' girls who must battle ther way t' success. It's no easy thing fer a youth t' git t' th' front with a purty name an' curly hair, an' it's doubly hard if his name is Dewey. Boys shouldn' be named till ther fifteen. That's th' time t' size 'em up an' name 'em Dan or Albert, or Kenneth or Stanley, or Godfrey or Cecil, or Steve or Norman, but beware o' th' name Bolivar. Never name a boy after a successful father t' grow up an' fail, an' what's still worse, never name a son after a worthless dad t' grow up an' try t' keep his identity under cover. Never name a scrawny, thin spaced son Robert jest because he has a rich uncle named Robert, fer money he gits that way won't do him no good. Don't give a son a double name t' slip up an' rearrange an' fool with all through life. A boy with an illustrious name won't git very fer unless he's endowed. He should not try t' start even with a great name. Jest think o' th' Lincolns an' Sumners, Grants an' Grovers we run into, practically all failures, luggin' about the names of illustrious idols, an' often goin' without food an' sleepin' in th' open. I used t' know a fairly successful feller named Felix Grubbs Craw. He wuz handicapped at both ends of his name an' in th' middle. His uncle had left him a little money t' tide over his first name, an' his mother had deeded him the family home t' help out his last name. He wuz a good, industrious feller an' got on fairly well, although his middle name made it very difficult. I often wonder what would have become o' him if he'd been turned adrift without funds. Never name a boy Al unless you want ever'buddy in town t' be runnin' t' him fer favors. An' another name that's allus taken advantage of is Jack. Th' girls love it, an' that's why so few Jacks are ever heard of after they reach thirty. Women seem t' git on fairly well with incongruous names, but nothin' kin hold a woman back if she's got a sweet disposition. It's a mistake, o' course, t' name a girl Goldie, fer so many o' them fail t' return when they go t' th' grocery.

Abe Martin's Sayings

WHILE failure in private business may not be a recommendation for a political office, it's nearly allus th' real incentive.

"Well, sir, it wuz th' best I could do at that time," said ole Dan Moss, when asked how in the world he ever happened t' marry his uncle's widder.

Miss Tawney Apple has contracted neuritis from chilled cocktail shakers.

A feller will stop at any kind of a hotel if his feet hurt.

Next t' settlin' back an' lightin' a nickel cigar at th' dinnertable, th' worst breach o' good taste is tryin' t' separate a fishbone from a mouthful o' mashed pertaters.

Say whatever else you please about Lon Moon, he's got th' best lookin' Bible class in town.

While Lisle Tharp wuz tryin' t' thumb his way t' Bloom Center, Butcher Joe Mopps drove along, an' taking a fancy t' his thumb, he hired him t' clerk in his meat-shop.

Lester Lark, o' th' *Weekly Sliphorn*, won th' Tell Binkley prize fer th' best write-up of a burnin' building, bein' th' only contestant that didn't say anything about th' flames "belchin' forth" an' th' structure bein' gutted.

Talk about hard luck, Mrs. Ike Lark has got an exclusive piece o' gossip, but nobuddy t' stay with her children while she puts it out.

FROM *Barbed Wire*

Luther Motts, founder an' president o' the "Fit-at-Fifty Club," dropped dead with his skates on.

Miss Fawn Lippincut got her new sunback dress on frontwards an' had to back all the way to the pust-office an' home again.

My idee o' takin' big chances is gittin' smart Alecky with a state fair policeman carryin' a heavy hickory cane.

"It's not allus necessarily th' liver, fer oftentimes bein' married'll cause th' same ugly, irritable, to h-ll with ever'buddy feelin'" said Dr. Mopps, as a patient put his shirt back on.

FROM *Abe Martin's Broadcast*

Indiana Writers' Project

The following yarns are selected from HOOSIER TALL STORIES *(1937), compiled and written by members of the Federal Writers' Project in Indiana. A foreword says:*

"From earliest times men in American small towns and rural communities have gathered at crossroads, stores, and taverns to swap yarns, and tell tales; so common is this yarn-swapping among Hoosiers that a time-honored institution exists from which the yarns are started on their rounds. This institution is called variously the 'Lazy' or 'Liars' Bench,' the 'Community Bench,' and the 'Cracker Barrel.' It is here that tall stories usually get their start.

"In Nashville, county seat of Brown County, the bench stands beneath the locust trees on the courthouse lawn. It is an old wooden seat with iron legs, and a single arm, and has occupied the same position winter and summer for a number of years. Its seating capacity is limited to six. Here the Brown County story-tellers swap yarns.

"There is an unwritten law that when this bench is full and other tale-tellers come to join those seated there, the one at the foot—the end without the arm—is pushed off to make room for the new recruits. Efforts are sometimes made to dislodge the man at the head, the iron arm blocks this move and as a result one of the middle men is pushed out when the grand shove begins. It is to this comfortable loafing place that Nashville women come whenever they cannot find their husbands nearer home.

"Gentryville has always had its loafing place since the days when the Gentry boys, Baldwin the blacksmith, Abe Lincoln, and Dennis Hanks, used to congregate around Jones' store. But it was not until 1894 that a definite place was established where a man

might go and be sure of an audience any time of day. A large heavy bridge plank was wedged between two locust trees near the entrance to one of the crossroad stores. The plank was thick and long, and with a brace in the center gave enough room for a number of men and boys who kept the bench full throughout the day and far into the night. As fast as one would leave some other would take his place.

"Here children came repeatedly with the announcement 'Pa, Ma wants you!' Still the story-telling continued. Sometimes it took two or three summons before Pa would leave the bench.

"From Fountain County comes the report that whenever the mendacious heroes of small town life foregather, this bench exists, and whenever the faithful meet on store platform or barber shop or garage, the tall stories are told. No one believes them unless it is the narrator who by repetition has come to believe his own myths. They cannot come in the category of lies for a lie is deliberate and is usually without value as entertainment but untruths they undoubtedly are. It requires a real effort of the imagination to produce some of the fearful and wonderful tales 'swapped' on these occasions."

Them Plaguey Indians

AN OLD woman who lived near the frontier during our disturbance with Great Britain had possessed a marvelous propensity for learning the news, and frequently used to make inquiries of the soldiers. On one occasion she called to a passing soldier whom she had frequently saluted before: "What's the news?"

"Why," said he, "the Indians have fixed a crowbar under Lake Erie, and are going to turn it over and drown the world." "Oh massy! massy! what shall I do?" she cried, and ran away to tell the neighbors of the danger and inquire of her minister how such a calamity might be averted. "Why," says he, "you need not be alarmed, we have our Maker's promise that He will not again destroy the world by water."

"I know that," returned the old lady hastily, "but He's nothing to do with it; it's them plaguey Indians."

A "Sockdolager"

SAM (THE name is fictitious, as the biggest liar is always well known in his community), a hunter famous in the vicinity of Vincennes both for his "tall stories" and his ability to bag game, was once overtaken and accosted by the game warden.

"What luck?" began the game warden's inquiry.

"Oh, plenty!" said Sam; and he related his day's experiences and elaborated upon them: "Why, I bagged 17 squirrels [squirrels were out of season at the time] and 23 rabbits and killed 35 birds today."

"I see you've been fishing too," urged the game warden. "Did you catch many?"

"Oh, not with a line," bragged Sam, "but I have six nets out and do pretty well with them."

"Say, do you know who I am?" asked the game warden, suddenly, thinking he had the goods on Sam.

"No," truthfully replied our hero.

"Well, I'm the game warden," he replied.

But Sam, undaunted, asked, "Do you know who I am?"

"No," snapped the game warden.

"Well," drawled Sam, "I am the biggest damn liar in the county."

Hot Marksmanship

HERE is a bird of a story which gives an idea of what crack shots the old settlers were in the days when folks depended a deal on their rifles and naturally took pains to practice whenever they could:

It seems that two old timers had some trouble with each other that couldn't get settled no matter what, so to make it quick and no fooling they figured the best way was to get into the woods by themselves and have it out with their guns. So they went out a ways and turned back to back and stepped off twenty paces apiece. It was the rule in such cases to aim at the other man's left eye—the "sight eye"—which naturally was the one left open when he was sighting a rifle, as you can try for yourself.

Well, these two old timers counted "three" together and fired, but blamed if either got so much as creased. They felt sort of ashamed at first, of course, but after they got to remembering how they hated each other and how there was no one looking on anyhow they went to loading up again, holding their place.

Well, they fired again, but no luck. There wasn't even the riffle of a hair to show for the powder and lead they'd used up trying to stir up the material for an obituary. But they were obstinate and determined, so they shot and shot until a dozen charges had been used up apiece. By that time they got to worrying what might happen if they run short of powder and ball for the next rumpus with the Indians, so they figured it would be best to call the show off.

Naturally this kind of weighed on them—calling the thing off on such account—but anyhow and someway they walked back midway and shook hands, still wondering what in

Tophet had come over their shooting. All at once one of them felt something hot under his boot and jumped. They both looked down. And darned if there wasn't a lump of hot lead!

Those two old buzzards had shot so straight at each other's left eye that every pair of bullets had met midbetween, and they had loaded and fired so fast that the next pair had met and melted into the one next before, so that in the end there was just one lump of lead that hadn't had time to cool when they called off the show!

Who Was Drunk?

It was on Pipe Creek that Tom Moore took rod and tackle one warm day in July and went to fish. As he had a thirsty nature and feared he would have nothing but creek water to drink, Tom took along a bottle of John Barleycorn.

He found a nice shady place along the stream to sit, baited his hook and cast his line far out into the water. He had sat there for some time before he thought of the bottle in his pocket, took it out and quenched his thirst which had suddenly become middling sharp. He put the bottle back in his pocket and in a little while fell asleep. On waking up, he found the pole had been dragged from his hand down to the water's edge where a snake was coiled, looking at the fisherman with more than ordinary interest for a snake.

Tom "sot agin," baited the hook and threw it into the water. Again his thirst took possession of him and he took another drink. He felt something nudging him in the side. As he looked down he saw the snake with mouth open and tongue extended suggestively. The fisherman poured some of the contents of the bottle into the snake's mouth, and it went scurrying off into the water. Soon it appeared with a catfish in its mouth and laid the fish down beside Tom. It nudged him again and opened its mouth and Tom gave it another drink. Again it disappeared into the stream and this time came up with a bass in its mouth. Tom kept up the game, giving it a drink and in return receiving a fish each time. He finally stopped fishing and just watched the snake, which now approached the bank with considerable difficulty. It proceeded in this wandering fashion for some time, getting more and more off its course, when suddenly two other snakes appeared on the scene. They slipped along on either side of their boon companion, one wrapping a coil around the neck and the other around its middle, and the three snakes disappeared among the weeds at the side of the stream.

Drive On!

JEFF DAWSON was said to be the laziest man in Fountain or any other county. His neighbors labored with him on behalf of his family, hard up because he was so lazy, but appeals were of no use. Finally the citizens told him in so many words that there was no need of a dead man walking around on top the ground and he could take his choice of getting down to work or being buried alive. He chose to be buried.

On the way to the cemetery, with Jeff in a coffin on the wagon, they met a man who inquired the reason for such unusual doings since the "corpse" was calmly puffing a corncob pipe. When it was explained to him, he offered to help Jeff get a start in life by giving him a bushel of corn. Jeff pondered this a moment and finally rose up to ask, "Is the corn shelled?" "Why, no!" replied the Good Samaritan in astonishment. Jeff resignedly lay back again in the coffin. "Drive on, boys," said he, "drive on!"

Ben Krit

Ben Krit (1898–   ) was born in Russia, came to the United States shortly before the outbreak of World War I. He graduated from Hyde Park High School in 1919 and has since been general-store clerk and country schoolteacher in North Dakota, dry-cleaner, Skid Row habitué, member of the Illinois Writers' Project, and a laboratory technician. Given a typewriter in lieu of a fee for cleaning out a basement in 1937, he used it to knock out a story accepted by the REFORM ADVOCATE *(now defunct), where several other stories and a column written by Krit appeared. He wrote for some of the little magazines, and won two prizes for stories published in the Chicago* DAILY NEWS. *"Benny the Bummer" appeared in the* DAILY NEWS *in 1940 as "Such a Life."*

Benny the Bummer

THAT'S the way it is with children—you can never tell the way they'll turn out. You try your best, figure and plan for them and then they go ahead and do as they please. Personally I can't complain because in my case things turned out all right but it is sure surprising at the way fate works out things without asking anybody. For example take a look at my two sons, Hymie the oldest boy and Benny the youngest.

My Benny was a bummer like there never was one. All the time it was baseball, football and swimming. Baseball and football I could stand yet, but his swimming was terrible.

Already when he was in public school while Hymie, that's my older boy, was busy with his lessons that loafer Benny was always swimming. So what do you think? When it came to graduation Hymie was the first in his class and Benny was so low down that his teacher graduated him just to get rid of him.

It's all right to swim. I ain't no fanatic, a kid's got to have some fun, but a boy who is already in highschool should forget this kind of foolishness. So already the first year Benny gets left behind and Hymie skips a grade. And why not? The boy, I mean Hymie, was always studying and reading. A regular professor he was. Everytime there was something important to do in school they call on Hymie. A regular somebody; a debater, a speaker, a chess player and on top of it he wrote poems too. His teacher used to tell me that if he got a little better they would have to invent a special mark that was good enough for him.

And like this it was all the time they were in highschool, Hymie was the best in everything and Benny was swimming.

"The Fish" the boys used to call him because he was all the time in the water. The minute he'd come home from school it was hurry up, give him supper.

"What's the matter," my wife used to ask him, "where's the fire?" "Got to go swimming," he'd answer, grab a piece of cake or a sandwich and run off to the gym.

"And what about lessons?" I'd ask him, "don't you have to do them? Look at Hymie he's already a year ahead of you and is going to get a free scholarship to college and what will you be? A tramp? A bummer?

"No," he answers, "a swimmer."

Well, graduation time came around and Hymie got the highest honors and a free scholarship to college. I'm telling you it was a pleasure to watch him on the stage and it made me cry from happiness when I heard the principal telling everybody what a smart boy Hymie was and what a great man he'll be.

Right after graduation I told Benny that he'd have to get a job because Hymie was going to college and I couldn't afford to keep them both in school.

"I got a job," he tells me, "$30.00 a week."

"And what are you going to do? Be the president of the First National Bank they should pay you $30.00 a week?" I ask him.

"No," he says, "I'm going to swim. I'm going to be a life guard on the beach."

"And what kind of monkey business is that?" I holler at him, "can't you get a job in a shoe store or an office and learn a business or why not help me in the store? I can use a boy."

"Too much work," he says, "I don't like to drag bundles on the third floor and have to listen to Mrs. Cohen complain about the vegetables or Mrs. Goldstein send me back to the store because the eggs don't smell so good. This job is a cinch, all I got to do is sit on a high chair and see that nobody gets drowned."

"So you're going to save people?" I laugh at him, "and you're so smart that you can't even make highschool in four years."

You think it helped all the hollering and talking I done? Nothing. So while Hymie was at home studying for college so he should catch up and graduate quicker, Benny was on the beach saving people.

And that wasn't enough yet so I started having telephone trouble. I mean about all the girls calling up Benny. He wasn't a life guard a month and already the telephone got so busy that nobody got a chance to use it. It didn't stop ringing from morning till night. My wife nearly got flat feet from running from the kitchen to the front room, where the telephone is, telling them when Bernard (no more Benny) would be home.

"You should talk to the boy, he shouldn't, God forbid, get in no trouble yet from all these girls," my wife tells me one day. So when the swimmer comes home and takes off the policeman hat he used to wear, I tell him, "Benny, better be careful."

"Don't worry, Pop," he says, "I'm a good swimmer."

"I know that," I say, "only be careful you don't drown in woman trouble."

"What woman trouble?" he asks me like he don't know from nothing.

"I mean about all these girls calling you up all the time."

"Oh, that," he laughs, "don't worry, I'll be all right."

"I hope so, sonny," I tell him, but I'm a little worried.

A couple of weeks later he comes home and shows me the paper. "Look, Pa," he says, "I'm in the news."

Sure enough there was his picture in the policeman hat and a bathing suit and right by his picture there was a girl's picture. At first I got so scared that I told my wife to call up Fanny's husband, the lawyer. But Benny and Hymie explained that it was all right, no trouble. It said in the paper that Benny saved a girl from drowning. My Benny was a hero.

And what a girl she was. A regular doll. And her father wasn't a nobody neither. Did you ever hear of the Tishel Furniture Company? That's him, the girl's father, I mean.

So pretty soon Mr. Tishel gives Benny a job in his store and Benny gets to be a salesman instead of a swimmer but Hymie goes back to college and in time he graduates, again the best in his class, with the highest honors and a bachelor of arts degree.

What about Benny? Nothing. He married Sally, that's the girl he saved from drowning, Tishel the furniture man's daughter, and he became a partner in the store.

And that is the funny part of this fate business I was talking about because it took me plenty of time, talking and carfare until I got Benny to give Hymie a job in his store.

Ring Lardner

Ring Lardner (1885–1933), born in Niles, Michigan, was named Ringgold Wilmer by his parents. He studied engineering for a while at the Armour Institute of Technology in Chicago, but soon quit school to work as a railroad freight agent. A short time later he was functioning as a reporter on the South Bend TIMES— *the first of a number of newspaper jobs. He achieved his initial literary prominence as a humorous sports writer in* YOU KNOW ME, AL *(1916). Before his death he had the satisfaction of being adopted by the intellectuals as a savagely serious, deadly effective satirist. One of his favorite targets for ridicule was the banality of the "show" business, particularly as expressed in the sterile idiocies and mawkish sentimentality of Tin Pan Alley tunesmiths. "Nora" is reprinted from* ROUND UP *(1929); "Dogs" and "Colleges for Cops" are reprinted from* FIRST AND LAST *(1926).*

Nora

"MR. HAZLETT, shake hands with Jerry Morris and Frank Moon. I guess you've heard of both of them."

The speaker was Louie Brock, producer of musical shows, who had cleared over half a million dollars in two years through the popularity of "Jersey Jane," tunes by Morris and lyrics by Moon.

They were in Brock's inner office, the walls of which were adorned with autographed pictures of six or seven of the more celebrated musical comedy stars and a too-perfect likeness of Brock's wife, whom he had evidently married in a dense fog.

"Mr. Hazlett," continued Brock, "has got a book which he wrote as a straight play, but it struck me right off that it was great material for a musical, especially with you two fellas to do the numbers. It's a brand-new idear, entirely opposite from most of these here musical comedy books that's all the same thing and the public must be getting sick of them by this time. Don't you think so, Jerry?"

"I certainly do," the tunesmith replied. "Give us a good novelty story, and with what I and Frank can throw in there to jazz it up, we'll run till the theater falls down."

"Well, Mr. Hazlett," said Brock, "suppose you read us the book and we'll see what the boys think of it."

Hazlett was quite nervous in spite of Brock's approval of his work and the fact that friends to whom he had shown it had given it high praise and congratulated him on his good fortune in getting a chance to collaborate with Morris and Moon—Morris, who had set a new style in melodies and rhythms and whose tunes made up sixty percent of all dance programs, and Moon, the ideal lyricist who could fit Jerry's fast triplets with such cute-sounding three-syllable rhymes that no one ever went to the considerable trouble of trying to find out what they meant.

"I've tried to stay away from the stereotyped Cinderella theme," said Hazlett. "In my story, the girl starts out just moderately well off and winds up poor. She sacrifices everything for love and the end finds her alone with her lover, impoverished but happy. She—"

"Let's hear the book," said the producer.

Hazlett, with trembling fingers, opened to the first page of his script.

"Well," he began, "the title is 'Nora' and the first scene—"

"Excuse me a minute," Morris interrupted. "I promised a fella that I'd come over and look at a big second-hand Trinidad Twelve. Only eight grand and a bargain if there ever was one, hey, Frank?"

"I'll say it's a bargain," Moon agreed.

"The fella is going to hold it for me till half-past three and its nearly three o'clock now. So if you don't mind, Mr. Hazlett, I wish that instead of reading the book clear through, you'd kind of give us a kind of a synopsis and it will save time and we can tell just as good, hey, Frank?"

"Just as good," said Moon.

"All right, Mr. Hazlett," Brock put in. "Suppose you tell the story in your own way, with just the main idear and the situations."

"Well," said Hazlett, "of course, as a straight play, I wrote it in three acts, but when Mr. Brock suggested that I make a musical show out of it, I cut it to two. To start with, the old man, the girl's uncle, is an Irishman who came to this country when he was about twelve years old. He worked hard and he was thrifty and finally he got into the building business for himself. He's pretty well-to-do, but he's avaricious and not satisfied with the three or four hundred thousand he's saved up. He meets another Irish immigrant about his own age, a politician who has a lot to say about the letting of big city building contracts. This man, Collins, has a handsome young son, John, twenty-three or twenty-four.

"The old man, the girl's uncle—their name is Crowley—he tries his hardest to get in strong with old Collins so Collins will land him some of the city contracts, but Collins, though he's very friendly all the while, he doesn't do Crowley a bit of good in a business way.

"Well, Crowley gives a party at his house for a crowd of his Irish friends in New York, young people and people his own age, and during the party young John Collins sees a picture of Crowley's beautiful niece, Nora. She's still in Ireland and has never been to this country. Young Collins asks Crowley who it is and he tells him and young Collins says she is the only girl he will ever marry.

"Crowley then figures to himself that if he can connect up with the Collinses by having his niece marry young John, he can land just about all the good contracts there are. So he cables for Nora to come over and pay him a visit. She comes and things happen just as Crowley planned—John and Nora fall in love.

"Now there's a big dinner and dance in honor of the Mayor and one of the guests is Dick Percival, a transplanted Englishman who has made fifty million dollars in the sugar business. He also falls in love with Nora and confesses it to her uncle. Old Crowley has always hated Englishmen, but his avarice is so strong that he decides Nora must get rid of John and marry Dick. Nora refuses to do this, saying John is 'her man' and that she will marry him or nobody.

"Crowley forbids her to see John, but she meets him whenever she can get out. The uncle and niece have a long stubborn battle of wills, neither yielding an inch. Finally John's father, old Collins, is caught red-handed in a big bribery scandal and sent to the penitentiary. It is also found out that he has gambled away all his money and John is left without a dime.

"Crowley, of course, thinks this settles the argument, that Nora won't have anything more to do with a man whose father is a crook and broke besides, and he gets up a party to announce the engagement between her and Dick. Nora doesn't interfere at all, but insists that young John Collins be invited. When the announcement is made, Nora says her uncle has got the name of her fiancé wrong; she has been engaged to John Collins since the first day she came to the United States, and if he will still have her, she is his. Then she and John walk out alone into the world, leaving Dick disappointed and Crowley in a good old-fashioned Irish rage."

"Well, boys," said Brock after a pause, "what do you think of it?"

The "boys" were silent.

"You see," said Brock, "for natural ensembles, you got the first party at What's-his-name's, the scene on the pier when the gal lands from Ireland, the Mayor's party at some hotel maybe, and another party at What's-his-name's, only this time it's outdoors at his country place. You can have the boy sing a love-song to the picture before he ever sees the gal; you can make that the melody you want to carry clear through. You can have love duets between she and the boy and she and the Englishman. You can write a song like 'East Side, West Side,' for the Mayor's party.

"You can write a corking good number for the pier scene, where the people of all nationalities are meeting their relatives and friends. And you can run wild with all the good Irish tunes in the world."

"Where's your comic?" inquired Morris.

"Mr. Hazlett forgot to mention the comic," Brock said. "He's an old Irishman, a pal of What's-his-name's, a kind of a Jiggs."

"People don't want an Irish comic these days," said Morris. "Can't you make him a Wop or a Heeb?"

"I'd have to rewrite the part," said Hazlett.

"No you wouldn't," said Morris. "Give him the same lines with a different twist to them."

"It really would be better," Brock put in, "if you could change him to a Heeb or even a Dutchman. I've got to have a spot for Joe Stein and he'd be a terrible flop as a Turkey."

"And listen," said Morris. "What are you going to do with Enriqueta?"

"Gosh! I'd forgot her entirely!" said Brock. "Of course we've got to make room for her."

"Who is she?" Hazlett inquired.

"The best gal in Spain," said Brock. "I brought her over here and I'm paying her two thousand dollars every week with nothing for her to do. You'll have to write a part for her."

"Write in a part!" exclaimed Morris. "She'll play the lead or she won't play."

"But how is a Spanish girl going to play Nora Crowley?" Hazlett asked.

"Why does your dame have to be Nora Crowley?" Morris retorted. "Why does she have to be Irish at all?"

"Because her uncle is Irish."

"Make him a Spaniard, too."

"Yes, and listen," said Moon. "While you're making the gal and her uncle Spaniards, make your boy a Wop. If you do that, I and Jerry have got a number that'll put your troupe over with a bang! Play it for them, Jerry."

Morris went to the piano and played some introductory chords.

"This is a great break of luck," said Moon, "to have a number already written that fits right into the picture. Of course, I'll polish the lyric up a little more and I want to explain that the boy sings parts of the lines, the gal the rest. But here's about how it is. Let's go, Jerry!"

Morris repeated his introduction and Moon began to sing:

> Somewhere in the old world
> You and I belong.
> It will be a gold world,
> Full of light and song.
> Why not let's divide our time
> Between your native land and mine?
> Move from Italy to Spain,
> Then back to Italy again?
>
> In sunny Italy,
> My Spanish queen,
> You'll fit so prettily
> In that glorious scene.
> You will sing me 'La Paloma';
> I will sing you 'Cara Roma;'
> We will build a little home, a
> Bungalow serene.
> Then in the Pyrenees,
> Somewhere in Spain,
> We'll rest our weary knees
> Down in Lovers' Lane,
> And when the breakers roll a-
> Cross the azure sea,
> Espanola, Gorgonzola;
> Spain and Italy.

"A wow!" cried Brock. "Congratulations, Jerry! You, too, Frank! What do you think of that one, Mr. Hazlett?"

"Very nice," said Hazlett. "The tune sounds like 'Sole Mio' and 'La Paloma.' "

"It sounds like them both and it's better than either," said the composer.

"That one number makes our troupe, Jerry," said Brock. "You don't need anything else."

"But we've got something else, hey, Frank?"
"You mean 'Montgomery'?" said Moon.
"Yeh!"
"Let's hear it," requested Brock.
"It'll take a dinge comic to sing it."
"Well, Joe Stein can do a dinge."
"I'll say he can! I like him best in blackface. And he's jus'
the boy to put over a number like this."

Morris played the introduction, strains that Hazlett was
sure he had heard a hundred times before, and Moon was off
again:

> I want to go to Alabam'
> That's where my lovin' sweetheart am,
> And won't she shout and dance for joy
> To see once more her lovin' boy!
> I've got enough saved up, I guess,
> To buy her shoes and a bran'-new dress.
> She's black as coal, and yet I think
> When I walk in, she'll be tickled pink.
>
> Take me to Montgomery
> Where it's always summery.
> New York's just a mummery.
> Give me life that's real.
> New York fields are rotten fields.
> Give me those forgotten fields;
> I mean those there cotton fields,
> Selma and Mobile.
>
> I done been away so long;
> Never thought I'd stay so long.
> Train, you'd better race along
> To my honey lamb.
> Train, you make it snappy till
> ('Cause I won't be happy till)
> I'm in the capital,
> Montgomery, Alabam'.

"Another knockout!" said Brock enthusiastically. "Boys, either one of those numbers are better than anything in 'Jersey Jane.' Either one of them will put our troupe over. And the two of them together in one show! Well, it's in!"

Hazlett mustered all his courage.

"They're a couple of mighty good songs," he said, "but I don't exactly see how they'll fit."

"Mr. Hazlett," said Jerry Morris. "I understand this is your first experience with a musical comedy. I've had five successes in four years and could have had five more if I wanted to work that hard. I know the game backwards and I hope you won't take offense if I tell you a little something about it."

"I'm always glad to learn," said Hazlett.

"Well, then," said Morris, "you've got a great book there, with a good novelty idear, but it won't go without a few changes, changes you can make in a half-hour and do not detract anything from the novelty. In fact, they will add to it. While you were telling your story, I was thinking of it from the practical angle, the angle of show business, and I believe I can put my finger right on the spots that have got to be fixed.

"In the first place, as Louie has told you, he's got a contract with Enriqueta and she won't play any secondary parts. That means your heroine must be Spanish. Well, why not make her uncle her father and have him a Spaniard, running a Spanish restaurant somewhere down-town. It's a small restaurant and he just gets by. He has to use her as cashier and she sits in the window where the people going past can see her.

"One day the boy, who is really an Italian count—we'll call him Count Pizzola—he is riding alone in a taxi and he happens to look in the window and see the gal. He falls in love with her at first sight, orders the driver to stop and gets out and goes in the restaurant. He sits down and has his lunch, and while he is eating we can put in a novelty dance number with the boys and gals from the offices that are also lunching in this place.

"When the number is over, I'd have a comedy scene between Stein, who plays a dinge waiter, and, say, a German customer who isn't satisfied with the food or the check or something. Louie, who would you suggest for that part?"

"How about Charlie Williams?" said Brock.

"Great!" said Morris. "Well, they have this argument and the dinge throws the customer out. The scrap amuses Pizzola and the gal, too, and they both laugh and that brings them together. He doesn't tell her he is a count, but she likes him pretty near as well as he likes her. They gab a while and then go into the Spanish number I just played for you.

"Now, in your story, you've got a boat scene where the gal is landing from Ireland. You'd better forget that scene. There was a boat scene in 'Sunny' and a boat scene in 'Hit the Deck,' and a lot of other troupes. We don't want anything that isn't our own. But Pizzola is anxious to take the gal out somewhere and let's see—Frank, where can he take her?"

"Why not a yacht?" suggested Moon.

"Great! He invites her out on a yacht, but he's got to pretend it isn't his own yacht. He borrowed it from a friend. She refuses at first, saying she hasn't anything to wear. She's poor, see? So he tells her his sister has got some sport clothes that will fit her. He gets the clothes for her and then we have a scene in her room where she is putting them on with a bunch of girl friends helping her. We'll write a number for that.

"Now the clothes he gave her are really his sister's clothes and the sister has carelessly left a beautiful brooch pinned in them. We go to the yacht and the Spanish dame knocks everybody dead. They put on an amateur show. That will give Enriqueta a chance for a couple more numbers. She and Pizzola are getting more and more stuck on each other and they repeat the Spanish song on the yacht, in the moonlight.

"There's a Frenchman along on the party who is greatly attracted by Enriqueta's looks. The Frenchman hates Pizzola. He has found out in some way that Enriqueta is wearing Pizzola's sister's clothes and he notices the diamond brooch. He figures that if he can steal it off of her, why, suspicion will be cast on the gal herself on account of her being poor, and Pizzola, thinking her a thief, won't have anything more to do with her, and he, the Frenchman, can have her. So, during a dance, he manages to steal the brooch and he puts it in his pocket.

"Of course Pizzola's sister is also on the yachting party. All of a sudden she misses her brooch. She recalls having left it on the clothes she lent to Enriqueta. She goes to Enriqueta and asks her for it and the poor Spanish dame can't find it. Then Pizzola's sister calls her a thief and Pizzola himself can't help thinking she is one.

"They demand that she be searched, but rather than submit to that indignity, she bribes a sailor to take her off the yacht in a small launch and the last we see of her she's climbing overboard to get into the launch while the rest of the party are all abusing her. That's your first act curtain.

"I'd open the second act with a paddock scene at the Saratoga race-track. We'll write a jockey number and have about eight boys and maybe twenty-four gals in jockey suits. Enriqueta's father has gone broke in the restaurant business and he's up here looking for a job as assistant trainer or something. He used to train horses for the bull-fights in Spain.

"The gal is along with him and they run into the Frenchman that stole the brooch. The Frenchman tries to make love to the gal, but she won't have anything to do with him. While they are talking, who should come up but Pizzola. He is willing to make up with Enriqueta even though he still thinks her a thief. She won't meet his advances.

"He asks the Frenchman for a light. The Frenchman has a patent lighter and in pulling it out of his pocket, he pulls the brooch out, too. Then Pizzola realizes what an injustice he has done the gal and he pretty near goes down on his knees to her, but she has been badly hurt and won't forgive him yet.

"Now we have a scene in the café in the club-house and Stein is one of the waiters there. He sings the Montgomery number with a chorus of waiters and lunchers and at the end of the number he and the Spanish gal are alone on the stage.

"She asks him if he is really going to Montgomery and he says yes, and she says she and her father will go with him. She is anxious to go some place where there is no danger of running into the Frenchman or Pizzola.

"The third scene in the second act ought to be a plantation in Alabama. Stein is working there and the Negroes are having a celebration or revival of some kind. Louie, you can get a male quartet to sing us some spirituals.

"Enriqueta's father has landed a job as cook at the plantation and she is helping with the housework. Pizzola and his sister follow her to Montgomery and come out to see her at the plantation.

"They are about to go up on the porch and inquire for her when they hear her singing the Spanish number. This proves to Pizzola that she still loves him and he finally gets his sister to plead with her for forgiveness. She forgives him. He tells her who he really is and how much dough he's got. And that pretty near washes it up."

"But how about our Japanese number?" said Moon.

"That's right," Morris said. "We'll have to send them to Japan before we end it. I've got a cherry-blossom number that must have the right setting. But that's easy to fix. You make these few changes I've suggested, Mr. Hazlett, and I feel that we've got a hit.

"And I want to say that your book is a whole lot better than most of the books they hand us. About the fella falling in love with the gal's picture—that's a novelty idear."

Hazlett said goodbye to his producer and collaborators, went home by taxi, and called up his bootlegger.

"Harry," he said, "what kind of whisky have you got?"

"Well, Mr. Hazlett, I can sell you some good Scotch, but I ain't so sure of the rye. In fact, I'm kind of scared of it."

"How soon can you bring me a case?"

"Right off quick. It's the Scotch you want, ain't it?"

"No," said Hazlett. "I want the rye."

Dogs

EVERY little wile you hear people talking about a man that they don't nobody seem to have much use for him on acct. of him not paying his debts or beating his wife or something and everybody takes a rap at him about this and that until finely one of the party speaks up and says they must be some good in him because he likes animals.

"A man can't be all bad when he is so kind to dogs." That is what they generally always say and that is the reason you see so many men stop on the st. when they see a dog and pet it because they figure that may be somebody will be looking at them do it, and the next time they are getting panned, why who ever seen it will speak up and say:

"He can't be all bad because he likes dogs."

Well friends when you come right down to cases they's about as much sence to this as a good many other delusions that we got here in this country, like for inst. the one about nobody wanting to win the first pot and the one about the whole lot of authors not being able to do their best work unlest they are ½ pickled.

But if liking animals ain't a virtue in itself I don't see how it proves that a man has got any virtues, and personly if I had a daughter and she wanted to get married and I asked her what kind of a bird the guy was and she said she don't know nothing about him except that one day she seen him kiss a leopard, why I would hold up my blessing till a few of the missing precints was heard from.

But as long as our best people has got it in their skull that a friendly feeling toward dumb brutes takes the curse off a bad egg, why I or nobody else is going to be a sucker enough to come out and admit that all the horses, rams and oxen in the world could drop dead tomorrow morning without us batting an eye.

Pretty near everybody wants to be well thought of and if liking dogs or sheep is a helping along these lines, why even if I don't like them, I wouldn't never loose a opportunity to be seen in their company and act as if I was haveing the time of my life.

But while I was raised in a kennel, you might say, and some of my most intimate childhood friends was of the canine gender, still in all I believe dogs is better in some climates than others, the same as oysters, and I don't think it should ought to be held against a man if he don't feel the same towards N.Y. dogs as he felt towards Michigan dogs, and I am free to confess that the 4 dogs who I have grew to know personly here on Long Island has failed to arouse tender yearnings anyways near similar to those inspired by the flea bearers of my youth.

And in case they should be any tendency on the part of my readers to denounce me for failing to respond whole heartily to the wiles of the Long Island breed let me present a brief sketch of some so as true lovers of the canine tribe can judge for themselfs if the fault is all mind.

NO. I

This was the dainty boy that belonged to Gene Buck and it was a bull dog no bigger than a 2 car garage and it wouldn't harm a hair of nobody's head only other animals and people.

Children were as safe with this pet as walking in the Pittsburgh freight yards and he wouldn't think of no more wronging a cat than scratching himself.

In fairness to Mr. Buck I'll state that a pal of his give him the dog as a present without no comment. Well they wasn't no trouble till Gene had the dog pretty near ½ hr. when they let him out. He was gone 10 minutes during which Gene received a couple of phone calls announcing more in anger than in sorrow the sudden deaths of 2 adjacent cats of noble berth so when the dog come back Gene spanked him and give him a terrible scolding and after that he didn't kill no more cats except when he got outdoors.

But the next day De Wolf Hopper come over to call and brought his kid which the dog thought would look better with one leg and it took 5 people to get him not to operate, so after that Gene called up the supt. of a dogs reform school and the man said he would take him and cure him of the cat habit by tying one of his victims around his neck and leaving it there for a wk. but he didn't know how to cure the taste for young Hoppers unlest De Wolf could spare the kid the wk. after they was finished with the cat.

This proposition fell through but anyway Gene sent the dog to the reformatory and is still paying board for same.

NO. 2

The people that lived 3 houses from the undersigned decided to move to England where it seems like you can't take dogs no more so they asked us did we want the dog as it was very nice around children and we took it and sure enough it was OK in regards to children but it shared this new owners feeling towards motorcycles and every time one went past the house the dog would run out and spill the contents and on Sundays when the traffic was heavy they would sometimes be as many as 4 or 5 motorcycle jehus standing on their heads in the middle of the road.

One of them finely took offence and told on the dog and the justice of the peace called me up and said I would have to kill it within 24 hrs. and the only way I could think of to do same was drown it in the bath tub and if you done that, why the bath tub wouldn't be no good no more because it was a good sized dog and no matter how often you pulled the stopper it would still be there.

NO. 3

The next-door neighbors has a pro-German police dog that win a blue ribbon once but now it acts as body guard for the lady of the house and one day we was over there and the host says to slap his Mrs. on the arm and see what happened so I slapped her on the arm and I can still show you what happened.

When you dance with mine hostess this sweet little pet dances right along with you and watches your step and if you tred on my ladys toe he fines you a mouth full and if you and her is partners in a bridge game he lays under the table and you either bid right and play right or you get nipped.

NO. 4

This is our present incumbrance which we didn't ask for him and nobody give him to us but here he is and he has got the insomonia and he has picked a spot outside my window to enjoy it but not only that but he has learnt that if you jump at a screen often enough it will finely give way and the result is that they ain't a door or window on the first floor that you couldn't drive a rhinoceros through it and all the bugs that didn't already live in the house is moveing in and bringing their family.

That is a true record of the dogs who I have met since takeing up my abode in Nassau county so when people ask me do I like dogs I say I'm crazy about them and I think they are all right in their place but it ain't Long Island.

Colleges for Cops

A MAN like I that has got a house full of children or kids as the case may be can't help from giveing a whole lot of thought to the school question and where to send them to school and etc., and the Mrs. keeps after me to put what some call my mind on the subject and come to some decision and we was talking it over the other night and I said you know it will cost hundreds of dollars to send them anywheres and she says yes but we have got to send them somewheres if only to relieve the congestion at home and if you don't send them nowheres it will cost hundreds of dollars just the same because we will half to hire 7 or 8 policemans to regulate traffic right here in the house because the way it is now you can't walk from one room to another without indulgeing in football tactics and we could send them to school for the same amt. of money which we would otherwise half to pay out for salary to traffic policemans and in fact policemans of all kinds is a high salaried profession.

Well a little wile after this I was talking to one of the kids themselfs and I asked him what he wanted to be when he growed up and he said he would like to be a policeman and all of a sudden I had a idear namely that if policemans is such a high salaried profession and if the boy wanted to be one of them why not sen him to the N.Y. school for policemans which I had read about same in the papers and this way you would be killing several birds with one and the same stone, namely get him out of the house, send him to school and learn him a profession which was not only his favorite profession but a profession which the rewards of which is wealth and undying notoriety.

But to come to find out the school referred to don't take in nobody as young as my little ones and in fact it ain't got no kindergarten or primary grades but was organized to train men that is already policemans to be better policemans and learn common patrolmans to be sergeants, lieutenants and finely captains of police.

It seems they's a lot more to advancing in the police profession than just serveing a certain number of years in this or that capacity and unless you show ability and get the right kind of education you will be a patrolman all your life and never a officer. The people that runs the school makes a effort to find out which is the most likeliest pupils and then they give them special training to fit them for officers like the officers training schools in the army.

But once in a wile in the more genteel precincts of the metropolis a dumb blue coat gets into their heads to pinch say a total stranger for beating a woman and find out later that it was his wife and he knowed what he was doing and besides that she liked it, so the city get sewed for false arrest all because a policeman was too dumb to tell the difference between work and play. The school probably learns you how to tell the differnce between wifes and women, husbands and friends, petty thiefs and bank messengers and etc., and when the pupil gets so he can make these distinctions at a glance he is promoted to a sergeant with permission to grow a mustache.

Part of the curriculum is no doubt made up of what is know as hypothetical questions like as follows:

"If you was walking on your beat and a little ways off from you they was a beautiful woman strolling along and dangling a purse in her hand and all of a sudden a tough egg jumped out of the alley and grabbed the purse and run as fast as he could run (1) would you diagnose it as justifiable or mild flirtation and (2) which of the 2 would you chase, he or she?"

Or

"Suppose you was standing on Riverside Drive and they was a woman and a baby in arms and the woman handed you the baby and asked you would you promise to hold it a wile and you promised and then the woman throwed herself in the river and was drowning, would you break your promise and drop the baby and jump in and save the woman or would you try and sell the baby a ticket to the policemans field day at Jamaica?"

These and many other tricks of the trade is learned to pupils in the school and I only wished they would of left my little boy matriculate as he takes after his mamma and would make a great captain of police.

Della T. Lutes

Della T. Lutes (188?–1942) was born and raised in the pleasant farming country of Southern Michigan. Her books and magazine articles are interlarded with recipes used by her mother in an effort to please the headstrong and domineering lord of the manor who was Della's father. "Michigan Political Rally" is reprinted from COUNTRY SCHOOLMA'AM *(1941).*

Michigan Political Rally

CURT BRIGGS drove the team up to the side of the road where Gran'pa Powell stood waving and stopped.

"Hi, Gramp," he said. "What you doin' here? Why ain't you gone t' the Rally?"

"Good reason why," Gran'pa replied tartly,—if a little thickly,—laying hold of the front wheel with both hands. He needed support. He was tidied and scrubbed, shaven and combed, dressed in a clean white shirt and his best suit, but he quite apparently was well along on the way to easing Mr. Harrison into the Presidential chair with proper lubrication.

"Dam' Demmycrats went off and left me."

"Well, come on, get in. Ma," his eyes twinkled at the good-natured woman on whom he could always depend, " 'd you ruther shove along and let Gran'pa set between us, or d'you think he ort to sit on the outside, or—"

"I'll get in back with the girls." The back of the seat was not too high to be stepped over easily, but modesty forbade such exhibition, so she got out of the wagon and climbed in again with Milly and me. Then she lifted Andy over the seat and put him in the back with Alan and Mabel. Gran'pa, with only a couple of struggling efforts, was seated in front.

"I'd ruther set hangin' out the tailboard," Mrs. Briggs confided to us in a whisper, " 'n sit on the windward side o' *him*." But there was neither venom nor censure in her tones—it was merely comment on a condition.

Gran'pa was garrulous, and considerably out of temper with his family. "I don't wish 'em no harm," he explained virtuously as we trotted briskly along, "but if the rims come off their wheels and they hev to ride on spokes every inch the way I shan't drop my tail and howl."

"How'd come to forget you?" Curt asked.

"Forget me—hell!" Gran'pa in his indignation lurched so far to the side that Curt reached out in alarm and drew him back. "*They* didn't forget me. They went off a purpose. Cal wouldn't o' done it"—paternal fidelity came to the exoneration of his son—"but that gol-darned old Stonewall Jackson *hen*—she said no Republican's goin' to ride in *her* wagon on 'lection day. *Her* wagon!" Vindictively he spat into the November dusk, balancing precariously on the edge of the seat. "Why, say—she ain't got, never had, and never will have a shirt to her back 't ain't beholden to me. Course," his voice grew meditative, "Cal ain't got no guts. Had, he wouldn't of married her in the first place. Still, you'd think," his voice changed to hurt peevishness, "he'd of stood up for me to go along on *'lection* night." After a little self-pitying pause he added, "I hope their wagon wheels come off and they roll in the ditch and—but—" At some sudden thought he came to rights and clapped hand to knee. "By cracky, I forgot! *That* ain't the worst of it!"

"Ain't it?" Curt was obviously amused. "What is the worst of it?"

"Why," Gran'pa was overwhelmed by the magnitude of whatever major catastrophe had occurred to him, "by the long-horned, rat-tailed son of a sowbelly—I clean forgot!"

"What you forgot, Gran'pa?" Curt urged the horses along. He wasn't going to turn back even if Gran'pa had forgotten his teeth.

"I forgot I put that jug o' cider under the front seat o' their wagon!"

Curt laughed. "Well," he said, "that's too bad. Did Ed go with 'em?"

"Naw. Ed went off this afternoon, ready for hell-raisin'." He suddenly burst into laughter, loud and raucous. He bent backward, he bent forward, he slapped his leg. He bent sideways and slapped Curt's leg. He shouted. Curt grunted. "Don't see what's so all-fired funny about that," he said. " 'Tain't likely it's the first time."

"No," said Gran'pa, gasping, "it ain't. But it's the first time a jug's rid there, right under Cal's backside, when he's give his word and promised M'lindy up hill an' down 't he wouldn't take a *ounce* o' likker along. And," he added with satisfaction, "there's a *gallon* of the hardest dam' cider you ever set tongue to in your life. By the holy hornspoon, won't M'lindy *sweat?*"

"They might not find it," Curt offered mildly.

"Sho-o-o! Find it? Why, Cal's feet'll scrape it time they've gone a quarter a mile. He'll hug it up 'tween his feet and I'll bet he'll hev to run into the hazel brush every half-mile. M'lindy'll think he took a dose o' physic."

The thought entertained him in silence for some time. Then alarm overtook him. "Jee-mite-a-cus!" he worried suddenly. "I hope he don't lap it all up 'fore I can find the wagon!"

He found the wagon all right, as we were assured not long after we had left the team and wagon at the livery stable. Curt had hurried away to hear Jimmie O'Donnell speak, and Alan was hectoring his mother to let him go and see where the big bonfire was to be held, when we passed them—Gran'pa and his renegade son, Cal. They had apparently just met, Gran'pa a little sobered from his ride, Cal altogether Republican in his attitude toward Mr. Benjamin Harrison, the tariff, the corruption fund, and Mr. James O'Donnell, whose qualifications for Congress they were discussing as we approached.

"*Course* you'll vote for Jimmie," Gran'pa was adjuring his son. "You'll vote straight Republican ticket and t' hell with M'lindy."

"Lesh go back and see 'f—wagon's a-right," Calvin persuaded, and they went.

We, Mrs. Briggs, Alan, Mabel, Milly with Andy clinging to her hand, and I, went up Main Street where there was a mob

of people to see the parade. We saw a few we knew. Mr. and
Mrs. Crawford and all the little Crawfords, she looking ripe
and fit to pop. "Mercy!" exclaimed Mrs. Briggs as we passed.
"I sh'd think she'd be scared to death to be here. She's two
weeks overdue now and she always drops 'em just like a cow."

Ike Sinclair and Hermie Powell ran past yelling and waving
torches of cattails soaked in kerosene, blazing high and dan-
gerously in the crowd. Seeing Alan they paused, turned, and
grabbed him by any clutch. "C'mon, Al," they screamed.
"The's going to be a gang of us in the p'rade." Like a shot
they were off and later, in the parade, we saw them with
about twenty other boys forming a rather picturesque brigade
in the procession, their cattail torches sputtering and blazing
yellow in the murky night.

We got ourselves good positions to watch the parade, on
the corner of Main and Mechanic, standing on the curb and
as close to the line of march as we could get.

The speech-making must have been at its height when we
heard a din of drums, a blare of trumpets, and a clangor of
tongues coming *down* Main Street from the west. The Republican parade was to form down by the depot and march *up*
Main Street, wheeling around onto Mechanic, where, a few
blocks out, the big bonfire was to be held.

"The *Demmycrats! It's the Demmycrats!* They've stole a
march!"

The Democrats, it seemed, had been inarticulate as to where
their parade was to form, what direction it was to go, or
whether, indeed, they were going to have a parade at all.
They had a huge pile of lumber of all sorts, so some stranger
standing near told us, ready for the bonfire, but what else they
were going to do nobody knew—but the Demmycrats. However, here they came borne upon the evil power of noise.
First there was a hayrack drawn by two teams of mules—
good big *hauling* mules with long twiddling ears like rabbits.
On each donkey was a red blanket which upon closer inspec-

tion proved to be a pair of red flannel drawers, the legs hanging free and swinging at the end of each a small sheep bell. Each donkey was ridden by a small boy well blacked and dressed in fancy costume of red and white.

A torch burned at the masthead where a huge and decidedly "colored" man sat and drove. On—and in and all over —the rack was a crew of blacked-up imitation minstrels in fancy costume. Some were dressed as women and these constantly pulled up their long full skirts to show white pantaletted legs. They all had banjos, guitars, mouth organs, jew's-harps, combs with paper over them—anything that would make a noise. And a noise they made. The wagon wheels, bound with red and white cambric, had strings of sleighbells intertwined, and clattered and bumped over rough pavement. There were bells attached to the tongue of the wagon and to the triangle of the rack that held the reins.

The "niggers" sang, "Shoo-Fly, Don't Bother Me, for I Belong to Company G," and waved huge fans of turkey's tail feathers tied to a stick. They sang "Camp Town Ladies Sing Dis Song: Doo-dah! Doo-dah Day!" They rattled and rolled and shrieked and whooped and drummed and tootled their way toward us down the street. If Jimmie O'Donnell could continue to speak over that racket he had a better voice than most. Apparently he didn't try. Those nearest the door, as Curt told us later, heard the din and, suspicions alert, had high-tailed it to the scene of preparation for the Republican parade and got the boys under way. The timing was not perfect but the *coup d'état* was all that we as spectators could have desired. The Republicans snaked their highly spectacular fire engine out the back way and up to the meeting point, together with a crowd of "Indians" dressed up in buckskin breeches and coats (made of white canvas dyed with walnut stain), many feathers, beads, headdresses, and equipped with tomahawks and burning torches. They too had a hayrack, in the bottom of which was a wigwam on which hung a coon-skin, along with the log cabin and hard cider.

The parade started. It moved into sight. The two proceeded toward each other—the colored contingent leading bands of music, companies of men waving banners, and small boys weaving in and out. The Indian crew approached from the east, and every few feet an "Indian" would leap from the float, grab some girl or woman and lug her (if he could for the kicking and screaming and yelling) toward the wagon. He never got her quite there, until once a big, painted-faced, big-nosed, panting "redskin" dashed into the crowd near us, grabbed up a little girl, and ran with her to the wagon and tossed her in. She screamed and fought and yelled for her mother, until finally a woman sprang from the crowd and ran into the street, demanding her child. The child had fainted, although we learned later that the man was her own father and she had been told what was going to happen, but the characterization and plot were so realistic that the child forgot all but her fear.

In a few minutes all was confusion. The two parades met head-on and in spite of all efforts of the management, direction, and leadership, the whole scene became more or less a riot, first of hilarity but developing into a free-for-all. Zouaves in their short jackets, fancy pants, and white puttees met with Civil War veterans and in a few minutes Republicans and Democrats had lost all party sense and fought for possession of a cigar-store Indian with all the ardor with which their forbears had fought for principle. Torches were brandished and flung with an abandon unsurpassed by even the Log Cabin campaign. Gran'pa Powell, his son Carl, and the leader of the Democratic rally stood together in the middle of the street and, to the tune of "Auld Lang Syne," sang:—

> Should good old cider be despised
>   And e'er neglected more,
> Should plain log cabins be despised
>   Our fathers built of yore?

> For the true old style, my boys—
> For the true old style,
> Let's take a nip o' cider yet
> For the true old style.

At least Gran'pa Powell sang; the others whistled, tootled, and tummed along with him or a couple of bars behind. Ed Powell and Sime Briggs were seen one minute with their arms entwined giving three cheers for Benjamin Harrison, and the next gripped in apparently mortal combat over a barberpole. No one had an atom of sense left, not even the spectators. The wheels of the Indian wagon locked with those of the dusky South until the mules laid back their ears and brayed and the Indians' horses ran away for a couple of blocks and then stopped in their tracks, apparently disgusted with such unsportsmanlike didos. Police, politicians, and plain citizens finally reduced the melee to order and each party picked up the tattered remnants of its glory and took itself off.

We followed the crowd to the bonfire. The Republican bonfire. Here was a huge tinderbox of railroad ties, tar barrels, lumber, anybody's gates that were not securely fastened, blinds from vacant houses, cellar doors from anybody's house, anything and everything that could be moved. As we approached, half a dozen fights were in progress. Democrat boys were either trying to retrieve their own property already appropriated by the opposing party, or laying ruthless hands on whatever they could to augment their own blaze.

A torch was applied to the oil-soaked edifice. It spit, purred, crackled—and burst into a roar of flame. The crowd fell back, for the heat was unbearable. Flames leaped to the skies. Boys and men yelled. With torches in their hands they danced around the roaring holocaust in a circle, yelling in a way that would have raised the scalp of any self-respecting Indian. They went mad. They threw on more fuel from any source —from houses, barns, woodsheds, privies. Nothing in the im-

mediate vicinity was safe. Privies especially were met with a
roar of applause. A contingent of zealous young Republicans
came from the opposing party's blaze bearing a kerosene barrel one-third full. The Democrats were hot behind them. The
Republicans threw the barrel on the blaze and the Democrats
showed every intent of throwing them after it. Officers and
bystanders intervened.

Nobody had thought of the weather for two hours. A few
drops of rain struck us on hands and faces. We looked up
and were met by a deluge. The fire sissed, spat, stunk, and
died down. People ran. We ran. Some people fell and others
clambered over them. Halfway to the livery stable to which
Curt Briggs with Andy in his arms was herding his family,
we saw those ahead of us swerving a little to the right, a
little to the left. A man lay in the road. Curt paused. It was
Gran'pa. Curt put Andy down and got Gran'pa to his feet.
We went on more slowly, drenched to the skin.

Ruth McKenney

Ruth McKenney (1911–   ), born in Mishawaka, Indiana, was educated spasmodically in Cleveland and Columbus, Ohio. While in the latter city she was a part-time reporter for the Columbus DISPATCH *when not studying at Ohio State University. Next she functioned as a regular member of the Akron* BEACON-JOURNAL *staff. Going to New York with her sister Eileen, later celebrated in a book and a play, she toiled on the* POST *from 1934 to 1936, when she forsook journalism for the life of a free-lance author.* MY SISTER EILEEN *(1939), most of which had appeared as sketches in the* NEW YORKER, *was succeeded by* INDUSTRIAL VALLEY *(1939),* THE MC KENNEYS CARRY ON *(1940), and* JAKE HOME *(1943). "No Tears, No Good" is reprinted from* MY SISTER EILEEN.

No Tears, No Good

THE NICELY brought up child of today lives on a prissy milk-and-water movie diet of colored cartoons, costume pictures with noble endings, and banal dramas starring his favorite radio comic. The Mickey Mouse vogue among the juniors demonstrates what fearful changes Will Hays, the Legion of Decency, and Aroused Parenthood have wrought in a mere twenty years or so.

My sister Eileen and I, movie fans when we were five and six, respectively, would have scorned Mickey Mouse in our youth; we preferred Theda Bara to Fatty Arbuckle, and that was the acid test.

We saw our first movie shortly after we saw our first airplane. The airplane was very nice, of course, and we had a school half-holiday to celebrate the glorious moment when an air machine first put landing gear on the dreary soil of Mishawaka, Indiana. That was in the early spring of 1918, and airplanes were very patriotic and thrilling, but in spite of the glamorous fellow who ran the queer machine, we liked the movie better than the airplane. The movie lasted longer.

Our first film was Chapter 3 of a serial which had to do with bandits, high cliffs, and pistols, Eileen was so small she was able to sneak under the ticket-seller's high box and get in free. The serial was shown that spring daily, not weekly, in a made-over garage not far from our schoolhouse. Chapter 1 of the adventures of, say, Death-Defying Desmond started on Monday at four o'clock sharp and the last installment ended at the Friday-afternoon matinée, amid the hoarse cheers of the excited audience. Admission price was a nickel, but no self-respecting child in our fairly prosperous neighborhood would have thought of stumbling down the dark aisles and throwing himself into a creaking wooden seat unless he were equipped with a bag of peanuts, price also five cents.

The peanuts were not merely for the inner man; the shells were used by the large and energetic audience to enliven the dull stretches in the scenario. To us, even the liveliest Western had a good many sleepy sequences, and, indeed, the whole audience could be bored into mass fidgets at the mere sight of a long subtitle, for few, if any, of the paying customers at those four-o'clock matinées could read—not, at least, with any ease. Nobody in the theater had the slightest idea of what the film was about, and nobody cared. We came to see the fights and the horse races over the mountains, and the jumping across chasms. Our attention wandered as soon as the scene shifted indoors, and two subtitles in a row were enough to start a peanut fight.

Thus, when the heroine began to plead with the villain for the hero's life, Benny Burns, a big boy in the third grade, would rise and shoot a peanut shell at his old enemy, Freddie Meriman. Freddie would respond in kind, and soon the darkened theater would be the scene of a fine free-for-all battle, with both sides eventually running out of peanut shells and resorting to books, hats, apples, and other deadly weapons. Piercing screams could sometimes be heard all the way out to the street, and the howls of the wounded would sooner or later seriously annoy the bored movie operator, upstairs in his booth. He and the ticket-seller were the only attendants, for in those days there were no laws about matrons, and for a nickel we did not have the dubious pleasure of hearing the regular pianist. In the midst of the joyous battle, then, the lights would suddenly go on, the heroine disappear from the screen, and the racket diminish slightly while the operator bawled, "Shut up, you brats, or I'll throw you all out."

"Ya-a-ah," we would all scream, Eileen's five-year-old shriek rising above the rest, "come on and do it!"

He never tried, though. He waited for comparative quiet, dimmed the lights, and put the heroine back on the screen, this time perhaps pleading, in one of those lightning developments, for her own life. The peanut battles were apparently more exciting than the serials, I remember little of that first spring movie season except a train wreck, but that train wreck will live in my memory as one of the most piquant experiences of my life.

In the film, a motorcar, a Motel T Ford was racing down a country road, pursued by something—I think it was a lot of bandits in another car. Just as the motorcar approached the crossing, a train appeared around a convenient bend. All this was old stuff; we were used to seeing motorcars and trains fight it out on the tracks.

But suddenly the camera switched from the general view of the automobile and the train, and on the screen appeared a huge pair of wheels—the train wheels. They grew larger and larger, revolving furiously. We were awed and horrified. The wheels were coming right for us; apparently, the motorcar was not to be run over, we were. Suddenly my sister Eileen screamed, and began trying to climb across the tense legs of the little boys in our row.

"Let me out, let me out!" she howled. "Ruth! Mamma! Help! It's coming!"

In the silence of the darkened movie house, Eileen's screams made a sensation. Other small girls burst into nervous sobs. Boys, even big boys in the third grade, began to whine dismally. On the screen the wheels were now rolling faster and faster, and the whole train loomed up, apparently about to descend upon us. In those days, when a cameraman had a good shot, he gave it plenty of footage, to let it sink in. Eileen's agonized howls and cries for help were now being drowned out by the panic-striken roar of the whole audience. There was a tremendous din, and the scuffle of dozens of frightened children trying to stumble out into the aisles and run for home and mother. At this point the lights went on and the train, wheels and all, disappeared from the screen.

"For Christ's sake!" bawled the infuriated movie operator from his booth. The attention of the horrified audience was now shifted from the thought of escape, to horror at hearing a bad word, a swear word, shouted so baldly from above. This was a polite neighborhood.

"This ain't real," the movie operator continued in his stentorian tones. "Nobody's going to get hurt. It's just a movie."

You could hear the soft rustle of everybody saying "Oh" to his neighbor, the diminishing sniffles, the blowing of noses, the regaining of creaking wooden seats. But before the lights went down, the ticket-seller, a mean-looking lady of what we thought was vast age, with side puffs over her ears, walked down the aisle.

"Who started this?" she demanded sternly. A dozen fingers pointed to my fat, tear-stained sister. Eileen tried to hide under her seat, but in vain. She was ordered out to the aisle.

"How old are you?" the ticket-seller demanded, in front of everybody.

"Theven," Eileen lied, in her most unfortunate lisp. A dozen voices contradicted her. "She's only in kindergarten," various old pals shouted gleefully.

"Little girls in kindergarten aren't allowed to come to the movies," the ticket-seller said grimly, and grabbed Eileen's chubby arm. Weeping dismally, my poor sister was ignominiously led out, with me tagging sorrowfully along in back. Unfortunately, this event made such a scandal that our mother heard of it, via other little girls' mothers, and we were forbidden to attend movies until we were older.

Older was next year, after we had moved to Cleveland. There were three movie houses within walking distance of our new home, and we settled down to delightful years of Saturday and Sunday afternoon film orgies.

Nobody censored our movie fare except ourselves. Mother

had no idea of what grim and gripping pictures we were seeing, for she never went to the movies herself. She was something of an intellectual, and back in 1919 and 1920 people who had pretensions to culture, at least in the Middle West, wouldn't have been caught dead in a movie house. Mother thought the films were exclusively for children and morons, like the comic strips in the newspapers. Cleveland had no Better Films for Children Committees in those days, and Ohio preachers and newspaper editorial-writers did not thunder, then, of the Movie Menace. Mother used to send us off to the neighborhood theaters with an innocent and loving heart.

"Don't sit through it more than twice," she would shout from the front porch as we skipped off, hand in hand, to the movies. We would return, hours later, exhausted from the hard seats and emotional duress.

We saw some bright and cheerful pictures, but I don't remember many of them. There was Fatty Arbuckle, of course, and two wonderful children who threw dishes at each other—the Lee sisters. We worshiped them. But most of the pictures we saw were, to us anyway, grim and awful tragedies. If there were happy endings, we never noticed them. Some of the pictures were so unbearably sad we could hardly stay to see them twice. We did, though.

We wore large, round hats with ribbons for these excursions to the movies. Once settled down in our seats, we held on anxiously to the hats. At the least sign of trouble on the screen, we put the hats in front of our eyes. Then we took turns peeking out to see if the film had taken a turn for the better. It makes me blanch to consider what we would have suffered if the films had been wired for sound when we were children. As it was, we could generally tell when the trouble was coming by the pianist, who used to begin thumping away at some very dread music. Of course, since we saw every film twice, in spite of our hat system of censorship we generally got the thread of the plot on the second time around. If we still couldn't quite make out what had happened, we stayed for the third show and were late for dinner.

We had no favorite movie stars at first, for the truth was that we hadn't really believed that movie operator. For a long time we thought the movies were real, and that the tragedies we saw were photographed, mysteriously, from real and horrible life. I gradually came to understand that the suffering heroine was only an actress, and I used to reassure Eileen loudly as she wept. "Don't cry," I would bawl through my own tears. "It's only a movie."

At last, though, we grew out of this primitive stage of movie response and developed into Wally Reid and Lon Chaney fans. Mr. Chaney, of course, we admired in a rather backhanded way. Each Chaney film was, for us, a terrible ordeal, through which we suffered and bawled and wept. As we staggered out of the theater, our pug noses swollen to red beets, we swore never to set eyes on the man again. But the next time we were back, groaning in our seats, fascinated and horrified. Finally "The Hunchback of Notre Dame" came along and very nearly finished me off. Even now, Eileen refuses to discuss that gruesome movie. Mr. Chaney was the hunchback, of course, and he suffered a peculiarly realistic and horrible beating in that old silent film. Eileen and I put our arms around each other, and howled steadily throughout the entire beating.

Mr. Reid, who came along a little earlier than the horror man, was a slightly more cheerful influence in our childhood, although his tragic death became, oddly enough, a family scandal. Our passion for Mr. Reid was shared by a young aunt of ours, who admired that jaunty actor with rather more enthusiasm than detachment. Now, my mother cared nothing for Mr. Reid but she was deeply attached to her only brother and she called him, as Mr. Reid's devoted fans called their idol, Wally.

Imagine her horror, then, one evening, when my young

aunt called up and wept over the phone, in broken accents, "Maggie, Maggie, Wally's dead!"

"Dead?" shouted my mother, electrifying everybody at our dinner table. "No! No! It isn't true!"

My aunt said, amid her tears, that it was true, alas. My mother began, naturally enough, to cry. My father, white and shaken, rushed to the phone, tenderly pushed his wife aside while she sobbed "Wally's dead," and picked up the receiver.

"How did it happen?" father began, in that somber tone of voice you use for these trying occasions. Then we heard him roar, "What? You're crazy!" He hung up with a frightful bang and shouted, "It's Wally Reid, the film actor!"

Eileen and I began to howl at once. We didn't know our uncle very well, but we certainly knew Wally Reid, and felt perfectly terrible about his death. We simply couldn't understand Mother's calloused revival when she heard the good news that her brother still lived. That famous telephone conversation started a family feud that lasted for years. Mother never forgave her young sister, and my aunt stated freely and frankly that she thought mother was a perfect idiot for not knowing that Wally Reid had been ill for days. People took their movies seriously those days, if they took them at all.

Nebraska Writers' Project

One of the most notable achievements of the Nebraska Writers' Project of the Works Projects Administration was the collection of Febold Feboldson stories by Paul R. Beath. These added a new name to the roster of American folk heroes. "Skunk Oil and the Punkin," reprinted here from NEBRASKA FOLK LORE PAMPHLET NO. 29, *compiled by the Nebraska Writers' Project, is an example of the invaluable work accomplished by the Project members in recording the recollections of old folks whose memories stretch far back into the past.*

▶

Skunk Oil and the Punkin

(GRANT ESSEX, of Lincoln, who is 80 years old, says he was told the following tall tale in Chase County during the 1880's.)

One of the first men I met after I had settled in Chase County, in the 80's, was an old fellow who had a claim on the Stinking Water River. He was a character who did a little bit of everything, from trapping and hunting to farming, but what he excelled in the most was lying. He could think up more lies in less time than anyone I have ever known. And I have heard some pretty good deviations from the truth in my day. But this man was the champion.

I don't recollect his real name, nor would it matter if I did, because to everyone in the community he was known as "Skunk Oil." He had been given this name because of his constant claims that a skunk's oil had the power to cure all diseases. Besides, Skunk Oil carried a bad odor with him, caused, I think, by his lack of interest in bathing. Then, too, he was constantly sweating, even in the coldest weather. It wasn't a pretty sight—or smell. But it was, so to speak, Skunk Oil's "trade mark," and as that you had to accept it.

One day, when I was out looking over the land in preparation for spring plowing, I saw Skunk Oil ambling along an old buffalo trail which led past my place. I had only met him once before, so I knew I was in for another lie, since a newcomer to the County was always legitimate prey for Skunk Oil.

But Skunk Oil, after our preliminary greetings were over, fooled around a while, talking about this and that before he got around to the whopper that I knew he was itching to tell. You see I had met up with him once before, on the first day of my arrival in the County, so I knew what he was leading up to. He finally got started by asking what I thought of the country and its possibilities. I answered by telling him I didn't think anyone could raise much but grass and, with luck, maybe a little hell.

"Man, you're plum wrong there," was his reply. "Ever hear about them punkins I raised over by the river? Well, you ought to have seen them."

I saw he was starting to warm up to his subject, so I looked doubtful and said I didn't think they'd grow over there.

He didn't reply for a moment or so because he was busy biting off a chew of navy plug that apparently was as tough as leather. Then, after he had succeeded in chewing off a big piece, he slowly replied: "I didn't think they would grow there myself, so I didn't attempt planting any punkin seeds. But one day, when I was dropping some corn seed along the river seven or eight punkin seeds showed up in the poke of corn. So I just naturally planted those seeds with the corn and forgot about them. The corn grew up and by the middle of the summer was better'n shoulder high. But I didn't go over to the field for a long time. I believed in letting good-enough be, so let the corn take care of itself. Besides I was having a great deal of pig trouble at this time."

"How was that?" I asked.

"Well, I had an old sow who had a litter of eleven little pigs that I turned loose to forage for themselves. It saved me the trouble of feeding them. For awhile they stayed near the soddie, but one day they didn't show up and it was the beginning of no end of trouble. I spent several weeks looking for them, but couldn't find so much as a trace of their where-abouts. Along in September I went to my corn patch, by the river, and what I saw nearly made me doubt my sanity."

"Why, what had happened?"

"The eight punkin seeds that had been mixed in with the seed corn I had planted had started growing in a big way, like the bean in 'Jack and the Beanstalk,' only for me they followed the ground. One punkin vine was especially big. It was at least eight feet thick and took off across the river like a big green snake, disappearing in a thicket on the opposite side of the river bank. This vine was so enormous that its top was above my head. I followed it to the bank, where I crawled upon it and walked across the river. It made a natural bridge which was strong enough to hold a team of oxen.

"Well, believe it or not, I followed this vine for seven miles into the open prairie, where, at its end, I found a tremendous punkin which must have been at least thirty feet high. It was a beautiful reddish-yellow, ripening in the fall air. From a distance, with the sun shining on it, it looked very much like a harvest moon. I had never seen anything like it before and probably never will again.

"As I was walking around it, looking it over, I heard a grunting, squealing sound come from its insides. It was a peculiar unearthly noise, which had me scared stiff for a few minutes until I happened to think of my missing pigs. It was them I heard. They were in the punkin, although I couldn't figure out how they had gotten there.

"So I hurried back to the soddie for a saw and axe, which I took back to the punkin. After two hours of sawing and cutting I managed to make a hole in the side. It was hard work, because the punkin's sides were as hard as plate iron. After I had finished making a good sized hole I crawled inside where, sure's you're born, were those pigs. They had growed so it was difficult to recognize them. Must have weighed 200 pounds apiece while the sow probably tipped the scales at half a ton.

"Now that I had found my pigs I was sure hankering to find out how they had gotten into the punkin. Nor did it take me long to get at the secret.

"The old sow had taken her litter to the corn patch where, when rooting around, she'd dug a hole into the side of the vine, and had gone inside, followed by her pigs. Here they had stayed, feeding on the vine and growing along with it.

In time it carried them across the river to the big punkin itself. This they made their headquarters. But there were many tracks in the vine itself, so they probably traveled back and forth a great deal.

"The punkin was too big to move, so I left the pigs there all winter and they used it for a snug cozy hog house. I walked over once a week to see how they were getting along. When the weather was nice I walked over on the top of the vine, but when it was cold I lighted a miner's lamp, which I had purchased from an old peddler, and used the inside of the vine. It made a fine tunnel.

"When spring came I hitched the team to my wagon and crossed the river on the vine (it was a perfect road) with the idea of loading one of the punkin seeds for another crop. I took Hank Billings, who lived up the river a ways, along to help me load the seed.

"Unfortunately we didn't have a rope and pulley, so were forced to raise the punkin seed with our hands. The seed slipped during the process and caught Hank under it, breaking his leg. Naturally this accident made him good and mad, since it meant he would be laid up for the greater part of the summer.

"So I was not surprised the next day when a committee of settlers called at my soddie and ordered me not to plant any more punkins. They said they were skeered of the punkin taking over the whole county if any more grew like the last one did, and there wasn't any sense in taking any unnecessary risks.

"I tried to answer their arguments by telling them what fine roads and bridges the vines would make, and of the punkin houses and barns that could be made from the heads. But they wouldn't listen to me and burned all my seeds, so I calculate the only punkins we will have from now on will be the ordinary garden variety which isn't good for anything except pies."

Kenneth W. Porter

Kenneth W. Porter (1905–   ) was born near Sterling, Kansas, and studied at Sterling College, the University of Minnesota, and Harvard. After holding several other teaching posts, he joined the faculty of Vassar in 1938, teaching history. He has written, among other books, JOHN JACOR ASTOR, BUSINESS MAN *(2 vols., 1931) and two volumes of verse,* THE HIGH PLAINS *(1938) and* NO RAIN FROM THESE CLOUDS. *"Kansas Grasshoppers" is reprinted from the latter volume.*

Kansas Grasshoppers

When streets were a living carpet of six-inch pile
and locomotive wheels spun helplessly
in the grease of smashed bodies
a small-town editor put into print
in Local News
a single line:
"A grasshopper was seen on the courthouse steps
      this morning."
And a farmer—
dredging up bucket after bucket of drowned bodies
from his only well—
hailed a neighbor:
"D'ye know
yesterday I tied my team to the fence
while I got out to see if the ground
was too hard to plow
and when I got back
a big grasshopper had eaten my horses
and was picking his teeth with the wagon-tongue!"
"Hell! That's nothin'!
I left my team to go down to the spring
and when *I* got back
two grasshoppers had eaten the team—
and were pitchin' horse-shoes to see who'd eat the
      wagon!"

Keith Preston

Keith Preston (1884–1927) was born in Chicago. His formal education began with APPLETON'S FIRST READER *and ended with "an oral examination for the Doctorate in Classics at the University of Chicago." He taught at the University of Indiana, Princeton University, and Northwestern University before he became a columnist on the Chicago* DAILY NEWS, *where he was book editor for a year before his death. The following poems are reprinted from* POT SHOTS FROM PEGASUS *(1929).*

Button, Button, Who Has the Button?

Consider Button Gwinnett now, whose greatest claim to fame
Is seen in the infrequency with which he signed his name.
He signed the declaration that made our nation free,
And then and there swore nevermore to scribble his B. G.

He never wrote in ladies' books of album-sentiments,
He never signed the dotted line for smooth persuasive gents,
He seldom wrote a letter and he never signed a check;
He wouldn't sign a legal form to save his lawyer's neck.

And what was the result of this for poor old Button Gwinnett?
He could not have foreseen, I ween, what signal fame was in it,
How opulent collectors would rummage high and low
For Button Gwinnett's autograph, that most unique John Doe.

It isn't much to look at, but it's very, very rare,
And the price that's put upon it only button kings can bear,
It's a warning to all great men who would make their lives sublime
Not to leave too many footprints upon the sands of time.

An Awful Responsibility

I am the captain of my soul;
  I rule it with stern joy;
And yet I think I had more fun,
  When I was cabin boy.

The Liberators

Among our literary scenes,
  Saddest this sight to me,
The graves of little magazines
  That died to make verse free.

Heart Blobs

In the manner of Edgar Guest

Home ain't home till you can spot,
  By thumb prints on the wall,
Just where each little tad and tot
  Played up and down the hall.
Oh, take away your spotless towns
  And marble halls, by cricky!
For home ain't home to him that frowns
  Because the walls are sticky.

No, home ain't home without a tint
  Above the cedar chest,
To show where laddie's peppermint
  Was forcibly impressed.
And home ain't home without a hint,
  A blot, a blob, a splotch
That keeps for aye the golden glint
  Of lassie's butter scotch.

If you would always have those spots
  That home ain't home without,
Feed taffy to the little tots,
  Let sorghum stand about!

For, folks, when all is done and said,
   I say, with father feeling,
Home's home where happy kiddies spread
   Molasses, floor to ceiling.

Vance Randolph

Vance Randolph (1892–   ) is widely accepted as the foremost authority on the customs and people of the Ozarks. Born in Pittsburg, Kansas, he worked on the APPEAL TO REASON *for a short time after graduating from the University of Kansas. He wrote scenarios in Hollywood, compiled a number of "A B C's" of this and that for the Vanguard Press when it was a labor publishing house financed by the Garland Fund, and wrote quite a few little and big blue books for Haldeman-Julius. His works include* THE OZARKS: AN AMERICAN SURVIVAL OF PRIMITIVE SOCIETY *(1932),* OZARK MOUNTAIN FOLKS *(1932),* HEDWIG *(1935), and* OZARK SUPERSTITIONS *(1947). "The Feather-grafter" is reprinted from* FROM AN OZARK HOLLER *(1933).*

The Feather-grafter

THE PRISONERS in the stone jail-house used to sing a good deal, and I often sat on the court-house lawn in order to hear their old-time songs. My collection of these folk-songs is the only one ever made in the Ozark country, I think, but I have never been able to find a publisher for it.

But no matter—this is the story of Jube Halliday, who called out from behind the bars to ask if he could "borry th' loan of a chaw." It is a very bad thing to be in jail without any tobacco, so I gave him the whole twist.

Jube and I used to talk through the barred window nearly every evening after that, but it did not occur to me to ask what he was in for—I simply took it for granted that the man was a moonshiner. When Jube realized this he hastened to set me right.

"Hell, no," he cried indignantly, "I never made a drap o' painter-sweat in all my born days! I'm a feather-grafter, an' they're a-holdin' me for th' sheriff o' Burdock County."

"Feather-grafter!" said I, "what do you mean, feather-grafter?"

Jube was astonished and a bit contemptuous.

"No foolin'?" he asked. "Mean t' tell me you don't know whut a feather-grafter is?"

I shook my head.

"My Gawd, feller, you shore must of been raised in a pore triflin' settlement. Whut did you-all sleep on—cornshucks?"

Without waiting for an answer he went on. "O' course, we never said *grafters* only jest 'mongst ourselves—th' name on th' wagon was *renovators*. You never heerd tell o' feather-renovators?"

And again I was forced to acknowledge my ignorance. Jube sighed as he took a fresh chaw and prepared to enlighten me.

"Wal, sir, when I j'ined up with 'em I didn't know no more 'bout th' business than whut you do, but I shore l'arnt a plenty, an' it didn't take me long neither.

"Our crew driv two good teams, an' th' biggest wagon had th' machine in it—a kind of flutter-wheel dingus, with a b'iler fixed so you could git up steam an' turn it into the machine. Soon as we come t' a good town th' boss he'd pitch th' tent an' fire up th' b'iler, while me an' Andy tuck th' leetle wagon out t' git th' business. We allus went t' th' fine big houses first, 'cause that's whar th' best featherbeds is at.

"Andy, he had a purty slick spiel 'bout how we could renovate feathers with steam. Hit cleaned 'em whiter'n snow, he says, an' put new life in 'em, an' kilt all th' bugs, an' ever'thing. Then mostly th' woman she'd holler out that thar wasn't no bugs in *her* featherbeds, an' go t' shut th' door on us, but Andy, he allus stuck his foot in, accidental like.

"Then he'd say oh, my goodness, lady, I know you ain't got no *bedbugs!* Whut I'm a-talkin' 'bout is these hyar feather-bugs. You rip that 'ar tick open jest a leetle bit an' I'll show ye! An' if thar ain't no bugs in them feathers I'll renovate th' hull thing free gratis for nothin', an' you cain't ask no better'n that, says he.

"Hit ain't no trouble t' rip a tick 'nough t' git a handful o' feathers out, an' lots o' women jest went an' done it without no more argyment. Andy he tuck an' spread the feathers out on a paper, an' poked 'em round with his pencil, an' all of a suddent he says looky hyar, lady, whut did I tell ye? An' shore 'nough, th' hull mess was jest a-crawlin' with leetle white bugs. You could see 'em plain without no specs, but when Andy put his magnifyin'-glass on 'em they looked big as mushrats. Wal, sir, when she seen them bugs th' woman mostly wanted her bed renovated right now, an' Andy he tells her we'll do it for ten cents a pound. We tuck th' featherbed out t' th' wagon an' weighed it, an' it come out forty pounds even, so he says we'll fix it better'n new for four dollars, an' she says all right.

"On th' way back t' th' tent Andy showed me how t' work them scales. You jest press your thumb down hard at th' top, an' th' dang thing reads ten pound light. So then I says hell, we're a-cheatin' ourselves, 'cause if this hyar bed weighs *fifty* pounds 'stead o' forty, we orter be gittin' *five* dollars 'stead o' four! But Andy he says you fool, them goose-feathers is worth fifty cents a pound in Saint Louis, so we jest take out ten pound an' sell 'em, an' keep th' money.

"I studied 'bout that a while, an' then I ask Andy whar does all them leetle bugs come from? He jest laughs louder'n ever. They ain't nothin' but wheat-bugs, says he, an' th' boss has got a big jar chuck full of 'em in th' wagon. An' then Andy he shows me how t' carry them bugs in a holler lead-pencil, so you kin jest pull th' rubber out an' scatter bugs in th' feathers easy as rollin' off'n a log. Thar's tricks in all trades, says he, an' this hyar is what is knowed as salesmanship.

"Wal, sir, soon as we got back t' camp th' boss he ripped open th' tick an' dumped it out—fifty pound o' th' finest goose-feathers you ever seen. Now, says he, you put twenty pound o' them feathers in th' whirler an' blow steam on 'em a while. An' so I done it. When we tuck them feathers out they was th' finest an' fluffiest ever growed on a goose, an' ever' dang feather was swole plumb t' a strut, big as these hyar ostriches! Seems like th' steam puffs 'em up thataway, same as popcorn. Fact is, they was swole so big we couldn't hardly git 'em back in th' tick.

"Me an' Andy hauled it back t' th' woman an' weighed it for her, an' I tuck note Andy never pressed his thumb down this time, neither. Hit come out forty-six pound, so Andy he says maybe thar is a leetle steam in it yit, but it'll settle back down t' forty in a week or two. So she give him th' four dollars, an' seemed like she was tickled t' death with th' job.

"Purty soon I says t' Andy, say, how much do you reckon we made off'n that 'ar featherbed? Oh, jest 'bout average, says he. Let's see, we got four dollars for cleanin' it, an' thirty pound o' prime goose-feathers. Take out th' shop-pound— that's one pound out o' ever' tick whut goes t' th' boss personal, t' pay for th' steam—an' we still got twenty-nine pound t' three ways amongst us. Feathers is worth fifty-cents a pound now, an' fifty times twenty-nine is fourteen-fifty. Fourteen-fifty an' four is eighteen-fifty. Yas, sir, we made eighteen dollars an' fifty cents out o' cleanin' that 'ar bed! We got six beds th' first day, so I figgured we must be makin' more'n a hundred dollars a day for th' three of us.

"We allus baled our feathers up of a night, an' sent 'em t' a feller name of Winterfield in Saint Louis. Had t' pay th' express man extry t' come an' git 'em atter dark—wouldn't do for folks t' git t' wonderin' whut he was a-shippin' so much. I found out later on how this hyar Winterfield was a-gittin' rich—he had nine more crews out that Summer besides us, all of 'em a-stealin' feathers hand over fist. Hit was Winterfield whut furnished th' outfit—th' machine an' th' horses an' th' wagons an' all like that.

"Th' main drawback t' feather-graftin' is that you cain't stay more'n three-four days in one place, on account th' beds allus goes flat soon as th' steam gits out of 'em, an' folks comes round wantin' t' know whut has went with their feathers. Some of 'em gits turrible worked up 'bout it too, an' mean.

"Allus 'bout th' third mornin' th' boss he'd say, well boys, this'll be our last day hyar, but don't go too strong. I ask Andy whut did th' boss mean by that? an' he says well, some fellers in this business'll do most anything, particular when they're a-gittin' ready t' leave town. Whut do they do? says I. Andy he says oh, sometimes they take all th' goose-feathers out, an' stuff th' tick full o' chicken-feathers. An' I have knowed fellers whut would jest grab th' hull dang bed an' run off with it, tickin' an' all. But our boss he don't never do nothin' like that on account it might git us a bad name, an' it don't pay in th' long run nohow. Honesty is th' best policy, says he.

"Wal, sir, I *thought* my coffee tasted kinder funny that night, but I drinked it anyhow. An' when I woke up next mornin', thar I was a-layin' on one measley leetle ol' quilt, an' th' hull caboodle of 'em was gone—horses an' wagons an' flutter-wheel an' ever'thing. Yas, sir, them dirty lowdown sneakin' crooks had jest snuck off in th' night, an' left me afoot, so's t' git out o' payin' my sheer o' th' money!

"An' that ain't all, neither. They had went an' stole a hull passel o' feather-beds unbeknownst t' me, an' them folks whut had lost their beds come down an' ketched me afore I could git out o' town. They rid me on a rail, an' throwed me in th' creek, an' booted me round somethin' scandalous. Said they was aimin' t' tar-an'-feather me, too, only nobody couldn't spare th' feathers! Some o' them fellers was a-laughin', but it warn't no joke t' me.—Them two scallywag partners was th' cause o' me gittin' in this hyar jail, too—but I'll tell you 'bout that tomorrow."

It was impossible for me to visit the jail on the morrow, however, and when I did come around several days later Jube Halliday was gone.

"Yas, sir," the sheriff told me, "they tuck him back t' Burdock County t' stand his trial. I reckon they'll hang him all right, 'less'n he kin play off crazy someway."

"Hang him! Good Lord, what did he do?"

"Why, he kilt a couple o' furriners down thar—jest walked up an' shot 'em down in cold blood. Claimed they had stole his feather-bed, or somethin'," said the sheriff.

Carl Sandburg

Carl Sandburg (1878–   ) was born in Galesburg, Illinois. At the age of thirteen he was compelled to leave school to help support his family and at seventeen he struck out for himself, riding the rods to the harvest fields, working as dishwasher, pick-and-shovel man, etc. After the Spanish-American War, in which he saw action in Cuba, he studied four years at Lombard College in Galesburg. He worked as a reporter on the Milwaukee LEADER, *a Socialist daily, and eventually became a Chicago newspaperman and poet, one of the group fostered by Harriet Monroe's* POETRY: A MAGAZINE OF VERSE. *His early wanderings and his constant contact with the common people are reflected in the earthy strength of his poetry, beginning with* CHICAGO POEMS *(1915) and continuing through several volumes to* THE PEOPLE, YES *(1936) from which "They Have Yarns" is reprinted. Sandburg's massive biography of Abraham Lincoln has occupied much of his time within recent years.*

They Have Yarns

They have yarns
Of a skyscraper so tall they had to put hinges
On the top two stories so to let the moon go by,
Of one corn crop in Missouri when the roots
Went so deep and drew off so much water
The Mississippi riverbed that year was dry,
Of pancakes so thin they had only one side,
Of "a fog so thick we shingled the barn and six feet out on the
    fog,"
Of Pecos Pete straddling a cyclone in Texas and riding it to the
    west coast where "it rained out under him,"
Of the man who drove a swarm of bees across the Rocky Moun-
    tains and the Desert "and didn't lose a bee,"
Of a mountain railroad curve where the engineer in his cab can
    touch the caboose and spit in the conductor's eye,
Of the boy who climbed a cornstalk growing so fast he would
    have starved to death if they hadn't shot biscuits up to him,
Of the old man's whiskers: "When the wind was with him his
    whiskers arrived a day before he did,"
Of the hen laying a square egg and cackling, "Ouch!" and of
    hens laying eggs with the dates printed on them,
Of the ship captain's shadow: it froze to the deck one cold
    winter night,
Of mutineers on that same ship put to chipping rust with rubber
    hammers,
Of the sheep counter who was fast and accurate: "I just count
    their feet and divide by four,"
Of the man so tall he must climb a ladder to shave himself,
Of the runt so teeny-weeny it takes two men and a boy to
    see him,
Of mosquitoes: one can kill a dog, two of them a man,

Of a cyclone that sucked cookstoves out of the kitchen, up the
    chimney flue, and on to the next town,

Of the same cyclone picking up wagon-tracks in Nebraska and
    dropping them over in the Dakotas,

Of the hook-and-eye snake unlocking itself into forty pieces, each
    piece two inches long, then in nine seconds flat snapping
    itself together again,

Of the watch swallowed by the cow—when they butchered her
    a year later the watch was running and had the correct time,

Of horned snakes, hoop snakes that roll themselves where they
    want to go, and rattlesnakes carrying bells instead of rattles
    on their tails,

Of the herd of cattle in California getting lost in a giant redwood
    tree that had hollowed out,

Of the man who killed a snake by putting its tail in its mouth
    so it swallowed itself,

Of railroad trains whizzing along so fast they reach the station
    before the whistle,

Of pigs so thin the farmer had to tie knots in their tails to keep
    them from crawling through the cracks in their pens,

Of Paul Bunyan's big blue ox, Babe, measuring between the eyes
    forty-two ax-handles and a plug of Star tobacco exactly,

Of John Henry's hammer and the curve of its swing and his
    singing of it as "a rainbow round my shoulder."

              "Do tell!"
              "I want to know!"
              "You don't say so!"
              "For the land's sake!"
              "Gosh all fish-hooks!"
              "Tell me some more.
              I don't believe a word you say
              but I love to listen
              to your sweet harmonica
              to your chin-music.
              Your fish stories hang together
              when they're just a pack of lies:
              you ought to have a leather medal:

you ought to have a statue
carved of butter: you deserve
a large bouquet of turnips."
"Yessir," the traveler drawled,
"Away out there in the petrified forest
everything goes on the same as usual.
The petrified birds sit in their petrified nests
and hatch their petrified young from petrified eggs."

A high pressure salesman jumped off the Brooklyn Bridge and
was saved by a policeman. But it didn't take long to sell
the idea to the policeman. So together they jumped off the
bridge.

One of the oil men in heaven started a rumor of a gusher down
in hell. All the other oil men left in a hurry for hell. As he
gets to thinking about the rumor he had started he says to
himself there might be something in it after all. So he leaves
for hell in a hurry.

"The number 42 will win this raffle, that's my number." And
when he won they asked him whether he guessed the number or had a system. He said he had a system, "I took up
the old family album and there on page 7 was my grandfather and grandmother both on page 7. I said to myself
this is easy for 7 times 7 is the number that will win and
7 times 7 is 42."

Once a shipwrecked sailor caught hold of a stateroom door and
floated for hours till friendly hands from out of the darkness
threw him a rope. And he called across the night, "What
country is this?" and hearing voices answer, "New Jersey,"
he took a fresh hold on the floating stateroom door and
called back half-wearily, "I guess I'll float a little farther."

An Ohio man bundled up the tin roof of a summer kitchen and
sent it to a motor car maker with a complaint of his car not
giving service. In three weeks a new car arrived for him and
a letter: "We regret delay in shipment but your car was
received in a very bad order."

A Dakota cousin of this Ohio man sent six years of tin can
accumulations to the same works, asking them to overhaul
his car. Two weeks later came a rebuilt car, five old tin cans,
and a letter: "We are also forwarding you five parts not
necessary in our new model."

Thus fantasies heard at a filling station in the midwest. Another
relates to a Missouri mule who took aim with his heels at
an automobile rattling by. The car turned a somersault, lit
next a fence, ran right along through a cornfield till it came
to a gate, moved onto the road and went on its way as
though nothing had happened. The mule heehawed with
desolation, "What's the use?"

Another tells of a farmer and his family stalled on a railroad
crossing, how they jumped out in time to see a limited express knock it into flinders, the farmer calling, "Well, I
always did say that car was no shucks in a real pinch."

When the Masonic Temple in Chicago was the tallest building
in the United States west of New York two men who would
cheat the eyes out of you if you gave 'em a chance, took an
Iowa farmer to the top of the building and asked him, "How
is this for high?" They told him that for $25 they would go
down in the basement and turn the building around on its
turn-table for him while he stood on the roof and saw how
this seventh wonder of the world worked. He handed them
$25. They went. He waited. They never came back.

This is told in Chicago as a folk tale, the same as the legend of
Mrs. O'Leary's cow kicking over the barn lamp that started
the Chicago fire, when the Georgia visitor, Robert Toombs,
telegraphed an Atlanta crony "Chicago is on fire, the whole
city burning down, God be praised!"

Nor is the prize sleeper Rip Van Winkle and his scolding wife
forgotten, nor the headless horseman scooting through
Sleepy Hollow

Nor the sunken treasure-ships in coves and harbors, the hideouts
of gold and silver sought by Coronado, nor the Flying

Dutchman rounding the Cape doomed to nevermore pound his ear nor ever again to take a snooze for himself

Nor the sailor's caretaker Mother Carey seeing to it that every seafaring man in the afterworld has a seabird to bring him news of ships and women, an albatross for the admiral, a gull for the deckhand

Nor the sailor with a sweetheart in every port of the world, nor the ships that set out with flying colors and all the promises you could ask, the ships never heard of again,

Nor Jim Liverpool, the riverman who could jump across any river and back without touching land he was that quick on his feet,

Nor Mike Fink along the Ohio and Mississippi, half wild horse and half cock-eyed alligator the rest of him snags and snapping turtle. "I can out-run, out-jump, out-shoot, out-brag, out-drink, and out-fight, rough and tumble, no holts barred, any man on both sides of the river from Pittsburgh to New Orleans and back again to St. Louis. My trigger finger itches and I want to go redhot. War, famine and bloodshed puts flesh on my bones, and hardship's my daily bread."

Nor the man so lean he threw no shadow: six rattlesnakes struck at him at one time and every one missed him.

Max Shulman

Max Shulman (1919–   ) was born in Saint Paul, Minnesota, and harassed the faculty of the University of Minnesota first with an indiscreet column in the student newspaper, the MINNESOTA DAILY, *and later by his disrespectful editing of the campus humor magazine,* SKI-U-MAH. *While a sergeant in the Army Air Forces he wrote* BAREFOOT BOY WITH CHEEK *(1943), following it with* THE FEATHER MERCHANTS *(1944) and* THE ZEBRA DERBY *(1945). The latter he describes as "the third in a series of fourteen books, the work to be called, in toto,* REMEMBRANCE OF THINGS PAST" *which "will be condensed to three pages in the* READER'S DIGEST *and printed under the title: 'Hernia Can Be Cured.'" The following selection is reprinted from* BAREFOOT BOY WITH CHEEK *(1943).*

Asa Hearthrug Joins Alpha Cholera

AFTER I left the Health Service I went for a walk. I wanted to think about all the wonderful things that had happened to me. I could scarcely believe that in just a few days I was going to walk into a university class, a belonger, a cog in a great machine where everyone puts his nose to the grindstone and pulls together. I glowed all over as I walked upon the handsome promenade called fraternity row.

Minnesota has one of the finest fraternity rows in the country. Behind luxuriant, well-kept lawns stand the ornate but tasteful fronts of the fraternity houses. Doric columns adorn their façades, and through the leaded panes of their windows I could see gay, well-dressed young men lounging casually in the living rooms. My fellow students, I thought rapturously. I gave a little jump in my unbridled joy. As I landed, two cunningly hinged sidewalk stones gave way, and I hurtled into a pit below.

"We got one," someone yelled. Immediately two youths beset me and tied me with baling wire. Then I was carried through a devious tunnel into the living room of a fraternity house. "We got one, Roger," announced my bearers.

The one called Roger was sitting at a table playing Michigan rummy with three others. "O.K.," he said. The others drew guns, and each one walked over to a door. "Untie him," Roger commanded.

The two who had brought me in produced an acetylene torch and loosed me. Roger pulled out a buffer and dental floss and got his teeth ready. Then he smiled. "I'm Roger Hailfellow, the president. I'm certainly glad that you decided on this fraternity. Yes sir, you can't find a better fraternity than Alpha Cholera. How about that, fellows?" he asked, turning to the three who were guarding the exits.

"Friend, you did right," they said to me.

"I'll tell you, chum," said Roger, putting his arm around me, sticking a cigarette in my mouth, and lighting it, "there's fraternities and there's fraternities. I don't like to knock anybody, but there's some bad fraternities as well as good fraternities. A fellow who joins a bad fraternity is almost as bad off as a fellow who don't join no fraternity at all. And you know how bad off a fellow is who don't join no fraternity at all. Damn barb." Roger spat angrily.

The three at the doors fired shots into the wall to indicate their feelings about a fellow who didn't join any fraternity.

"But you're lucky," Roger continued, sticking another cigarette in my mouth and lighting it. "You picked the best fraternity first crack off the bat. How about that, fellows,"

"Friend, you did right," they said.

"Yes sir, the very best. Alpha Cholera isn't one of those little upstart fraternities. No sir. Do you know when we were founded?"

"No," I said.

"Five hundred B.C. Alpha Cholera was founded in ancient Greece by three fellows named Aeschylus, Sophocles, and Euripides. They did not give their last names. Even in those days people knew a good thing when they saw one, and all the right people in Greece joined Alpha Cholera. The spring formal at the Parthenon was the high spot of the social year in Athens. They had the best orchestra in the country, Oedipus Rex. 'Fling and flex with Oedipus Rex' was his slogan.

"But just like it is today, Alpha Cholera was choosy about who it let in. The mayor of Athens, Nick, tried to get his son into the fraternity, but Alpha Cholera was not going to take nobody with a ram's head. It meant banishment.

"So the members hied themselves off to Rome. They were

carried most of the way on the back of their sergeant at arms, a chap named Aeneas. When they finally reached Rome, they were so exhausted that they collapsed on the ground. They would have perished, had it not been for a passing she-wolf who suckled them.

"In Rome Alpha Cholera did not fare well. The members were relentlessly hunted out and murdered by the barbarous Romans. Finally there was only one Alpha Cholera left, a fellow Androcles. He hid for a time in the basement of a sympathetic Roman candlestick maker named Phelps or Mazinik. Eventually Androcles was apprehended, and it was decided that he was to be thrown to the lions.

"While thousands of spectators sat in the Colosseum and roared for blood, Androcles bravely entered the lion's cage. The beast rushed at him. Stout-hearted Androcles proceeded to grapple. Unwittingly, as he seized the lion's paw, he gave him the secret Alpha Cholera handshake. The lion paused. He licked Androcles' face and refused to do further battle. He, too, was an Alpha Cholera, Swahili chapter.

"Androcles was spared and lived to carry forward the torch of Alpha Cholera. After his death, we know that Alpha Cholera continued to exist, but we are not sure of the details. We believe that there was a chapter in Pompeii. When the noted archaeologist, Dudley Digs, excavated the ruins of Pompeii, he found a corpse wearing a pin that bore the initials A.C. We think that stood for Alpha Cholera. Digs, himself, holds to another theory. The corpse who was wearing the pin also held a dulcimer in his hand, and Digs believes that A.C. meant "Ad Carthage" where the Roman musicians' union was going to hold its convention the year of the Pompeiian disaster.

"Be that as it may, we know that somehow Alpha Cholera went forward unbrokenly. In the writings of Cellini we find this passage: 'I saw this night a comely wench upon the thoroughfare. After pleasant amenities she accompanied me to my quarters where we deported ourselves pleasantly until she, seeing a bauble upon my blouse, expressed a desire for it. I gave her that and other things and having done, hit her in the mouth, took back the bauble, and flung her from my casement.' The bauble was, of course, an Alpha Cholera pin.

"We are certain, too, that Robespierre was an Alpha Cholera. The motto for the French Revolution was originally 'Liberty, Equality.' Robespierre inserted the 'Fraternity.'

"And who do you think brought Alpha Cholera to America? The pilgrim fathers, no less. They were an Alpha Cholera chapter in London, but they lost the lease on their house when their landlady, the old lady of Threadneedle Street, found out that they were dancing on Saturday nights. She hated dancing since years before when she had gone out with an adagio dancer named Ike, who had snatched her purse and thrown her into a passing circus wagon where she had been assaulted four times by an orang-utan. So the pilgrim fathers came to America where nobody could interfere with their Saturday-night hops."

"My. You certainly have an illustrious history," I exclaimed, removing the cigarettes from my mouth so I could talk.

"Friend, you said right," said the three at the doors.

"Now, you just sit here and smoke a cigarette while I get you a pledge card to sign," Roger said, inserting another cigarette in my mouth.

"Well, wait a minute," I protested. "I really hadn't intended to join a fraternity today. I was just walking along the sidewalk here when I happened to fall into your pit. I really wasn't thinking about joining a fraternity. I hope you understand I have nothing against your fraternity. It seems to be a totally admirable institution. And I certainly do appreciate all these cigarettes I am smoking. I am grateful, too, for the time you have spent telling me all about Alpha Cholera. But, to be perfectly frank, I wasn't even thinking about joining a fraternity—at least, not today."

The three with guns moved in on me. Roger waved them back. "Of course," he said simply. "How stupid of me. You want a little time to think it over. Well, why don't you have lunch here, and perhaps we can talk about it some more?"

"Oh, I don't think I should. You have done too much for me already."

"Oh, pooh," said Roger. "It's nothing. Harry, go get something to eat for our friend."

One of the doorkeepers left.

"Really, Roger." I cried, "you shouldn't!"

"Tut, tut," Roger said. "I want you to think of the Alpha Cholera house as your home away from home."

I felt a lump rise in my throat. "I think that's the nicest thing anybody has ever said to me," I said simply.

Roger lowered his eyes modestly. Harry came in with my lunch. I looked, and for a moment I thought my senses were deceiving me, for Harry had laid a plate of hominy grits before me, and they were arranged to spell out:

> *Alpha Cholera is glad you're here.*
> *Eat these grits in all good cheer.*

Unable to speak, I looked at Roger. He smiled reassuringly and bade me eat. As I started to eat, the three at the doors came over to Roger. They all patted me on the shoulder, and then, putting their arms about one another, proceeded to sing this song.

> *"Stand, good men, take off your hat*
> *To Alpha Cholera, our swell frat.*
> *In our midst you'll find no rat,*
> *And don't let anyone tell you that.*

> *"Be you lean or be you fat,*
> *Join Alpha Cholera, our swell frat.*
> *Since long ago, when first we mat,*
> *Our swell bunch is together yat."*

As their last soft chords died, I could see through the leaded panes of the windows the flaming orb of the sun expire gently into the west. The earth was bathed in the soft pastel of the vanishing day.

"Want some salt on those grits?" Roger asked gently.

I shook my head, for my tears were salt enough. Understanding, Roger perceived my condition and said, "Let's go, fellows. He wants to be alone for a while." They patted my throbbing shoulders and left, still singing the Alpha Cholera song in close harmony.

I finished the grits and licked the plate so they wouldn't have to wash it. Then I wiped my nose on my sleeve and let my thoughts take possession of me. If somebody had told me before I came to the University that my fellow students were going to make such a to-do over me, I would have cried, "Go to, sirrah, and make not light of my innocence." But it was all true. Here was I, a complete stranger, taken without question into the bosom of my fellows. Ah, alma mater, you are indeed my adopted mother, I thought.

Roger and the others returned. "How was it?" Roger asked.

"The lunch? It was divine."

"Well, that gives you a rough idea of the kind of cuisine we have at Alpha Cholera. And hominy grits is only an example of what you'll get. We often have peanut-butter sandwiches, baked beans, turnip greens, and head cheese. And on legal holidays we always have mackerel."

"No!" I exclaimed.

"Yes," said Roger. "And would you believe it, our kitchen shows a profit year after year. But enough. Let's get down to business. Are you ready to join?"

The three at the doors had put their guns in their holsters. Now they drew them again.

"Well," I said, "how much does it cost?"

"Why, bless you," Roger said, "don't **you** worry about

that. Come with me. I'll introduce you to some of the fellows."

He took me by the hand and led me upstairs to the dormitory. "We have one of the biggest B.M.O.C.'s in Alpha Cholera," he said, as we walked up the stairs.

"What's a B.M.O.C.?" I asked.

"A Big Man on Campus," he explained.

We stopped in front of a room near the head of the stairs. "This room belongs to Eino Fflliikkiinnenn," Roger said reverently.

"Not Eino Fflliikkiinnenn, the football player!" I cried.

"Yes," said Roger. "He will be your fraternity brother."

I was all shaky inside as we entered Fflliikkiinnenn's room. He was standing in a corner beating his head methodically against the wall. "He's toughening up for the football season," Roger whispered.

"Eino," Roger called, "here's a man who wants to meet you. He is going to pledge Alpha Cholera."

Eino grabbed my hand in a hearty grip. "Ay tink dot's real nice," he said. "Ay am happy to call you my brudder."

I did not trust myself to speak.

"Did I do good, Roger?" said Eino.

"Yes, Eino," Roger answered. "Now let go of his hand and go back to your exercises."

"Say, Roger," Eino said, "you didn' pay me yat dis mont'."

"Is that so?" said Roger. "Well, it's just an oversight. I'll see that you get your money right away."

"You batter," Eino said. "Ay got a goot offer from Mu Beta Fistula to live over dere. Dey pay on time too."

"I'll see that you get your money. Don't worry," said Roger.

"You batter," Eino said, "and cash. No more beer chips."

We left.

"Just think of being a fraternity brother of Eino Fflliikkiinnenn's," Roger said to me.

"I can't imagine anything more heavenly," I answered.

Roger rubbed his hands. "Well, then, should I get the pledge card?"

"Well, I don't know, I really wasn't thinking of joining a fraternity. I just happened to be walking by when I fell into—"

"Let's go take a look at our record collection," Roger interrupted.

We went downstairs to a large radio phonograph with an enclosed record cabinet. "We got everything," Roger said, "Goodman, Shaw, Basie, Dorsey, Herman, anything you want. All the new stuff too. Just got a new Andrews sister disc today. 'Death and Transfiguration' on one side, 'Dope Me, Doctor, with a Sulfa Drug' on the other. Or maybe you like the heavier stuff. Symphonic. We got all you want. 'Filigree on Derrière's Variation of a Theme of Merde' recorded by the Rush City Four. And 'Afternoon of a Prawn.' Anything you want."

But again he was taking me somewhere. I followed him into a room piled waist high with pictures of girls. "Pictures here of every girl on the campus. Name, address, age, height, weight, habits, and food and liquor capacity written on the back. Also achievement records of all the fellows who have ever taken her out. Join Alpha Cholera and be sure what you're getting into."

"Land sakes," I said admiringly.

"Now will you pledge?" Roger asked.

I took his two hands in mine and looked him in the eyes. "Whatever you think best, Roger," I said simply.

He rubbed his hands rapidly, starting a minor conflagration on his cuffs. "Now, I suppose you want to discuss finances. Well, just you don't worry about that at all. I'll call our treasurer, and we'll have every little thing all straightened out as fast as you can say Jack Robinson. You'll like our treasurer."

Roger left and came back in a few minutes with the treasurer. "This is our treasurer, Shylock Fiscal," he said.

"Well, you finally got one," he said to Roger.

Roger smiled modestly.

"I was about to go to work," Shylock said.

"Where there's life there's hope," Roger reminded him.

"I just about gave up," Shylock confessed. "It's getting worse each year, what with the other houses serving meat and keeping a dozen B.M.O.C.'s and—"

"That reminds me," Roger interrupted. "Eino wants to get paid."

"Give him some beer chips," suggested Shylock.

"No, he wants cash."

"Cash, huh? Well, let's see what we can get from this turnip." Shylock turned to me. "I'm Shylock Fiscal," he said cheerily. "Just call me Shy. Everybody does. I guess its because I'm not. Heh, heh, heh."

"Heh, heh, heh," laughed Roger.

I joined the general merriment. How good it was to share a good joke with good men.

"So you've decided to join Alpha Cholera?" Shylock continued. "Friend, you did right. You'll never regret it. There's nothing like a good fraternity, and Alpha Cholera is the best, isn't it, Roger?"

"Yes," Roger admitted.

"Yes sir. You can't beat a good fraternity. Good fellows living together in a good house, sharing each other's problems, making contacts that are going to be their most precious possessions in later life. But I don't have to tell you about the advantages. Anyone looking at you can tell that you know what the score is."

I blushed becomingly.

Shylock leaned closer and put his hand on my knee. "The surprising thing," he said, "is how reasonable Alpha Cholera is. I mean, looking at it intelligently. You and I know that in this world you don't get something for nothing; the best thing you can hope for is to get a lot of a little. And that's what you get when you join Alpha Cholera.

"Take dues, for instance. We charge $100 a month. I'll admit that $100 is a tidy sum. But remember, if you were going to take a suite in a hotel downtown while you went to school you'd pay a lot more. And besides, you'd be living alone. You wouldn't have all these swell kids to live with and share your problems. Furthermore, $100 a month dues keeps out the riffraff. You can be sure that you're living with the best people at Alpha Cholera.

"Now then, there's meals. Breakfast—$1.75. Lunch—$2.50. Dinner—$4.00. Now you know as well as I do that you can't pay too much for a good meal, attractively served in pleasant surroundings. How about that, Roger?"

"Yes," said Roger.

"And laundry. You just throw your dirty clothes down the chute, and the next time you see them, they're spick-and-span, all ready to wear. None of that wet-wash stuff here. No sir. And all for $12.50 a week.

"Then there's national dues; Alpha Cholera isn't one of your dinky one-chapter houses. Not on your life. You'll find an Alpha Cholera house on every major campus in the country. And that's important. Whenever you visit another college, you don't have to pay four or five dollars a night for a hotel room. You just go to the Alpha Cholera and they'll put you up without charging you a cent. National dues are $40 a month.

"And that's it, friend. That's every red cent you'll pay for being an Alpha Cholera, except naturally $5.00 a month for the telephone, a quarter a day for hot water, and $300 for your handsome zircon Alpha Cholera pin. Of course there'll be special events from time to time, but we won't worry about those now, will we?"

"No," said Roger.

"Now that you know all the facts about Alpha Cholera, are you ready to make your decision?" Shylock asked. "We want you to go into this thing with your eyes open. This is the most important step you have ever taken in your life, and we don't want you to regret it. We want you to *want* to join Alpha Cholera; otherwise we don't want you. The decision is entirely up to you. We have acquainted you with the facts, and that is all we can do. Now, you take your time and think it over. We'll give you ninety seconds."

I knew it was an important decision, and I took the full allotted time. As they twisted my arms, I mentally weighed the considerations in the case. There was only one answer I could reasonably, honestly, and conscientiously give.

"I'll pledge," I said.

We shook hands silently all around, not trusting ourselves to speak.

"Shy," said Roger, after we had choked back our tears, "you tell him about the pledge period while I get everything ready for the ceremony." He left.

"Now," said Shylock, "you are going to be pledged in just a few minutes. For six months after that you are going to be a pledge. Then you get initiated and become what is called an active. During your pledge period you are sort of a little brother to the actives. You come to us with your problems and we give you advice about whatever you want to know. We choose your clothes and your girls for you. You just let us actives worry about everything."

I nuzzled against his sleeve. "There, there," he said quietly.

"All ready," called a voice from down the hall, and I left with Shylock for the pledging ceremony. (The ritual that followed is very secret, and I must ask the readers to keep the ensuing account in strictest confidence.)

We entered a room lit dimly by candles. A group of young men sat cross-legged in a circle on the floor. In the corner of the room on a dais Roger sat, dressed in a curiously inscribed robe. Frankincense and myrrh burned in an icon on the wall. Shylock led me to the center of the circle. He chanted:

> *"I bring a man*
> *Into this clan."*

> *"Hubba, gubba,*
> *Goodrich rubba,"*

intoned the circle.

A barefoot maiden in a white gown entered bearing a young ram above her head. She deposited the ram in Roger's lap.

> *"Ram, bam,*
> *Thank you ma'am,"*

he said.

He drew a curiously inscribed kriss from his robe and slit the ram's throat. He dipped his finger in the blood and, beckoning me to the dais, made a curious inscription on my forehead.

"He's been washed in the blood of the ram," repeated the circle. Then they sang:

> *"Blood, thud,*
> *Fuddy dud."*

They leaped to their feet. Each put his hands on the hips of the one in front of him. They proceeded to move around me in a curious dance consisting of three steps and a kick. regularly repeated. After a while they resumed their positions and chanted:

> *"Simba, marimba,*
> *Richard himba."*

The lights went on, and suddenly their smiling faces were

shaking my hand. Tears streamed uncheckable from my little eyes. "My brothers! My brothers!" I cried hoarsely.

Now I was on their shoulders, and they were giving three cheers and a tiger for me.

"By the way," said Shylock, "what's your name?"

"Asa Hearthrug," I answered.

"Oh, Jesus," he said.

Vincent Starrett

Vincent Starrett (1886–), Toronto-born, but a resident of Chicago since childhood, served a journalistic apprenticeship on the INTER-OCEAN *and the* DAILY NEWS. *He edited* THE WAVE, *a creditable "little" magazine, and looks like and is a bibliophile, a discoverer and appreciator of obscure tomes long immured in dustbins. He is the person to whom Chicagoans in search of abstruse literary information usually turn. A founder of the Baker Street Irregulars, a band of zealots pledged to keep green the memory of Sherlock Holmes, he has written a number of detective novels, as well as verse, short stories, literary critiques, and just about everything else. "Hell, Said the Duchess" and "Embattled Virgin" are reprinted from* AUTOLYCUS IN LIMBO *(1943).*

Hell, Said the Duchess

Hell, said the Duchess, and her voice was hard,
What's the world coming to, I'd like to know?
Mutton is up a penny, rents are slow,
Butter's so dear we'll soon be using lard.
Months have elapsed since I have held a card
Higher than six or seven; and my toe
Is sticking through my stocking. What I owe
Causes them sleepless nights at Scotland Yard.

Politics gives me twinges in the head;
Half of the world is bellowing for war,
And half is—Well, at least here comes the tea.
Just one more rubber, then a spot of bed:
I can't think when I've had so poor a score—
And you, sir, take your hand from off my knee!

Embattled Virgin

Between the sheets of publicized hotels
In scenic nooks and corners of the nation,
Miss Philomena stubbornly repels
Impatient lovers of her own creation;
In tossing bunks of trains and ocean liners,
She lies awake and cocks a cautious ear
For ribald males who eyed her in the diners
With what she fancies was an evil leer.

Bright-eyed and fearful in her virgin bed
She cowers, having no one to defend her,
As flagrant pictures riot in her head
Through nights of happy struggle and surrender;
Alert in every rustle to discover
The stealthy footstep of a maddened lover.

Booth Tarkington

Booth Tarkington (1869–1946) was born in Indianapolis. Beginning with THE GENTLEMAN FROM INDIANA *(1899), he wrote a long series of novels of varying excellence which received public acclaim in varying degrees. His eminent position as a humorous writer about the real or fancied woes of childhood appears to be secure. "Penrod and Harold Ramorez" is reprinted from* PENROD.

Penrod and Harold Ramorez

(Penrod is here approaching one of the fateful crises of his young life. It is almost time for him to don the befrilled costume of the child Sir Lancelot he is to wear in a sissified pageant under the direction of Mrs. Lora Rewbush, and he is devoting his remaining moments of freedom to a more pleasant and more manly occupation.)

PENROD slid down from the fence, and with slow and thoughtful steps entered a one-storied wing of the stable, floored with cement and used as a storeroom for broken bric-à-brac, old paintbuckets, decayed garden-hose, worn-out carpets, dead furniture, and other condemned odds and ends not yet considered hopeless enough to be given away.

In one corner stood a large box, a part of the building itself: it was eight feet high and open at the top, and it had been constructed as a sawdust magazine from which was drawn material for the horse's bed in a stall on the other side of the partition. The big box, so high and towerlike, so commodious, so suggestive, had ceased to fulfil its legitimate function; though, providentially, it had been at least half full of sawdust when the horse died. Two years had gone by since that passing; an interregnum in transportation during which Penrod's father was "thinking" (he explained sometimes) of an automobile. Meanwhile, the gifted and generous sawdust-box had served brilliantly in war and peace: it was Penrod's stronghold.

There was a partially defaced sign upon the front wall of the box; the donjon-keep had known mercantile impulses:

The O.K. RaBiT Co.
PENROD ScHoFiELD AND co.
iNQuiRe FOR PRicEs

343

This was a venture of the preceeding vacation, and had netted, at one time, an accrued and owed profit of $1.38. Prospects had been brightest on the very eve of cataclysm. The storeroom was locked and guarded, but twenty-seven rabbits and Belgian hares, old and young, had perished here on a single night—through no human agency, but in a foray of cats, the besiegers treacherously tunnelling up through the sawdust from the small aperture which opened into the stall beyond the partition. Commerce has its martyrs.

Penrod climbed upon a barrel, stood on tiptoe, grasped the rim of the box; then, using a knot-hole as a stirrup, threw one leg over the top, drew himself up, and dropped within. Standing upon the packed sawdust, he was just tall enough to see over the top.

Duke had not followed him into the storeroom, but remained near the open doorway in a concave and pessimistic attitude. Penrod felt in a dark corner of the box and laid hands upon a simple apparatus consisting of an old bushel-basket with a few yards of clothes-line tied to each of its handles. He passed the ends of the lines over a big spool, which revolved upon an axle of wire suspended from a beam overhead, and, with the aid of this improvised pulley, lowered the empty basket until it came to rest in an upright position upon the floor of the storeroom at the foot of the sawdust-box.

"Eleva-ter!" shouted Penrod. "Ting-ting!"

Duke, old and intelligently apprehensive, approached slowly, in a semicircular manner, deprecatingly, but with courtesy. He pawed the basket delicately; then, as if that were all his master had expected of him, uttered one bright bark, sat down, and looked up triumphantly. His hypocrisy was shallow: many a horrible quarter of an hour had taught him his duty in this matter.

"El-e-*vay*-ter!" shouted Penrod sternly. "You want me to come down there *to* you?"

Duke looked suddenly haggard. He pawed the basket feebly again and, upon another outburst from on high, prostrated himself flat. Again threatened, he gave a superb impersonation of a worm.

"You get in that el-e-VAT-ter!"

Reckless with despair, Duke jumped into the basket, landing in a dishevelled posture, which he did not alter until he had been drawn up and poured out upon the floor of sawdust with the box. There, shuddering, he lay in doughnut shape and presently slumbered.

It was dark in the box, a condition that might have been remedied by sliding back a small wooden panel on runners, which would have let in ample light from the alley; but Penrod Schofield had more interesting means of illumination. He knelt, and from a former soap-box, in a corner, took a lantern without a chimney, and a large oil-can, the leak in the latter being so nearly imperceptible that its banishment from household use had seemed to Penrod as inexplicable as it was providential.

He shook the lantern near his ear: nothing splashed. There was no sound but a dry clinking. But there was plenty of kerosene in the can; and he filled the lantern, striking a match to illumine the operation. Then he lit the lantern and hung it upon a nail against the wall. The sawdust floor was slightly impregnated with oil, and the open flame quivered in suggestive proximity to the side of the box; however, some rather deep charring of the plank against which the lantern hung offered evidence that the arrangement was by no means a new one, and indicated at least a possibility of no fatality occurring this time.

Next, Penrod turned up the surface of the sawdust in another corner of the floor, and drew forth a cigar-box in which were half a dozen cigarettes, made of hayseed and thick brown wrapping paper, a lead-pencil, an eraser, and a small note-book, the cover of which was labelled in his own handwriting: *English Grammar. Penrod Schofield. Room 6, Ward School Nomber Seventh.*

The first page of this book was purely academic: but the study of English undefiled terminated with a slight jar at the top of the second: "Nor must an adverb be used to modif—"
Immediately followed:

HARoLD RAMoREZ THE RoADAGENT
OR WiLD LiFE AMoNG THE
ROCKY MTS.

And the subsequent entries in the book appeared to have little concern with Room 6, Ward School Nomber Seventh.

The author of *Harold Ramorez*, etc., lit one of the hayseed cigarettes, seated himself comfortably, with his back against the wall and his right shoulder just under the lantern, elevated his knees to support the note-book, turned to a blank page, and wrote, slowly and earnestly:

CHAPITER THE SIXTH

He took a knife from his pocket, and, broodingly, his eyes upon the inward embryos of vision, sharpened his pencil. After that, he extended a foot and meditatively rubbed Duke's back with the side of his shoe. Creation, with Penrod, did not leap, full-armed, from the brain; but finally he began to produce. He wrote very slowly at first, and then with increasing rapidity; faster and faster, gathering momentum and growing more and more fevered as he sped, till at last the true fire came, without which no lamp of real literature may be made to burn.

Mr. Wilson reched for his gun but our hero had him covered and soon said Well I guess you don't come any of that on me my freind.

Well what makes you so sure about it sneered the other

bitting his lip so savageley that the blood ran. You are nothing but a common Roadagent any way and I do not propose to be bafled by such, Ramorez laughed at this and kep Mr. Wilson covred by his ottomatick

Soon the two men were struggling together in the deathroes but soon Mr Wilson got him bound and gaged his mouth and went away for awhile leavin our hero, it was dark and he writhd at his bonds writhing on the floor wile the rats came out of their holes and bit him and vernim got all over him from the floor of that helish spot but soon he manged to push the gag out of his mouth with the end of his toungeu and got all his bonds off

Soon Mr Wilson came back to tant him with his helpless condition flowed by his gang of detectives and they said Oh look at Ramorez sneering at his plight and tanted him with his helpless condition because Ramorez had put the bonds back sos he would look the same but could throw them off him when he wanted to Just look at him now sneered they. To hear him talk you would thought he was hot stuff and they said Look at him now, him that was going to do so much, Oh I would not like to be in his fix

Soon Harold got mad at this and jumped up with blasing eyes throwin off his bonds like they were air Ha Ha sneered he I guess you better not talk so much next time. Soon there flowed another awful struggle and siezin his ottomatick back from Mr Wilson he shot two of the detectives through the heart Bing Bing went the ottomatick and two more went to meet their Maker only two detectives left now and so he stabbed one and the scondrel went to meet his Maker for now our hero was fighting for his very life. It was dark in there now for night had falen and a terrible view met the eye Blood was just all over everything and the rats were eatin the dead men.

Soon our hero manged to get his back to the wall for he was fighting for his very life now and shot Mr Wilson through the abodem Oh said Mr Wilson —— —— (*the dashes are Penrod's.*)

Mr Wilson stagerd back vile oaths soilin his lips for he

was in pain Why you —— —— you sneered he I will get
you yet —— —— you Harold Ramorez

The remainin scondrel had an ax which he came near our
heros head with but missed him and ramand stuck in the wall
Our heros amunition was exhaused what was he to do, the
remanin scondrel would soon get his ax lose so our hero
sprung forward and bit him till his teeth met in the flech
for now our hero was fighting for his very life. At this the
remanin scondrel also cursed and swore vile oaths. Oh sneered
he —— —— —— you Harold Ramorez what did you bite
me for Yes sneered Mr Wilson also and he has shot me in
the abodmen too the ——

Soon they were both cursin and reviln him together Why
you —— —— —— —— —— sneered they what did you
want to injure us for —— you Harold Ramorez you have
not got any sence and you think you are so much but you
are no better than anybody else and you are a —— ——
—— —— —— ——

Soon our hero could stand this no longer. If you could learn
to act like gentlmen said he I would not do any more to you
now and your low vile expresions have not got any effect on
me only to injure your own self when you go to meet your
Maker Oh I guess you have had enogh for one day and I
think you have learned a lesson and will not soon atemp to
beard Harold Ramorez again so with a tantig laugh he cooly
lit a cigarrete and takin the keys of the cell from Mr Wilson
poket went on out

Soon Mr Wilson and the wonded detective manged to
bind up their wonds and got up off the floor —— —— it I
will have that dasstads life now sneered they if we have to
swing for it —— —— —— —— him he shall not escape us
again the low down —— —— —— —— ——

CHAPTER SEVENTH

A mule train of heavily laden burros laden with gold from
the mines was to be seen wondering among the highest clifts
and gorgs of the Rocky Mts and a tall man with a long silken

mustash and a cartigde belt could be heard cursin vile oaths
because he well knew this was the lair of Harold Ramorez
Why —— —— —— you you —— —— —— —— mules
you sneered he because the poor mules were not able to go
any quicker —— you I will show you Why —— —— ——
—— —— —— it sneered he his oaths growing viler and viler
I will whip you —— —— —— —— —— —— —— you sos
you will not be able to walk for a week —— —— you you
mean old —— —— —— —— —— —— —— —— mules you
    Scarcly had the vile words left his lips when—

"Penrod!"

It was his mother's voice, calling from the back porch.

Simultaneously, the noon whistles began to blow, far and
near; and the romancer in the sawdust-box, summoned prosa-
ically from steep mountain passes above the clouds, paused
with stubby pencil halfway from lip to knee. His eyes were
shining: there was a rapt sweetness in his gaze. As he wrote,
his burden had grown lighter; thoughts of Mrs. Lora Rewbush had almost left him; and in particular as he récounted
(even by the chaste dash) the annoyed expressions of Mr.
Wilson, the wounded detective, and the silken moustached
mule-driver, he had felt mysteriously relieved concerning the
Child Sir Lancelot. Altogether he looked a better and a
brighter boy.

"Pen-*rod!*"

The rapt look faded slowly. He sighed, but moved not.

"Penrod! We're having lunch early just on your account,
so you'll have plenty of time to be dressed for the pageant.
Hurry!"

There was silence in Penrod's aerie.

"*Pen*-rod!"

Mrs. Schofield's voice sounded nearer, indicating a threatened approach. Penrod bestirred himself: he blew out the lantern, and shouted plaintively:

"Well, ain't I coming fast's I can?"

"Do hurry," returned the voice withdrawing; and the kitchen door could be heard to close.

Languidly, Penrod proceeded to set his house in order.

Replacing his manuscript and pencil in the cigar-box, he carefully buried the box in the sawdust, put the lantern and oil-can back in the soap-box, adjusted the elevator for the reception of Duke, and, in no uncertain tone, invited the devoted animal to enter.

Duke stretched himself amiably, affecting not to hear; and when this pretence became so obvious that even a dog could keep it up no longer, sat down in a corner, facing it, his back to his master, and his head perpendicular, nose upward, supported by the convergence of the two walls. This from a dog, is the last word, the *comble* of the immutable. Penrod commanded, stormed, tried gentleness; persuaded with honeyed words and pictured rewards. Duke's eyes looked backward; otherwise he moved not. Time elapsed. Penrod stooped to flattery, finally to insincere caresses; then, losing patience, spouted sudden threats. Duke remained immovable, frozen fast to his great gesture of implacable despair.

A footstep sounded on the threshold of the store-room.

"Penrod, come down from that box this instant!"

"Ma'am?"

"Are you up in that sawdust-box again?" As Mrs. Schofield had just heard her son's voice issue from the box, and also, as she knew he was there anyhow, her question must have been put for oratorical purposes only. "Because if you are," she continued promptly, "I'm going to ask your papa not to let you play there any—"

Penrod's forehead, his eyes, the tops of his ears, and most of his hair, became visible to her at the top of the box. "I ain't playing!" he said indignantly.

"Well, what *are* you doing?"

"Just coming down," he replied, in a grieved but patient tone.

"Then why don't you *come?*"

"I got Duke here. I got to get him *down*, haven't I? You don't suppose I want to leave a poor dog in here to starve, do you?"

"Well, hand him down over the side to me. Let me—"

"I'll get him down all right," said Penrod. "I got him up here, and I guess I can get him down!"

"Well then, *do* it!"

"I will if you'll let me alone. If you'll go on back to the house I promise to be there inside of two minutes. Honest!"

He put extreme urgency into this, and his mother turned toward the house. "If you're not there in two minutes—"

"I will be!"

After her departure, Penrod expended some finalities of eloquence upon Duke, then disgustedly gathered him up in his arms, dumped him into the basket and, shouting sternly, "All in for the ground floor—step back there, madam—all ready, Jim!" lowered dog and basket to the floor of the storeroom. Duke sprang out in tumultuous relief, and bestowed frantic affection upon his master as the latter slid down from the box.

Penrod dusted himself sketchily, experiencing a sense of satisfaction, dulled by the overhanging afternoon, perhaps, but perceptible: he had the feeling of one who has been true to a cause. The operation of the elevator was unsinful and, save for the shock to Duke's nervous system, it was harmless; but Penrod could not possibly have brought himself to exhibit it in the presence of his mother or any other grown person in the world. The reasons for secrecy were undefined; at least, Penrod did not define them.

Bert Leston Taylor

Bert Leston Taylor (1866–1921), was born in Goshen, Massachusetts, and got his academic learning at the College of the City of New York. He adorned several newspaper jobs in the East, married Rhode Islander Emma Bonner in 1895, and five years later took out for Chicago, where, as "B. L. T.," conductor of the "Line-o'-Type or Two" column in the Chicago TRIBUNE, *he provided innocent—sometimes acidulous—merriment for his contributors, his readers, and himself for nigh onto twenty years.* THE SO-CALLED HUMAN RACE *(1922), from which the following selections are reprinted, is a garland of Taylor's columns with a preface by Henry B. Fuller, author of* THE CLIFF-DWELLERS.

Gilded Fairy Tales

(Revised and regilded for comprehension of the children
of the very rich)

THE BABES IN THE WOOD

I

ONCE upon a time there dwelt in a small but very expensive cottage on the outskirts of a pine forest a gentleman with his wife and two children. It was a beautiful estate and the neighborhood was the very best. Nobody for miles around was worth less than five million dollars.

One night the gentleman tapped at his wife's boudoir, and receiving permission to enter, he said: "Pauline, I have been thinking about our children. I overheard the governess say to-day that they are really bright and interesting, and as yet unspoiled. Perhaps if they had a fair chance they might amount to something."

"Reginald," replied his wife, "you are growing morbid about those children. You will be asking to see them next." She shrugged her gleaming shoulders, and rang for the maid to let down her hair.

"Remember our own youth and shudder, Pauline," said the gentleman. "It's a shame to allow Percival and Melisande to grow up in this atmosphere."

"Well," said the lady petulantly, "what do you suggest?"

"I think it would be wise and humane to abandon them. The butler or the chauffeur can take them into the wood and lose them and some peasant may find and adopt them, and they may grow up to be worthy citizens. At least it is worth trying."

"Do as you please," said the lady. "The children are a collaboration; they are as much yours as mine."

This conversation was overheard by little Melisande, who had stolen down from her little boudoir in her gold-flowered nightdress for a peep at her mamma, whom she had not seen for a long, long time. The poor child was dreadfully frightened, and crept upstairs weeping to her brother.

"Pooh!" said Percival, who was a brave little chap. "We shall find our way out of the wood, never fear. Give me your pearl necklace, Melisande."

The wondering child dried her eyes and fetched the necklace, and Percival stripped off the pearls and put them in the pocket of his velvet jacket. "They can't lose us, sis," said he.

II

In the morning the butler took the children a long, long way into the woods, pretending that he had discovered a diamond mine; and, bidding them stand in a certain place till he called, he went away and did not return. Melisande began to weep, as usual, but Percival only laughed, for he had dropped a pearl every little way as they entered the wood, and the children found their way home without the least difficulty. Their father was vexed by their cleverness, but their mamma smiled.

"It's fate, Reginald," she remarked. "They were born for the smart set, and they may as well fulfill their destinies."

"Let us try once more," said the gentleman. "Give them another chance."

When the servant called the children the next morning Percival ran to get another pearl necklace, but the jewel cellar was locked, and the best he could do was to conceal a four-pound bunch of hot house grapes under his jacket. This time they were taken twice as far into the wood in search of the diamond mine; and alas! when the butler deserted them Percival found that the birds had eaten every grape he had dropped along the way. They were now really lost, and wandered all day without coming out anywhere, and at night they slept on a pile of leaves, which Percival said was much more like camping out than their summer in the Adirondacks. All next day they wandered, without seeing sign of a road or a chateau, and Melisande wept bitterly.

"I am so hungry," exclaimed the poor child. "If we could only get a few *marrons glacés* for breakfast!"

"I could eat a few macaroons myself," said Percival.

III

On the afternoon of the third day Percival and Melisande came to a strange little cottage fashioned of gingerbread, but as the children had never tasted anything so common as gingerbread they did not recognize it. However, the cottage felt soft and looked pretty good to eat, so Percival bit off a piece of the roof and declared it was fine. Melisande helped herself to the doorknob, and the children might have eaten half the cottage had not a witch who lived in it come out and frightened them away. The children ran as fast as their legs could work, for the witch looked exactly like their governess, who tried to make them learn to spell and do other disagreeable tasks.

Presently they came out on a road and saw a big red automobile belonging to nobody in particular. It was the most beautiful car imaginable. The hubs were set with pigeon blood rubies and the spokes with brilliants; the tires were set with garnets to prevent skidding, and the hood was inlaid with diamonds and emeralds. Even Percival and Melisande were impressed. One door stood invitingly open and the children sprang into the machine. They were accustomed to helping themselves to anything that took their fancy; they had inherited the instinct.

Percival turned on the gas. "Hang on to your hair, sis!" he cried, and he burnt up the road all the way home, capsizing the outfit in front of the mansion and wrecking the automobile.

Their mamma came slowly down the veranda steps with a strange gentleman by her side. "These are the children, Edward," she said picking them up, uninjured by the spill. "Children, this is your new papa."

The gentleman shook hands with them very pleasantly and said he hoped that he should be their papa long enough to get really acquainted with them. At which remark the lady smiled and tapped him with her fan.

And they lived happily, after their fashion, ever afterward.

LITTLE RED RIDING-HOOD

I

Once upon a time there was a little girl who was the prettiest creature imaginable. Her mother was excessively fond of her, and saw her as frequently as possible, sometimes as often as once a month. Her grandmother, who doted on her even more, had made for her in Paris a little red riding hood of velvet embroidered with pearl passementerie, which became the child so well that everybody in her set called her Little Red Riding-Hood.

One day her mother said to her: "Go, my dear, and see how your grandmother does, for I hear she has been ill with indigestion. Carry her this filet and this little pot of foie gras."

The grandmother lived in a secluded and exclusive part of the village, in a marble cottage situated in the midst of a wooded park. Little Red Riding-Hood got out of the motor when she came to the park, telling the chauffeur she would walk the rest of the way. She hardly passed the hedge when she met a Wolf.

"Whither are you going?" he asked, looking wistfully at her.

"I am going to see my grandmother, and carry her a filet and a little pot of foie gras from my mamma."

"Well," said the Wolf, "I'll go see her, too. I'll go this way and you go that, and we shall see who will be there first."

The Wolf ran off as fast as he could, and was first at the door of the marble cottage. The butler informed him that Madame was not at home, but he sprang through the door, knocking the servant over, and ran upstairs to Madame's boudoir.

"Who's there? asked the grandmother, when the Wolf tapped at the door.

"Your grandchild, Little Red Riding-Hood," replied the Wolf, counterfeiting the child's voice, "who has brought you a filet and a little pot of foie gras."

II

The good grandmother, who had eaten nothing for two days except a mallard, with a pint of champagne, cried out hungrily, "Come in, my dear."

The Wolf ran in, and, falling upon the old lady, ate her up in a hurry, for he had not tasted food for a whole week. He then got into the bed, and presently Little Red Riding-Hood tapped at the door.

The Wolf pitched his voice as high and unpleasant as he could and called out, "What is it, Hawkins?"

"It isn't Hawkins," replied Little Red Riding-Hood. "It is your grandchild, who has brought you a filet and a little pot of foie gras."

"Come in, my dear," responded the Wolf. And when the child entered he said: "Put the filet and the little pot of foie gras on the gold tabouret, and come and lie down with me."

Little Red Riding-Hood did not think it good form to go

to bed so very, very late in the morning, but as she expected
to inherit her grandmother's millions she obediently took off
her gold-flowered frock, and her pretty silk petticoat, and her
dear little diamond stomacher, and got into bed, where, amazed
at the change for the better in her grandmother's appearance,
she said to her:

"Grandmother, how thin your arms have got!"

"I have been dieting, my dear."

"Grandmother, how thin your legs have got!"

"The doctor makes me walk every day."

"Grandmother, how quiet you are!"

"This isn't a symphony concert hall, my dear."

"Grandmother, what has become of your diamond-filled
teeth?"

"These will do, my dear."

And saying these words the wicked Wolf fell upon Little
Red Riding-Hood and ate her all up.

The London Busman Story

I.—*As George Meredith might have related it*

"Stop!" she signalled.

The appeal was comprehensible, and the charioteer, as-
siduously obliging, fell to posture of checking none too volant
steeds.

You are to suppose her past meridian, nearer the twilight of
years, noteworthy rather for matter than manner; and her
visage, comparable to the beef of England's glory, well you
wot. This one's descent was mincing, hesitant, adumbrating
dread of disclosures—these expectedly ample, columnar, massive. The day was gusty, the breeze prankant; petticoats,

bandbox, umbrella were to be conciliated, managed if possible; no light task, you are to believe.

" 'Urry, marm!"

The busman's tone was patiently admonitory, dispassionate. A veteran in his calling, who had observed the ascending and descending of a myriad matrons, in playful gales.

" 'Urry, marm!"

The fellow was without illusions; he had reviewed more twinkling columns than a sergeant of drill. Indifference his note, leaning to ennui. He said so, bluntly, piquantly, in half a dozen memorable words fetching yawn for period.

The lady jerked an indignant exclamation, and completed, rosily precipitate, her passage to the pave.

II.—*As Henry James might have written it*

We, let me ask, what are we, the choicer of spirits as well as the more frugal if not the undeservedly impoverished, what, I ask, are we to do now that the hansom has disappeared, as they say, from the London streets and the taxicab so wonderfully yet extravagantly taken its place? Is there, indeed, else left for us than the homely but hallowed 'bus, as we abbreviatedly yet all so affectionately term it—the 'bus of one's earlier days, when London was new to the unjaded sensorium and "Europe" was so wonderfully, so beautifully dawning on one's so avid and sensitive consciousness?

And fate, which has left us the 'bus—but oh, in what scant and shabby measure!—has left us, too, the weather that so densely yet so congruously "goes with it"—the weather adequately enough denoted by the thick atmosphere, the slimy pavements, the omnipresent unfurled umbrella and the stout, elderly woman intent upon gaining, at cost of whatever risk or struggle, her place and portion among the moist miscellany to whom the dear old 'bus—But perhaps I have lost the thread of my sentence.

Ah, yes—that "stout, elderly woman"; so superabundant whether as a type or as an individual; so prone—or "liable"— to impinge tyrannously upon the consciousness of her fellow-traveller, and in no less a degree upon that of the public servant, who, from his place aloft, guides, as it is phrased, the destinies of the conveyance. It was, indeed, one of the most notable of these—a humble friend of my own—who had the fortune to make the acute, recorded, historic observation which, with the hearty, pungent, cursory brevity and point of his class and *métier*—the envy of the painstaking, voluminous analyst and artist of our period—But again I stray.

She was climbing up, or climbing down, perplexed equally, as I gather, by the management of her *parapluie* and of her— *enfin*, her petticoats. The candid anxiety of her round, underdone face, as she so wonderfully writhed to maintain the standard of pudicity dear—even vital—to the matron of the British Isles appealed—vividly, though mutely—to the forbearance that, seeing, would still seem *not* to see, her foot, her ankle, her *mollet*—as I early learned to say in Paris, where, however, so exigent a modesty is scarely . . . well, scarcely.

"Madam," the gracious fellow said in effect, "*ne vous gênez pas.*" Then he went on to assure her briefly that he was an elderly man; that he had "held the ribbons," as they phrase it, for several years; that many were the rainy days in London; that each of these placed numerous women—elderly or younger—in the same involuntary predicament as that from which she herself had suffered; and that so far as he personally was concerned he had long since ceased to take any extreme delight in the—*Bref*, he was charming; he renewed my fading belief—fading, as I had thought, disastrously but immitigably—in the capacity of the Anglo-Saxon for *esprit;* and I am glad indeed to have taken a line or so to record his *mot*.

III.—*As finally elucidated by Arnold Bennett*

Maria Wickwyre, of the Five Towns, emerged from muddy Bombazine Lane and stood in the rain and wind at Pie Corner, eighty-four yards from the door of St. Jude's chapel, in the Strand. She was in London! Yes, she was on that spot, she and none other. It might have been somewhere else; it might have been somebody else. But it wasn't. Wonderful! The miracle of Life overcame her.

She had arms. Two of them. They were big and round, like herself. One held a large parcel ("package" for the American edition); the other, an umbrella. She also had two legs. She stood on them. If they had been absent, or if they had weakened, she would have collapsed. But they held her up. Ah, the mysteries of existence! More than ever was she conscious of her firm strong underpinning. Maria waved her umbrella and her parcel and stopped a 'bus. The driver was elderly, wrinkled, weatherbeaten. Maria got in and rode six furlongs and some yards to Mooge Road, and then she stopped the 'bus to get out.

If she was conscious of her upper members and their charges, she was still more conscious of her lower ones. If she had her parcel and her umbrella to think about, she also had her stockings and petticoats to consider. The wind blew, the rain drizzled, the driver looked around, wondering why Maria didn't get out and have done with it.

"If he should see them!" she gasped. (You know what she meant by "them.") Her round, broad face mutely implored the 'busman to look the other way.

He wearily closed his eyes. He had been rumbling through the Strand for thirty years. "Lor', mum," he said, "legs ain't no treat to me!"

Maria collapsed, after all, and took the 4:29 for home that same afternoon.

Mr. Dubbe's Program Study Class

(Accompanying the Symphony Orchestra Concerts)

Reported by Miss Poeta Pants

I—THE NEAPOLITAN SIXTH

MR. CRITICUS FLUB-DUBBE's program study class began the season yesterday afternoon with every member present and keenly attentive. After a preparatory sketch of old Italian music, Mr. Dubbe told us about the Neapolitan Sixth, which, he said, had exercised so strong an influence on music that, if Naples had never done anything else, this alone would have insured to the city fame in history.

"The Neapolitan Sixth," said Mr. Dubbe, "is so called because the composers of the Neapolitan school of opera were the first to introduce it freely. D. and A. Scarlatti were at the head of the school and were well-known musicians. Bach, who was not so well known, also used this sixth."

"Which used it first?" asked Mrs. Givu A. Payne.

"Bach, of course," replied Mr. Dubbe. "Bach used everything first."

"Dear old Bach!" exclaimed Miss Georgiana Gush.

"The Neapolitan Sixth," continued Mr. Dubbe, "is usually found in the first inversion; hence the name, the sixth indicating the first inversion of the chord."

"How clever!" said Mrs. Gottem-Allbeat.

"It is an altered chord, the altered chord being the supertonic. The real character of the chord is submediant of the subdominant key; that is, it is a major chord, and the use of such a major chord in the solemn minor tonalities is indicative of the superficialities of the Italian school—a desire for a change from the strict polyphonic music of the times. Even the stern Bach was influenced."

"The Italians are so frivolous," said Mrs. Boru-Stiffe.

"A reign of frivolity ensued," went on Mr. Dubbe. "Not only was Italian music influenced by this sixth, but Italian art, architecture, sculpture, even material products. Take, for example, Neapolitan ice-cream. Observe the influence of the sixth. The cream is made in three color tones—the vanilla being the subdominant, as the chord is of subdominant character; the strawberry being the submediant, and the restful green the lowered supertonic or altered tone."

"What is the pineapple ice?" asked Miss Gay Votte.

"The pineapple ice is the twelfth overtone," replied Mr. Dubbe.

"There doesn't seem to be anything that Mr. Dubbe doesn't know," whispered Mrs. Fuller-Prunes to me with a smile.

I should say there wasn't!

After the lecture we had a lovely hand-made luncheon. Miss Ellenborough presided at the doughnuts and Mrs. G. Clef poured. It was such a helpful hour.

II

"You remember," said Mr. Dubbe, "that Herr Weidig, in his lecture on the wood winds, gave a double bassoon illustration from Brahms' 'Chorale of St. Anthony,' which you are to hear to-day. But Herr Weidig neglected to mention the most interesting point in the illustration—that the abysmal-toned double bassoon calls attention to the devil-possessed swine, St. Anthony being the patron saint of swine-herds. I want you to listen carefully to this swine motive. It is really extraordinary." Mr. Dubbe wrote the motive on the blackboard and then played it on his double bassoon, which, he said, is one of the very few in this country.

"The bassoon," said Mr. Dubbe, "was Beethoven's favorite

instrument. I go further than Beethoven in preferring the double bassoon. Among my unpublished manuscripts are several compositions for this instrument, and my concerto for two double bassoons is now in the hands of a Berlin publisher.

"But to recur to the Brahms chorale. You should know that it makes the second best variations in existence. The best are in the Heroic Symphony. The third best are Dvorák's in C major."

"C. Major—that's the man who wrote *Dorothy Vernon*," giggled Miss Vera Cilly.

"I am not discussing ragtime variations," said Mr. Dubbe, severely.

"Not knocking anybody," whispered Miss Gay Votte.

"Another interesting point in connection with this week's program," resumed Mr. Dubbe, "is the river motive in Smetana's symphonic poem, 'The Moldau.' Three flutes represent (loosely speaking; for, as I have often told you, music cannot represent everything) the rippling of the Moldau, a tributary of the Danube. If the composer had had a larger river in mind he would have used nine flutes. If this composition of Smetana's seems rather unmusical, allowance must be made for him, as the poor man was deaf and couldn't hear how bad his own music was."

"Wasn't Beethoven deaf?" asked Miss Sara Band.

"Only his physical ears were affected," replied Mr. Dubbe. "Smetana's soul ears were also deaf."

At the close of the lecture Miss Ellenborough gave us a surprise in the way of raised doughnuts made in the form of a G clef. Mrs. Gottem-Allbeat poured.

III

There was an ominous flash in Dr. Dubbe's eye when he arose to address the class. "We have this week," he began, "a program barbarous enough to suit the lovers of ultra-modern music. There is Saint-Saëns' overture 'Les Barbares,' to begin with. This is as barbaric as a Frenchman can get, and is interesting chiefly as a study of how not to use the trumpets. But for sheer barbarity commend me to Hausegger's 'Barbarossa.' Here we find the apotheosis of modern exaggeration. Hausegger strove to make up for unimportant themes by a profuse use of instruments. Only one theme, which occurs in the third movement, is of any account, and that is an imitation of an old German chorale. In this most monotonously muted of tone-poems the composer forgot to mute one instrument—his pen."

"My! but Dr. Dubbe is knocking to-day," whispered Miss Sara Band.

"The thing is in C major and opens with a C major chord," continued Dr. Dubbe. "That is the end of the C major; it never returns to that key. This is modern music. Take the third movement. It opens with a screeching barbershop chord. A little later ensues a prize fight between two themes, which continues till one of them is knocked out. In this edifying composition, also, snare drum sticks are used on the kettle drums. More modern music. Bah!"

I have never seen Dr. Dubbe so irritated.

"Let us turn to something more cheerful," resumed Dr. Dubbe; and seating himself at the piano he played the Schubert C minor impromptu. "On the second page," he said, "where the key becomes A flat major, occurs a harmony which looks and sounds like a foreign chord. Treated harmonically it is a second dominant formation, and should read C flat, D natural, A flat, diminished seventh of the key of the dominant. Schubert does not, however, use it harmonically, otherwise the B natural would read C flat. These notes are enharmonic because, though different, they sound the same."

"How clear!" exclaimed Miss Gay Votte.

"But Schubert, instead of progressing harmonically, goes directly back into the tonic of A flat major."

"How careless of him!" said Mrs. Givu A. Payne.

"Schubert uses it in its natural position. If the enharmonic C flat were used the chord would then be in its third inversion. Each diminished seventh harmony may resolve in sixteen different ways."

"Mercy!" murmured Mrs. Fuller-Prunes. "How much there is to know."

Dr. Dubbe passed his hand across his brow as if wearied. "I shall never cease to regret," he said, "that Schubert did not write C flat. It would have been so much clearer."

After the lecture Miss Ellenborough gave us another surprise—doughnuts made in the shape of flats. Dr. Dubbe ate five, saying that D flat major was his favorite key.

I rode down in the elevator with him and he repeated his remark that Schubert had unnecessarily bemuddled the chord.

"I am sure you made it very plain," I said. "We all understand it now."

"Do you, indeed?" he replied. "That's more than I do."

Of course he was jesting. He understands everything.

IV

Dr. Dubbe was in his element yesterday. The trinity of B's —Bach, Beethoven, and Brahms—or, as Dr. Dubbe put it, the "trinity of logicians," was much to his taste: a truly Gothic program.

"But what a contrast is the second half," said Dr. Dubbe. "In the first we have the Kings of absolute music. In his youth Beethoven strayed from the path (for even he must sow his musical wild oats), but in his maturer years he produced no music that was not absolute. But in the second half we have Berlioz and program music."

"I thought program music was music suitable for programs," said Mrs. Givu A. Payne.

"Berlioz," continued Dr. Dubbe, "instituted the 'musical

reform' in Germany—the new German school of Liszt and Wagner. Berlioz's music is all on the surface, while Brahms' music sounds the depths. He uses the contra-bassoon in about all of his orchestral compositions (you will hear it to-day), and most of his piano works take the last A on the piano. If his bass seems at times muddy it is because he goes so deep that he stirs up the bottom."

"How clear!" exclaimed Miss Gay Votte.

"Take measure sixty-five in Berlioz's 'Dance of the Sylphs,'" said Dr. Dubbe. "The spirits hover over Faust, who has fallen asleep. The 'cellos are sawing away drowsily on their pedal point D (probably in sympathy with Faust), and what sounds like Herr Thomas tuning the orchestra is the lone A of the fifth. The absent third represents the sleep of Faust. This is a trick common to the new school. Wagner uses it in 'Siegfried,' in the close of the Tarnhelm motive, to illustrate the vanishing properties of the cap. In measure fifty-seven of the Ballet you will find a chord of the augmented five-six, a harmony built on the first inversion of the diminished seventh of the key of the dominant, with lowered bass tone, and which instance resolves into the dominant triad. Others claim that this harmony is a dominant ninth with root omitted and lowered fifth."

"It has always seemed so to me," said Mrs. Fuller-Prunes. But I don't believe she knows a thing about it.

"I think it's all awfully cute," said Miss Georgiana Gush.

"The harmony," resumed Dr. Dubbe, frowning, "really sounds like a dominant seventh, and may be changed enharmonically into a dominant seventh and resolve into the Neapolitan sixth. This is all clear to you, I suppose?"

"Oh, yes," we all replied.

Dr. Dubbe then analyzed and played for us Brahms' Symphony, after which Miss Ellenborough first served doughnuts made in the shape of a Gothic B. We all had to eat them—one for Bach, one for Beethoven, and one for Brahms.

V

Dr. Dubbe did not appear enthusiastic over this week's program. I guess because there was no Bach or Brahms on it. But we enjoyed his lecture just the same.

"Raff was the Raphael of music," said Dr. Dubbe. "He was handicapped by a superabundnce of ideas, but, unlike Raphael, he did not constantly repeat himself. This week we will have a look at his Fifth Symphony, entitled 'Lenore.' "

"Oh!" exclaimed Miss Georgiana Gush, "that's the one the hero of 'The First Violin' was always whistling."

"As you all know," said Dr. Dubbe, "this symphony is based on Bürger's well-known ballad of 'Lenore,' but as only the last movement is concerned with the actual ballad, I will confine my remarks mainly to that. I wish, however, to cal your attention to a curious harmony in the first movement Upon the return of the first theme, the trombones break in upon a dominant B major harmony with what is apparently a dominant C major harmony, D, F, and B. But the chords are actually enharmonic of D, E sharp and B. This is a dominant harmony in F sharp. Listen for these trombone chords and pay special attention to the E sharp—a tone that is extremely characteristic of Raff."

"I think I have read somewhere," said Mrs. Givu A. Payne "that Raff was exceedingly fond of E sharp."

"He was," said Dr. Dubbe. "He often said he didn't see how he could get along without it. But to resume:

"The fourth movement opens with Lenore's lamentation over her absent lover and her quarrel with her mother—the oboe being the girl and the bassoon her parent. Lenore foolishly curses her fate (tympani and triangle), and from that moment is lost. There is a knock at the door and her dead lover appears with a horse and suggests something in the nature of an elopement. Not knowing he is dead, Lenore acquiesces, and away they go (trumpets, flutes and clarinets)

" 'T is a wild and fearful night. Rack scuds across the moon's wan face (violas and second violins). Hanged men rattle in their chains upon the wayside gibbets (triangle and piccolo). But on, on, on go the lovers, one dead and the other nearly so.

"At last they reach the grave in the church-yard, and death claims the lost Lenore ('cellos and bass viols *pizzicato*). For a conclusion there is a coda founded on the line in the ballad, '*Gott sei der Seele gnädig.*' It is very sad."

Dr. Dubbe seemed much affected by the sad tale, and many of us had to wipe tears away. But Miss Ellenborough came to our rescue with some lovely doughnuts made in the shape of a true lovers' knot. These, with the tea, quite restored us.

VI

There really wasn't any study class this week—that is, Dr. Dubbe did not appear. While the class waited for him and wondered if he were ill a messenger brought me the following note:

> My Dear Poeta: Kindly inform the class that there will be no lecture this week. I cannot stand for such a trivial program as Herr Thomas has prepared.
>
> C. F. D.

"He might have told us sooner," said Miss Georgiana Gush.

"Why, yes; he knew last week what the next program would be," said Mrs. Faran-Dole.

"The eccentricity of genius, my dear," remarked Mrs. Gottem-Allbeat. "Genius is not tied down by rules of conduct of any sort."

"Well," said Mrs. Givu A. Payne, "I don't blame him for not wanting to analyze this week's program. There isn't a bit of Bach or Brahms on it."

"Ladies," said Miss Ellenborough, coming forward with a

gentleman who had just arrived, "let me introduce Mr. Booth Tarkington, of Indiana. Mr. Tarkington came up to attend the lecture, but as Dr. Dubbe will not be here Mr. Tarkington had kindly consented to give us a doughnut recital, so to speak."

"Oh, how lovely!" we all exclaimed.

"Mr. Tarkington," added Miss Ellenborough, "is well known as the author of the Beaucaire doughnut, the pride of Indiana doughnutdom."

Saying which Miss Ellenborough removed the screen that conceals her work table and Mr. Tarkington, in an incredibly short time, produced a batch of Beaucaires. They were really excellent, and we didn't leave a single one. Mr. Everham Chumpleigh Keats poured.

After tea we all adjourned to the concert, which we enjoyed immensely, in spite of the absence of Bach and Brahms. Not knocking Dr. Dubbe.

James Thurber

James Thurber (1894–   ) was born in Columbus, Ohio, in a family whose extraordinary and continuous predicaments enliven MY LIFE AND HARD TIMES *(1933), from which the following sketches are reprinted. As might be guessed from "University Days," Thurber attended Ohio State University. Bad vision, which has plagued him since he lost the sight of one eye in a boyhood accident involving a bow and arrow, kept him from active duty in World War I, but he served as a code clerk for the State Department in Washington. He was a reporter on the Columbus* DISPATCH *for a time, then went to Paris, where he joined the staff of the Paris edition of the Chicago* TRIBUNE. *Coming back in 1926, he met E. B. White of the* NEW YORKER— *the beginning of a long relationship with the man and the magazine, an early result of which was a collaboration,* IS SEX NECESSARY? *(1929). Though Thurber's disarmingly simple drawings complement his prose and vice versa, each can be enjoyed without the other.* MY LIFE AND HARD TIMES *is comparatively uncomplicated Thurber. Later books, such as* THE MIDDLE-AGED MAN ON THE FLYING TRAPEZE *(1935) and* LET YOUR MIND ALONE *(1937) are apt to induce one to concur with Malcolm Cowley when he says: "Entering Thurber's middle-class world is like wandering into a psychiatric ward and not being quite sure whether you are a visitor or an inmate. The author himself bustles around in a white jacket, but sometimes he stops to say in a pleasant, matter-of-fact voice, 'You know, they don't suspect. They think I'm a doctor.'"*

The Day the Dam Broke

MY MEMORIES of what my family and I went through during the 1913 flood in Ohio I would gladly forget. And yet neither the hardships we endured nor the turmoil and confusion we experienced can alter my feeling toward my native state and city. I am having a fine time now and wish Columbus were here, but if anyone ever wished a city was in hell it was during that frightful and perilous afternoon in 1913 when the dam broke, or, to be more exact, when everybody in town thought that the dam broke. We were both ennobled and demoralized by the experience. Grandfather especially rose to magnificent heights which can never lose their splendor for me, even though his reactions to the flood were based upon a profound misconception; namely, that Nathan Bedford Forrest's cavalry was the menace we were called upon to face. The only possible means of escape for us was to flee the house, a step which grandfather sternly forbade, brandishing his old army sabre in his hand. "Let the sons —— —— come!" he roared. Meanwhile hundreds of people were streaming by our house in wild panic, screaming "Go east! Go east!" We had to stun grandfather with the ironing board. Impeded as we were by the inert form of the old gentleman—he was taller than six feet and weighed almost a hundred and seventy pounds--we were passed, in the first half-mile, by practically everybody else in the city. Had grandfather not come to, at the corner of Parsons Avenue and Town Street, we would unquestionably have been overtaken and engulfed by the roaring waters— that is, if there had *been* any roaring waters. Later, when the panic had died down and people had gone rather sheepishly back to their homes and their offices, minimizing the distances they had run and offering various reasons for running, city engineers pointed out that even if the dam had broken, the water level would not have risen more than two additional inches in the West Side. The West Side was, at the time of the dam scare, under thirty feet of water—as, indeed, were all Ohio river towns during the great spring flood of twenty years ago. The East Side (where we lived and where all the running occurred) had never been in any danger at all. Only a rise of some ninety-five feet could have caused the flood waters to flow over High Street—the thoroughfare that divided the east side of town from the west—and engulf the East Side.

The fact that we were all as safe as kittens under a cook-stove did not, however, assuage in the least the fine despair and the grotesque desperation which seized upon the residents of the East Side when the cry spread like a grass fire that the dam had given way. Some of the most dignified, staid, cynical, and clearthinking men in town abandoned their wives, stenog-raphers, homes, and offices and ran east. There are few alarms in the world more terrifying than "The dam has broken!" There are few persons capable of stopping to reason when that clarion cry strikes upon their ears, even persons who live in towns no nearer than five hundred miles to a dam.

The Columbus, Ohio, broken-dam rumor began, as I re-call it, about noon of March 12, 1913. High Street, the main canyon of trade, was loud with the placid hum of business and the buzzing of placid businessmen arguing, computing, wheedling, offering, refusing, compromising. Darius Con-ningway, one of the foremost corporation lawyers in the Mid-dle-West, was telling the Public Utilities Commission in the language of Julius Caesar that they might as well try to move the Northern star as to move him. Other men were making their little boasts and their little gestures. Suddenly some-body began to run. It may be that he had simply remembered, all of a moment, an engagement to meet his wife, for which he was now frightfully late. Whatever it was, he ran east on Broad Street (probably toward the Maramor Restaurant, a favorite place for a man to meet his wife). Somebody else began to run, perhaps a newsboy in high spirits. Another man, a portly gentleman of affairs, broke into a trot. Inside of ten minutes, everybody on High Street, from the Union Depot to the Courthouse was running. A loud mumble gradually crystallized into the dread word "dam." "The dam has broke!" The fear was put into words by a little old lady in an electric, or by a traffic cop, or by a small boy: nobody knows who, nor does it now really matter. Two thousand people were abruptly in full flight. "Go east!," was the cry that arose—east away from the river, east to safety. "Go east! Go east! Go east!"

Black streams of people flowed eastward down all the streets leading in that direction; these streams, whose headwaters were in the drygoods stores, office buildings, harness shops, movie theatres, were fed by trickles of housewives, children, cripples, servants, dogs, and cats, slipping out of the houses past which the main streams flowed, shouting and screaming. People ran out leaving fires burning and food cooking and doors wide open. I remember, however, that my mother turned out all the fires and that she took with her a dozen eggs and two loaves of bread. It was her plan to make Memorial Hall, just two blocks away, and take refuge somewhere in the top of it, in one of the dusty rooms where war veterans met and where old battle flags and stage scenery were stored. But the seething throngs, shouting "Go east!" drew her along and the rest of us with her. When grandfather regained full consciousness, at Parsons Avenue, he turned upon the retreating mob like a vengeful prophet and exhorted the men to form ranks and stand off the Rebel dogs, but at length he, too, got the idea that the dam had broken and, roaring "Go east!" in his powerful voice, he caught up in one arm a small child and in the other a slight clerkish man of perhaps forty-two and we slowly began to gain on those ahead of us.

A scattering of firemen, policemen, and army officers in dress uniforms—there had been a review at Fort Hayes, in the northern part of town—added color to the surging billows of people. "Go east!" cried a little child in a piping voice, as she ran past a porch on which drowsed a lieutenant-colonel of infantry. Used to quick decisions, trained to immediate obedience, the officer bounded off the porch and, running at full tilt, soon passed the child, bawling "Go east!" The two of them emptied rapidly the houses of the little street they were on. "What is it? What is it?" demanded a fat, waddling man who intercepted the colonel. The officer dropped behind and asked the little child what it was. "The dam has broke!" gasped the girl. "The dam has broke!" roared the colonel. "Go east! Go east! Go east!" He was soon leading, with the exhausted child in his arms, a fleeing company of three hundred persons who had gathered around him from livingrooms, shops, garages, backyards, and basements.

Nobody has ever been able to compute with any exactness how many people took part in the great rout of 1913, for the panic, which extended from the Winslow Bottling Works in the south end to Clintonville, six miles north, ended as abruptly as it began and the bobtail and ragtag and velvet-gowned groups of refugees melted away and slunk home, leaving the streets peaceful and deserted. The shouting, weeping, tangled evacuation of the city lasted not more than two hours in all. Some few people got as far east as Reynoldsburg, twelve miles away; fifty or more reached the Country Club, eight miles away; most of the others gave up, exhausted, or climbed trees in Franklin Park, four miles out. Order was restored and fear dispelled finally by means of militiamen riding about in motor lorries bawling through megaphones: "The dam has *not* broken!" At first this tended only to add to the confusion and increase the panic, for many stampeders thought the soldiers were bellowing "The dam has now broken!," thus setting an official seal of authentication on the calamity.

All the time, the sun shone quietly and there was nowhere any sign of oncoming waters. A visitor in an airplane, looking down on the straggling, agitated masses of people below, would have been hard put to it to divine a reason for the phenomenon. It must have inspired, in such an observer, a peculiar kind of terror, like the sight of the *Marie Celeste*, abandoned at sea, its galley fires peacefully burning, its tranquil decks bright in the sunlight.

An aunt of mine, Aunt Edith Taylor, was in a movie theatre on High Street when, over and above the sound of the piano in the pit (a W. S. Hart picture was being shown), there rose the steadily increasing tromp of running feet. Persistent shouts rose above the tromping. An elderly man, sitting near my aunt, mumbled something, got out of his seat, and went up the aisle at a dogtrot. This started everybody. In an instant the audience was jamming the aisles. "Fire!" shouted a woman who always expected to be burned up in a theatre; but now the shouts outside were louder and coherent. "The dam has broke!" cried somebody. "Go east!" screamed a small woman in front of my aunt. And east they went, pushing and shoving and clawing, knocking women and children down, emerging finally into the street, torn and sprawling. Inside the theatre, Bill Hart was calmly calling some desperado's bluff and the brave girl at the piano played "Row, Row! Row!" loudly and then "In My Harem." Outside, men were streaming across the Statehouse yard, others were climbing trees, a woman managed to get up onto the "These Are My Jewels" statue, whose bronze figures of Sherman, Stanton, Grant, and Sheridan watched with cold unconcern the going to pieces of the capital city.

"I ran south to State Street, east on State to Third, south on Third to Town, and out east on Town," my Aunt Edith has written me. "A tall spare woman with grim eyes and a de-

termined chin ran past me down the middle of the street. I
was still uncertain as to what was the matter, in spite of all
the shouting. I drew up alongside the woman with some effort, for although she was in her late fifties, she had a beautiful easy running form and seemed to be in excellent condition.
'What is it?' I puffed. She gave me a quick glance and then
looked ahead again, stepping up her pace a trifle. 'Don't ask
me, ask God!' she said.

"When I reached Grant Avenue, I was so spent that Dr.
H. R. Mallory—you remember Dr. Mallory, the man with
the white beard who looks like Robert Browning?—well, Dr.
Mallory, whom I had drawn away from at the corner of Fifth
and Town, passed me. 'It's got us!' he shouted, and I felt sure
that whatever it was *did* have us, for you know what conviction Dr. Mallory's statements always carried. I didn't know at
the time what he meant, but I found out later. There was a
boy behind him on roller-skates, and Dr. Mallory mistook the
swishing of the skates for the sound of rushing water. He
eventually reached the Columbus School for Girls, at the corner of Parsons Avenue and Town Street, where he collapsed,
expecting the cold frothing waters of the Scioto to sweep him
into oblivion. The boy on the skates swirled past him and Dr.
Mallory realized for the first time what he had been running
from. Looking back up the street, he could see no signs of
water, but nevertheless, after resting a few minutes, he jogged
on east again. He caught up with me at Ohio Avenue, where
we rested together. I should say that about seven hundred
people passed us. A funny thing was that all of them were on
foot. Nobody seemed to have had the courage to stop and
start his car; but as I remember it, all cars had to be cranked
in those days, which is probably the reason."

The next day, the city went about its business as if nothing
had happened, but there was no joking. It was two years or
more before you dared treat the breaking of the dam lightly.
And even now, twenty years after, there are a few persons,

like Dr. Mallory, who will shut up like a clam if you mention the Afternoon of the Great Run.

University Days

I PASSED all the other courses that I took at my University, but I could never pass botany. This was because all botany students had to spend several hours a week in a laboratory looking through a microscope at plant cells, and I could never see through a microscope. I never once saw a cell through a microscope. This used to enrage my instructor. He would wander around the laboratory pleased with the progress all the students were making in drawing the involved and, so I am told, interesting structure of the flower cells, until he came to me. I would just be standing there. "I can't see anything," I would say. He would begin patiently enough, explaining how anybody can see through a microscope, but he would always end up in a fury, claiming that I could *too* see through a microscope but just pretended that I couldn't. "It takes away from the beauty of flowers anyway," I used to tell him. "We are not concerned with beauty in this course," he would say. "We are concerned solely with what I may call the *mechanics* of flars." "Well," I'd say, "I can't see anything." "Try it just once again," he'd say, and I would put my eye to the microscope and see nothing at all, except now and again a nebulous milky substance—a phenomenon of maladjustment. You were supposed to see a vivid, restless clock-work of sharply defined plant cells. "I see what looks like a lot of milk," I would tell him. This, he claimed, was the result of my not having adjusted the microscope properly, so he would readjust it for me, or rather, for himself. And I would look again and see milk.

I finally took a deferred pass, as they called it, and waited a year and tried again. (You had to pass one of the biological sciences or you couldn't graduate.) The professor had come back from vacation brown as a berry, bright-eyed, and eager to explain cell-structure again to his classes. "Well," he said to me, cheerily, when we met in the first laboratory hour of the semester, "we're going to see cells this time, aren't we?" "Yes, sir," I said. Students to the right of me and to the left of me and in front of me were seeing cells; what's more, they were quietly drawing pictures of them in their notebooks. Of course, I didn't see anything.

"We'll try it," the professor said to me, grimly, "with every adjustment of the microscope known to man. As God is my witness, I'll arrange this glass so that you see cells through it or I'll give up teaching. In twenty-two years of botany, I—" He cut off abruptly for he was beginning to quiver all over, like Lionel Barrymore, and he genuinely wished to hold onto his temper; his scenes with me had taken a great deal out of him.

So we tried it with every adjustment of the microscope known to man. With only one of them did I see anything but blackness of the familiar lacteal opacity, and that time I saw, to my pleasure and amazement, a variegated constellation of flecks, specks, and dots. These I hastily drew. The instructor, noting my activity, came back from an adjoining desk, a smile on his lips and his eyebrows high in hope. He looked at my cell drawing. "What's that?" he demanded, with a hint of a squeal in his voice. "That's what I saw," I said. "You didn't, you didn't, you *did*n't!" he screamed, losing control of his temper instantly, and he bent over and squinted into the microscope. His head snapped up. "That's your eye!" he shouted. "You've fixed the lens so it reflects! You've drawn your eye!"

Another course that I didn't like, but somehow managed to pass, was economics. I went to that class straight from the botany class, which didn't help me any in understanding either subject. I used to get them mixed up. But not as mixed up as another student in my economics class who came there direct from a physics laboratory. He was a tackle on the football team, named Bolenciecwcz. At that time Ohio State University had one of the best football teams in the country, and Bolenciecwcz was one of its outstanding stars. In order to be eligible to play it was necessary for him to keep up in his studies, a very difficult matter, for while he was not dumber than an ox he was not any smarter. Most of his professors were lenient and helped him along. None gave him more hints, in answering questions, or asked simpler ones than the economics professor, a thin, timid man named Bassum. One day when we were on the subject of transportation and distribution, it came Bolenciecwcz's turn to answer a question. "Name one means of transportation," the professor said to him. No light came into the big tackle's eyes. "Just any means of transportation," said the professor. Bolenciecwcz sat staring at him. "That is," pursued the professor, "any medium, agency, or method of going from one place to another." Bolenciecwcz had the look of a man who is being led into a trap. "You may choose among steam, horse-drawn, or electrically propelled vehicles," said the instructor. "I might suggest the one which we commonly take in making long journeys across land." There was a profound silence in which everybody stirred uneasily, including Bolenciecwcz and Mr. Bassum. Mr. Bassum abruptly broke this silence in an amazing manner. "Choo-choo-choo," he said, in a low voice, and turned instantly scarlet. He glanced appealingly around the room. All of us, of course, shared Mr. Bassum's desire that Bolenciecwcz should stay abreast of the class in economics, for the Illinois game, one of the hardest and most important of the season, was only a week off. "Toot, toot, too-tooooooot!" some student with a deep voice moaned, and we all looked encouragingly at Bolenciecwcz. Somebody else gave a fine

imitation of a locomotive letting off steam. Mr. Bassum himself rounded off the little show. "Ding, dong, ding, dong,"
he said, hopefully. Bolenciecwcz was staring at the floor now,
trying to think, his great brow furrowed, his huge hands
rubbing together, his face red.

"How did you come to college this year, Mr. Bolenciecwcz?" asked the professor. "*Chuf*fa chuffa, *chuf*fa
chuffa."

"M'father sent me," said the football player.

"What on?" asked Bassum.

"I git an 'lowance," said the tackle, in a low, husky voice,
obviously embarrassed.

"No, no," said Bassum. "Name a means of transportation.
What did you *ride* here on?"

"Train," said Bolenciecwcz.

"Quite right," said the professor. "Now, Mr. Nugent, will
you tell us—"

If I went through anguish in botany and economics—for
different reasons—gymnasium work was even worse. I don't
even like to think about it. They wouldn't let you play games
or join in the exercises with your glasses on and I couldn't see
with mine off. I bumped into professors, horizontal bars, agricultural students, and swinging iron rings. Not being able to
see, I could take it but I couldn't dish it out. Also, in order
to pass gymnasium (and you had to pass it to graduate) you
had to learn to swim if you didn't know how. I didn't like
the swimming pool, I didn't like swimming, and I didn't like
the swimming instructor, and after all these years I still don't.
I never swam but I passed my gym work anyway, by having
another student give my gymnasium number (978) and swim
across the pool in my place. He was a quiet, amiable blonde
youth, number 473, and he would have seen through a microscope for me if we could have got away with it, but we
couldn't get away with it. Another thing I didn't like about
gymnasium work was that they made you strip the day you
registered. It is impossible for me to be happy when I am

stripped and being asked a lot of questions. Still, I did better than a lanky agricultural student who was cross-examined just before I was. They asked each student what college he was in—that is, whether Arts, Engineering, Commerce, or Agriculture. "What college are you in?" the instructor snapped at the youth in front of me. "Ohio State University," he said promptly.

It wasn't that agricultural student but it was another a whole lot like him who decided to take up journalism, possibly on the ground that when farming went to hell he could fall back on newspaper work. He didn't realize, of course, that that would be very much like falling back full-length on a kit of carpenter's tools. Haskins didn't seem cut out for journalism, being too embarrassed to talk to anybody and unable to use a typewriter, but the editor of the college paper assigned him to the cow barns, the sheep house, the horse pavilion, and the animal husbandry department generally. This was a genuinely big "beat," for it took up five times as much ground and got ten times as great a legislative appropriation as the College of Liberal Arts. The agricultural student knew animals, but nevertheless his stories were dull and colorlessly written. He took all afternoon on each of them, on account of having to hunt for each letter on the typewriter. Once in a while he had to ask somebody to help him hunt. "C" and "L," in particular, were hard letters for him to find. His editor finally got pretty much annoyed at the farmer-journalist because his pieces were so uninteresting. "See here, Haskins," he snapped at him one day, "why is it we never have anything hot from you on the horse pavilion? Here we have two hundred head of horses on this campus—more than any other university in the Western Conference except Purdue —and yet you never get any real low down on them. Now shoot over to the horse barns and dig up something lively." Haskins shambled out and came back in about an hour; he said he had something. "Well, start it off snappily," said the editor. "Something people will read." Haskins set to work and in a couple of hours brought a sheet of typewritten paper to the desk; it was a two-hundred word story about some disease that had broken out among the horses. Its opening sentence was simple but arresting. It read: "Who has noticed the sores on the tops of the horses in the animal husbandry building?"

Ohio State was a land grant university and therefore two years of military drill was compulsory. We drilled with old Springfield rifles and studied the tactics of the Civil War even though the World War was going on at the time. At 11 o'clock each morning thousands of freshmen and sophomores used to deploy over the campus, moodily creeping up on the old chemistry building. It was good training for the kind of warfare that was waged at Shiloh but it had no connection with what was going on in Europe. Some people used to think there was German money behind it, but they didn't dare say so or they would have been thrown in jail as German spies. It was a period of muddy thought and marked, I believe, the decline of higher education in the Middle West.

As a soldier I was never any good at all. Most of the cadets were glumly indifferent soldiers, but I was no good at all. Once General Littlefield, who was commandant of the cadet corps, popped up in front of me during regimental drill and snapped, "You are the main trouble with this university!" I think he meant that my type was the main trouble with the university but he may have meant me individually. I was mediocre at drill, certainly—that is, until my senior year. By that time I had drilled longer than anybody else in the Western Conference, having failed at the military at the end of each preceding year so that I had to do it all over again. I was the only senior still in uniform. The uniform, which, when new, had made me look like an interurban railway conductor, now that it had become faded and too tight made me look like Bert Williams in his bellboy act. This had a definitely bad effect on my morale. Even so, I had become by sheer practise little short of wonderful at squad manoeuvres.

One day General Littlefield picked our company out of the whole regiment and tried to get it mixed up by putting it through one movement after another as fast as we could execute them: squads right, squads left, squads on right into line, squads right about, squads left front into line etc. In about three minutes one hundred and nine men were marching in one direction and I was marching away from them at an angle of forty degrees, all alone. "Company, halt!" shouted General Littlefield. "That man is the only man who has it right!" I was made a corporal for my achievement.

The next day General Littlefield summoned me to his office. He was swatting flies when I went in. I was silent and he was silent too, for a long time. I don't think he remembered me or why he had sent for me, but he didn't want to admit it. He swatted some more flies, keeping his eye on them narrowly before he let go with the swatter. "Button up your coat!" he snapped. Looking back on it now I can see that he meant me although he was looking at a fly, but I just stood there. Another fly came to rest on a paper in front of the general and began rubbing its hind legs together. The general lifted the swatter cautiously. I moved restlessly and the fly flew away. "You startled him!" barked General Littlefield, looking at me severely. I said I was sorry. "That won't help the situation!" snapped the general, with cold military logic. I didn't see what I could do except offer to chase some more flies toward his desk, but I didn't say anything. He stared out the window at the faraway figures of co-eds crossing the campus toward the library. Finally, he told me I could go. So I went. He either didn't know which cadet I was or else he forgot what he wanted to see me about. It may have been that he wished to apologize for having called me the main trouble with the university; or maybe he had decided to compliment me on my brilliant drilling of the day before and then at the last minute decided not to. I don't know. I don't think about it much any more.

Raymond Weeks

Raymond Weeks (1863–   ) was born in Tabor, Iowa. Graduating from Harvard with a Ph.D. degree, he taught Romance Languages at the University of Missouri (1895–1908) and at Columbia University (1908–1929), after which he retired to his farm near Manakin, Virginia. Weeks is one of the considerable group of writers first to achieve national prominence through the medium of John T. Frederick's magazine, MIDLAND. *Weeks' favorite domain is the Kingdom of Callaway, an appellation seriously applied by the citizens of that section of Missouri depicted by him. The kingdom seceded from the Union during the Civil War, and has always held itself a bit aloof from its neighbors. Aside from recapturing the past as it was lived in the Kingdom of Callaway, Weeks has striven to make the dread science of mathematics not only painless but amusing in his* THE BOYS' OWN ARITHMETIC *(1924). "The Fat Women of Boone," originally printed in* MIDLAND, *January, 1925, is reprinted here from* THE HOUND-TUNER OF CALLAWAY.

The Fat Women of Boone

BOONE COUNTY is located near the center of the State of Missouri. The inhabitants are polite, and all come from distinguished ancestors. The soil is rich, the crops are bountiful. No farm there is complete without its mintbed, and all are complete. For three continuous generations, this county possessed men, who, one after the other and at times several together, held the State record for consumption of whiskey. Its horses and hounds are famous. It produces more beautiful women and brave men than all the rest of the State combined, as the inhabitants will admit. It is there that one finds cooking that would be fabulous elsewhere, and it is there that the best stories in the country take place and are told without embellishment, exactly as they happened, generation after generation.

Way out in Jackson County people knew of the crown of laurel on the brow of Boone, and felt it an honor to entertain a traveler from that favored county, even if he was traveling rapidly westward and looking behind him. Judge, then, of their good fortune when Col. Jack Avidon of Boone arrived at Westport by stage, in search of his third cousin, Juliette Major, wife of Sam Major of Westport. And think of Linwood's good fortune: Sam Major had died the year before and Juliette had married Willie Simpson and was living on the Simpson farm, in the center of Linwood! To Linwood, then, came Col. Avidon and was not long in being shown to the Simpson farm, and if there didn't stand Juliette picking cherries!

"Are you Juliette?"

"Yes, sir. May I enquire who you are?"

"Suttenly. I'm your cousin Jack Avidon of Boone."

They had never seen each other before, but blood—Boone County blood—will tell: they rushed into each other's embrace. A quarter of an hour later, Col. Avidon was comfortably seated in a chair near the cherry tree, holding a dew gemmed glass of mint julep in his hand, while Juliette picked cherries and both of them talked at once.

An auspicious beginning of a visit which was to last a month. The good news spread through the country. Two farmers met:

"Hev you huhd the news? Col. Jack Avidon of Boone is visitin' his cousin Juliette Simpson. Let's go down Sundy evnin'."

They went, and many went, and they all returned more than once, so great was the interest and admiration aroused by the distinguished visitor. They saw a sad-faced man of uncertain age, thin, like all thoroughbreds, and of sallow skin. He wore a drooping mustache and the inherited goatee. His eyes, placed just a shade closer together than they might otherwise have been, had a far-away look of invincible melancholy. There were perpendicular wrinkles running down each cheek and disappearing in the shadow of his uncropped mustache. He had the high forehead of a Boone County idealist, and his thin hair fell over it carelessly. One felt him to be a man of distinguished honor and ability, crushed by some stroke of fortune.

And he was a strong man! He did not parade his private misfortunes or talk untidily about himself. It was not until a balmy night, a week after his arrival, that he told the story of his life to Juliette and Willie. They were seated in the open air about a table on which were the Jackson and Boone County essentials of good conversation. The story will be set down in his own words but with no attempt to render the melodious, soft speech of Col. Avidon.

"Juliette's great-great-grandparents and mine, Thomas and

Lucy Avidon, were born in Fauquier County, Virginia, and emigrated to Madison County, Kentucky, and thence we came in 1821 to Boone County, Missouri. I was born in Madison County, and that fact, as you will see, is at the base of my bad luck, though the blame really belongs to the fat women of Boone.

"Well, I inherited a fair fortune from my parents, and at twenty-seven I owned a flourishing dry-goods store at the county seat, Columbia, one of the best towns in the State. My health was fine, my habits regular—I never take more than a certain number of drinks a day (or rarely), and I eat, smoke and sleep with great regularity. I was a graduate of the University—whatever that means—I possessed a fair library, several farms, some fine horses and hounds. My success at cards was all that an honorable gentleman's could be. I attended every party that was given, summer or winter, day or night, and I knew and called by their Christian names all the girls and most of the women, not only of Boone, but of the Kingdom of Callaway—ever hear about the Kingdom of Callaway? No? I'll tell you sometime, but there's other fish to be fried to-night. As for my appearance, without being what you'd call handsome, I was interesting to look at. In fact, some scores of ladies have used stronger language than this in the not remote past, but all that's in the discard now. . . .

"I had two assets: my name was Jack, and I was a bachelor. Ever notice about the name Jack? My mother said to me once, when I was such a little boy that she thought I'd forget it: 'Little pet, I named you Jack so that all the girls would be crazy about you. You'll thank me some time!' And I did, though the time came when the charm didn't work any longer, as you'll see. . . . As for being a bachelor, well! it certainly helped business a pile! There was always a dozen or two girls thought I was in love with them. . . .

"My life since I was twenty—excuse me for talking about myself: you asked me to!—my life since I was twenty might be divided into three zones: the lean zone, the fat zone, and the zone of ruin. Let me explain.

"For nigh onto twenty years, I preferred lean women, then I realized I'd been a-wasting my time, and I preferred fat women. The fat zone lasted about seven years, and then began the zone of ruin, which is still running, and running hard.

"I glide rapidly over the lean zone. What is a lean woman? A woman who has missed being fat, a wisp of straw, a chicken that's all feathers, a promissory note that'll never be paid, a building that's all front, a shadow which never had a substance, a smile with nothing behind it, a deceit and a lie!

"As for fat women, I cannot speak of them with all the admiration I used to feel, for they have trampled me under foot, but, relatively speaking, how wonderful they are! how lordly and Jove-like in their gait! how sure and steadfast in appearance! how substantial in the promises they hold out! how alluring! how all-embracing! Instead of being small and mean, they are broad and rotund, succulent, frank, honest, generous, jolly, full of amiable surprises, the snares of nature! At least, such was my opinion for close to seven years—and even now, who knows? I may say all this in the presence of cousin Juliette, who's neither fat nor lean, though her face is set in the right direction. All the women of our family have been perfect.

"Well! all through the war, I was faithful to my dream of plump women. I returned at its close, to find that my business had been carefully managed and that I was richer than ever. It was time to think of carrying out a dear secret plan of mine, which was to marry and go back to Madison County, Kentucky, to live. You see, my mother, as long as she lived, talked about going 'back home' to live, and you know how a young man is influenced by the desire of a mother whom he idolizes. I had visited Madison several times, and was determined to reestablish the family in its Kentucky home. We had always taken the *Richmond Register*, the oldest newspaper published in Madison County, and I used to read every line in its columns, including advertisements.

"This paper was my undoing. I have cursed a thousand times an article which it published, two full columns and more, on the fat women of Madison. The writer, with every indication of truthfulness, gave the individual weights, with names and addresses, of fifteen women of Madison, whose united avoirdupois was 3,165 pounds, or an average of 211 pounds. This was formidable. The writer claimed the record for the entire United States.

"After finishing the article, I passed my hand over my brow: in Moses' name, was Boone going to sit still under this affront? With the paper in my hand, I ran out of the store and accosted five or six of the principal citizens. I proposed an immediate campaign, a census of heavy females, but, to my surprise, the proposition left them cold. Some said: 'No use, Jack, we could never beat that record.' 'Not beat that record?' I cried, and my latent admiration for fat women lent force to my cry. 'Not beat that record? Of course we can beat it! In the matter of fat women, we can defy the world!' Then one man said: 'I don't believe in courting disaster. Even supposing that we have the goods, they wouldn't let themselves be weighed.' 'Not let themselves be weighed? They *love* to be weighed! I have them trained to eat out of my hand! You ought to see one of them enter my store and go tripping up to the scales and smile when I weigh her! I tell you, I've made a study of these fat women. They're as docile as pet ducks, and as for avoirdupois, I want to show you some figures—' and I drew out pencil and pad, but those fellows only went away laughing—the cowards! They did not have an ounce of patriotism! Such weaklings are the ruin of a community and ought to be put in the pillory.

"What was I to do? For one thing, I decided to keep my own counsel—to keep my own counsel and bide my time. I made no further mention of the article in the *Richmond Register* and locked the paper up in my desk.

"In the course of the next six months, all the fat women of Boone, except two, Carry Trevillian and Bonnie Phillips, who were good for 440 pounds between them, came into my store, and I got them all! It was lovely to see them trip toward the scales the first thing, while I came bustling up: 'Morning, Miss Nancy! I'll bet you a box of candy that you've lost five pounds since you was here last!' And then I weighed her, taking lots of time to prolong her pleasure, and she stood there on the scales, smiling and sort of spreading out her feathers, and of course she won the bet!

"I was determined to add one important detail which the chap back in Madison had omitted—the age of the contestants. Not an easy matter in some cases, though I usually succeeded, something like this: 'How old are you, Miss Irene? Twenty-eight?' 'Go 'way, Col. Jack! You know I'm only twenty-six!' In a few cases, I had to discover their ages by exterior means. Then it occurred to me that it would be a fine plan to publish portraits in the article I was preparing. Here I had no difficulty at all. You know that a woman is always glad to give her portrait to a man, especially one who received six wounds in defence of the Confederacy. Oh! I've forgot to mention one other detail I secured, and that was their measure 'round the waist line. Not so hard to get as you'd think. You see, I ordered from St. Louis two dozen extra-extra long belts of red leather two inches wide, with large, bright buckles. I kept these belts locked in a drawer of the store, and offered one as a present to each possible entry. The fat ladies of course were delighted. They purred like kittens while I put the belt on them. In this way I got their waist line. . . .

"Well! I'm prolonging this story beyond all reason! Pardon me, Willie, if I fill up my glass a third time—or is it a fourth? My article was at last finished. I had been corresponding with the editor of the *Richmond Register*, and he sure was keen on that article! It contained a scientific record of the fifteen entries finally selected by me. I have their names and all the details in a note-book. Let me give you a sample from memory. 'Flossie Jessup, maiden name Evans, age 31, address. Rocheport, Boone County, Missouri, girth 69½ inches, weight 223 pounds, 7 ounces.' As published, this record stood under Flossie's full-length portrait. Or this, of Maggie. Maggie was my pride—she led all the rest. Under her full length appeared her record: Maggie Marland, maiden name Richardson, age 35, address, Sturgeon, Boone County, Missouri, girth 74 inches, weight 267 pounds 3 ounces. The total avoirdupois of my contestants was 3,405 pounds and some ounces, an average of 227 pounds per, as against 3,165 pounds and an average of 211 pounds for Madison.

"My article was sworn to before Judge John DeWilton Robinson.

"I had ordered two hundred copies of my article, and when they arrived, I could hardly control myself with joy. Fool that I was, I was dancing on my own tombstone!

"My plans had been carefully formed. As soon as the papers came, I locked them up, then sent to all of the fifteen heavyweights an invitation for them and all their families: place, at my best farm, known as 'Blue Waters'; time, a week from next Saturday at 11 o'clock; if weather bad, then the following Saturday, etc., to satisfaction.

"If I'd stopped there, it wouldn't have been so bad, but those papers were burning me up with impatience. Why postpone the pleasure of the fat ladies? I asked myself. Why not let them know at once of the glory I'd brought them? I sent out my man on horseback with fifteen copies of the *Richmond Register*, each one nicely wrapped and addressed.

"The day arrived, and a perfect day it was. Ever pass a few days in Boone in late October? Wonderful! The air still soft, the trees a little bare, but all spangled with gold and crimson; the rich crops mostly gathered, except that here and there they hadn't been able to pick all the apples, persimmons without end; golden pumpkins in the fields; fat herds in the pastures. . . .

"I was proud of my farm, of its stables, horses, cows, sheep and hogs. Everything was in order. I had arranged for a big dinner—a real Boone County dinner, the sort our grandmothers talk about. I had hired four black women to help my servants in cooking and serving. Tables were set out of doors for seventy-five guests.

"Will you believe me? Not one guest appeared! From eleven o'clock to four, I walked up and down, champing my bit and looking at my watch every three minutes. What had happened? I counted on my fingers forty times to be sure there was no mistake about the date. What! could it be that I, Jack Avidon, had escaped death in the army a hundred times to see myself insulted in this manner? And the servants and hired help conversing in low tones and pitying me!

"I spent the night at 'Blue Waters,' and such a night! No sleep for me, but in the morning something was waiting for me—fifteen big red belts hanging scornfully on the riders of the worm fence out in front! Then I understood. . . .

"I drove back to town the next morning, trying to convince myself that nothing had happened. But it had. Do you know, I didn't sell five dollars' worth of stuff all day. By afternoon, the news got out, and more than a score of prominent citizens dropped in to condole with me and see a copy of the article. And if they didn't laugh right before me!

"While I was talking in the back of the store with my friend Major Rollins and two young men, R. B. Price and Jerry Dorsey—I was standing with my back to the door—just as I was repeating 'I never meant no harm,' I felt some danger coming from behind and saw a look of apprehension in the countenances of my friends, who were facing the door. Just as I was about to turn around—but I'd better pause to make a confession to you.

"I had included among the Fat Women of Boone Miss Millie McBride, though there were three or four heavier than her whom I had excluded. Please note that there was nothing dishonest in this. My monograph was not entitled 'The Fifteen Fattest Women of Boone,' but 'The Fat Women of Boone.' By including Millie, who was nineteen years of age and weighed a bare 204 pounds, I not only was conferring immortality on her, but I was holding in reserve, like a well-trained officer, my heavy squadrons, in case Madison came back at us. Do you see?

"But why Millie, you inquire. Simply because I had decided to marry her and retire to Madison County. . . .

"Now what do you suppose it was that I felt coming and that my frightened friends saw? It was Millie McBride! Before I could turn around and grab her arm, she had shaken down my neck and into my hair a bottle of greasy, foul smelling hair-oil. Of all things—hair oil on Jack Avidon! And could it be the purring voice which I had so admired that was saying:

" 'Never meant no harm! You leper! You bevel-edged alligator! You snipe! You varmint! You idiot!'

"She was actually beating me over the head. As I warded off some of her blows, I uttered the bitterest words in the world:

" 'Et tu, Brute!'

" 'Don't you call me no names!'

"She made a lunge to catch and strangle me instantly in her embrace. I escaped by dodging under her arm, leaped over the counter and rushed out the back door. My friends had already vanished, how or where I never knew. . . .

"What humiliation! What disaster! Millie McBride was the only one of the fifteen prize-winners to put foot in the store as long as I owned it, but they were all doing to me outside the store what she had done inside, only worse if anything. They were ruining my trade and my reputation. My business went down almost to nothing. I made a brave fight, but what was the use? I had to let my clerks go. Oh! the hours passed in that store, without as much as one customer opening the door! Those fifteen fat women, who had been purring kittens, had become ferocious rhinoceroses and were trampling me to pulp. After five months of heroic resistance, I sold out at a loss and retired from business.

"Since then, I have spent several months traveling. I went to Madison County, but resentment against me was too strong. Madison, like Boone, is closed to me forever. I visited a cousin in Doniphan County, Missouri, and he introduced me to the niece of his wife. She was low and fat and beautiful. Everything looked favorable on the surface, but, as an honest man, I felt obliged to make a confession about the fat women of Boone and to show her the article. Her manner changed, and, through a mutual friend, my cousin was asked to request me to cease my attentions. I came from there to Westport. You people have been mighty good to me, but I haven't seen what I want. It looks like a man of my age, with sixty thousand dollars in the bank, three farms and a house in town ought to be able to find a wife, but *I* can't, and it looks like 'good-night' to Jack."

"But, cousin Jack," said Juliette after a moment's silence, "you are hard to please! Fat women of charm and good birth don't grow on bushes."

"I'm done with fat women! Never again for me! The sight of a fat woman fills me with terror! No, I'm cured!"

"What sort of a wife do you want, Jack?"

"Well, she must be hand-picked, of good family, honest and generous, neither fat nor lean."

"Cousin Jack, do you know, I think I have in mind just the woman you want!"

"Is she fat?"

"No!"

"Lean?"

"No, just right—about like me, only prettier."

"I don't believe that, nor does Willie. Is she of good family?"

"None better hereabouts."

"A good house-keeper?"

"Fine!"

"Kind to servants?"

"Very."

"Is she a good listener?"

"To one who talks like you do! . . . Jack, the more I think of her, the more I see that she's made for you!"

"Tell me her given name."

"We call her Kennie—it's short for Kentucky."

"Where does she live, Juliette?"

Juliette pointed off into the night beyond the forest: "She lives in that direction. She will admire you for your courage and patriotism in that affair of the fat women of Boone, and for your six wounds in defence of the Confederacy. She's a noble heart, Jack! We more than like her—we love her!"

Long after the others had gone, Col. Jack Avidon, late of Boone, sat before his replenished glass, looking off into the night in the direction his cousin had indicated, and glancing from time to time at the splendid constellations above him, redressors, perhaps, of unmerited misfortune. . . . "Who knows? . . . Juliette is a good judge . . . Perhaps after all . . . Kennie . . ."

Will Wharton

Will Wharton (1908–   ) was born in Saint Louis, Missouri, and was educated at Christian Brothers College and Washington University. At the latter institution he contributed verse and prose to THE ELIOT *and* THE WASHINGTONIAN, *campus literary magazines. He was associate editor and business manager of* THE ANVIL, *and now edits the* HOUR GLASS, *house organ for a piston-ring manufacturing firm. "Bachelor Girl's Lament anent Inflation" and "Bird Lover" have not been previously published.*

Bachelor Girl's Lament anent Inflation

'Tis the voice of the maiden,
I hear her complain,
Sure, the city's no Aidenn
To quote poor Verlaine

And it rains in my heart as
It rains on the ville.
Sodden shoes fall apart as
Bill follows old bill

And the debits have swallowed
The credits, the while
Wage increases are followed,
O'ertaken a mile

By advances in prices
Till one is inclined
To indulge in old vices,
Be wickedly kind.

Oh, I've dreamed of a union
Approved by the church
But as June follows June and
I'm left in the lurch

I have learned from my mission
What everyone knows:
Many men proposition
But few will propose

For of pleasures connubious
Plus underpaid work

Is becoming more dubious
The maltreated clerk

And my nights are refulgent
With gentlemen swart
Who would cheaply indulge in
The lecherer's art,

Bleat of love's demolition
Midst moon, June and rose,
Grunt an old proposition—
But never propose!

Bird Lover

I love the peahen, modest bird
Of which the name is seldom heard.

She humbly picks pistachio nuts
While to and fro the peacock struts.

I don't see how she can endure
A life so hidden and obscure.

But maybe she can understand
Her feathers aren't in much demand

And though at fate she fumes and frets
She won't end up by decking hets.

I love to hear the parakeet
On rainy days sing tweet-tweet-tweet.

I'm over fond of gazing at
The ghostly vulture and the bat

Although they're not so sanitary
As is the twittering canary.

I like, though I have never met,
The stately African umbrette.

But I weep into my Scotch and sodo
When I think of the fate of the dodo.

Wendell Wilcox

Wendell Wilcox (1906–   ) was born in Albion, Michigan, but became a citizen of Chicago at the age of five. He was graduated from the University of Chicago in 1929. He says: "In my fourth year in college I became conscious of a passionate interest in writing. Six months after leaving college I did in actuality become a writer and have been one steadily ever since." His work has appeared in HARPER'S BAZAAR, *the* NEW YORKER, STORY, DECADE, MANUSCRIPT, *and other publications. A story of his was reprinted in the O. Henry Memorial Award stories for 1944. For his first novel,* EVERYTHING IS QUITE ALL RIGHT *(1945), Wilcox deliberately chose a commonplace theme—a love affair between a servant girl and her employer—about ordinary people living dull, uneventful lives, but his gift for illuminating the prosaic lends the book liveliness and strength. Gertrude Stein said of Wilcox in* EVERYBODY'S AUTOBIOGRAPHY, *contrasting him to slick and meretricious popular writers: "Wendell Wilcox is not in their tradition, he has a feeling for meaning that is not beyond what the words are saying and of course that does make more brilliant writing and that is what he is doing." "With Everything So Scarce" is published here for the first time.*

With Everything So Scarce

IN THE evenings when there was nothing else to do Evelyn Oakes and Mable Brockhurst would sit at the kitchen table and talk about the times.

"It's a relief to me," Mable would say. "I never really liked doing anything for a man. Cooking meals, washing dishes, getting up in the morning and all that rot." Being a war widow brought her nothing but pleasure and rest.

But Evelyn Oakes always talked about how hard the times were for women.

"I could be faithful forever," she would say, "even if I was to die of it." These sad words would make her pull her handkerchief so hard that she often tore it.

In fact she was getting very nervous so that sometimes she stayed home from work all day and just moped about the place, thinking of Edward Oakes who'd been gone over six months now, serving his country. Sometimes she thought a little of Karl Martin who had been her first husband and a little too about George Farley, her second, a man she had never really liked but who she had begun to feel would be better than nobody at all about a year after Karl had his truck accident.

Often she stood in the window watching people go by in the street, thinking about those days when Karl had gone and George had not yet come, because those days were so like the present ones.

When Edward's letters stopped coming she began staying home even oftener. She wrote the government about Edward but they wrote back and said they didn't know where he was any more, maybe he was lost.

"Don't worry," Mable said, "they're all the time getting lost. They turn up eventually on a raft listening to doves or sitting in bushes with black girls, according to the kind of temperament they have."

"I could be faithful for ten years," Evelyn said, "but it's pretty damn hard when you can't tell where they are or whether they're ever coming home or not. I think the government's pretty damn careless with those boys. How much do they think we girls can stand, anyhow?"

"Speak for yourself," Mable said. "I love standing it."

"If you'd go to work more it 'ud take your mind off it," Mable suggested, but it was no good. On bad days she didn't seem to be able to face that restaurant. She seemed to just relish moping.

She was moping by the window one afternoon when a man stopped in the street and looked up at her. She looked down into his face for a second and then she let the lace curtain fall between their glances.

"I think that man was interested in me," she told Mable. "I think he saw how sad and lonely I was looking and he wanted to help me out."

"Just how do you mean, help you out?" Mable asked.

"Nothing vulgar, Mable, I assure you. I could be faithful if this war took another ten years."

"Ha, ha, ha," Mable said in a coarse way. She was free of men and of all thought of love and she could be coarse and careless like this without any bitterness.

Evelyn stood in the window a great deal after that. She was careful to have her hair fixed and her face nicely painted. She held her handkerchief to her eyes. Three husbands, she thought, all gone, and the last one just wasted. It wasn't like a truck accident or being separated because of abuse. But she never saw the man who had looked up at her again.

One night on the way home from the movies Evelyn suddenly stopped under a tree and grabbed Mable's arm.

"The jig's up," she said in a hoarse, enigmatic voice.

"What on earth do you mean?"

"I mean . . . I mean if I knew just exactly when he was coming home, if he was coming at all, that is . . . well, if I did, I guess I could stand it."

"I guess what you mean is, the jig's just starting," Mable said coarsely.

"I wasn't cut out for this kind of a life. There are things you and the government neither one of you understand, Mable Brockhurst. You never felt any need for affection or the masculine presence, but God made me a warm type."

She bought herself a new dress, a new hat, and a new pair of shoes with very high heels that gave her a wonderful sway when she walked. She had her hair fixed all fresh and corn yellow and cut in a long page boy bob because she felt that together with the high heels it made her look a little taller and thinner. She had got quite broad and needed these little aids. Every night she and Mable went to the bars and drank beer.

"It kind of distracts me," she said.

"We hope so, good God," Mable replied.

But nothing happened. Nothing at all.

"I think my charm is broken," Evelyn told Mable.

"My opinion is, you're trying too hard," Mable said. "You're being just a little too seductive. Men like to do the catching."

"Maybe it's they can feel this atmosphere of grief I have about me," Evelyn said. She felt her sorrow had tainted her in some mysterious way that the boys could feel even if they might not be deep enough to grasp its meaning. "Still, some folks find a little tragedy interesting," she added. She was thinking, of course, of the man who had looked at her through the window.

"Oh, Evelyn," Mable said in disgust. She hated this kind of nonsense.

But when Evelyn took her bath she would often sit for half an hour on end thinking: oh, if only I could wash off this accursed sorrow. She really felt it was ruining her. She felt like an old spoiled apple.

One hot June morning she let down completely. She put on an old blue cotton dress and a pair of run down low heeled shoes that she had used to use to wait table in. An umbrella, she felt, would be too cumbersome for the lake shore. So she poked around in the closet 'til she found a big black straw hat that Mable had used for gardening years ago and for some reason had never thrown out. She took an unusually large lunch, one big enough to last all day.

The park along the drive was deserted. Beyond the white line of the rocks the lake was blue and motionless, the sky intensely blue and innocent of clouds. Evelyn stretched herself out under a bush. She covered her face with her hat and lay still. She listened to the sound of motors passing on the drive. Insects buzzed. Sweat welled up out of her skin. Ants began crawling, but, in a moment, she no longer noticed them; for, out of pure sorrow, she had fallen asleep.

At noon she woke and felt the need of movement. She crossed the drive, and finding a copse of young willows sat herself down on a rock in the midst of them. Her hat brim just barely reached the surface of the little trees. She opened her newspaper and began to read.

Her approach to print was one of evocative meditation. She would glance down at the page and then away over the rocks, thinking of whatever line her eye had fallen on until the sky faded and she seemed to see for a while a confused and quivering projection of what the print intended. When the vision faded she would turn the sheet and gaze again. Suddenly, through one such vision of trampled hospital nurses lying dead in their own blood, she became aware of a face which she had been unconsciously watching for some time and which had been watching her.

She stirred on her rock, straightening her skirt, but it was too late, she realized, either for modesty or coquetry. It occurred to her at this moment that often the most careful work seems to have been done along the wrong lines entirely.

Sometimes you work and pray and work again and it all seems in vain, and then one day when the whole business has been dropped and maybe even forgotten, it all comes easily, making it seem as if all effort were useless, or else that the gift were given only to those who neither ask nor act.

When she opened her lunch bag and held it out to him, he came over to her quite naturally, like a horse to oats.

"These jelly sandwiches have got kind of soggy," she said, "but the lettuce in the peanut butter ones keeps 'em from soaking up."

He was a tall man and very narrow. His bones showed everywhere and his skin drooped under his paps and down around a slightly protuberant stomach. His gray eyes had an invisible look and there was dirt under his finger and toe nails. His hair had been hacked off rather irregularly. As he stood there in a pair of cotton bathing trunks that had faded from red to rose, accepting her proffered dainties, he put her in mind of John the Baptist in his leather loin cloth, eating bugs. She laughed a little, it seemed so likely that this one too had made his meal off insects.

Later, when he put on what was left of an old blue serge suit that was everywhere a little too small, and a collarless shirt and a dirty straw hat, his appearance did not seem too much altered.

Mable got home late that evening. She'd been to the movies and had stopped on the way back for a glass of beer. She tried to pretend that the sight of Mr. Quinn sitting with Evelyn at the kitchen table did not surprise her any, but her politeness was pretty cold. She manoeuvred Evelyn into the bathroom.

"Get that hood out of the house," she said.

"He's not a hoodlum," Evelyn answered.

"I know a hood when I see one. He'll murder us in our beds."

"I think you're wrong, Mable. I do wish you'd listen to me. He used to be a minister of the gospel."

Mable gave her a scornful look.

"Yes, truly. He's very strict. I know. I've been with him all day and he's been very strict all the time. Have you really looked at him good, Mable?"

"Yes, I have, and I think he has lice."

"Oh, Mable, he's really an awfully good man. Go take a good look at him."

She opened the door and shoved Mable into the hall.

Mr. Quinn was sitting with his feet on the window sill. His face had little or no expression, but he seemed to be looking a long way off, very deep into the sky, wondering. Evelyn squeezed Mable's arm. She wanted her to see in his attitude and gaze some favorable and sympathetic meaning.

All at once he turned his head and looked at Mable.

"You don't want me here," he said to her.

"I don't," she answered.

"But it's just as much my house as Mable's," Evelyn cried.

"It's got nothing to do with me at all," Mable said. "I can leave any time."

"You're afraid of me," Mr. Quinn said.

"I'm not afraid of anybody," Mable said.

Mr. Quinn stood up and reached for his hat and coat.

"I knew I shouldn't have come here," he said. "I shouldn't have eaten your sandwiches. I knew it was wrong." His voice was cold, but beneath the sound of it, hidden, there was something else, unhappiness and disappointment.

"Then why did you?" Mable answered with an equal coldness.

Evelyn began to cry.

Mr. Quinn put on his hat. He was looking at Mable.

"I don't know," he said. His stare was so cold that it

frightened her much more than any thought of hoods could have done. Her tongue seemed to fail her.

"Don't go," she said, but he didn't answer her, only stared a long time as if he thought that by merely watching her he could tell what he ought to do. Despite her fear she felt the situation was a little ridiculous. Mr. Quinn's red and wrinkled lip made her think of a turkey gobbler's wattles. She put her arm around Evelyn and patted her.

Mr. Quinn laid his hat back on the table. He returned to the window and looked out at the sky again. Mable began clearing the dishes from the table and Evelyn went quickly to the sink and ran water into the dish pan. In a little Mr. Quinn sat down on the chair. His movements were brittle and tentative. He sat on only half the chair.

Having Mr. Quinn in the house was really something of an advantage. "If a man won't work neither shall he eat," he said, and he made beds and did dishes and even swept and dusted occasionally.

"With everything so scarce and all," Evelyn said, "I feel we're just lucky, having a man like this."

Nor did he interfere with their pleasures. They still went to the movies and had a glass of beer once in a while even though Mr. Quinn refused himself such indulgences.

"I have got rid, in my time, of nearly all the vices excepting fornication," he said, "and I just somehow don't seem to be able to let go of that." It was because of this one failing that he had had to give up his preaching.

So while the girls pursued their usual amusements he walked in the park or sat home and read the Bible. But often as not they all three of them sat about the kitchen table, passing the evening in talk.

June went off happily and most of July, with no mishap between the three of them. It seemed that everything was going to work very nicely until one evening late in the month Evelyn and Mable, coming in from work, found Mr. Quinn standing by the kitchen table holding an envelope in his hand. He seemed to have been standing there ever since he found the letter, fully dressed and looking very stern.

"What is this?" he said. He held up the envelope for them to see.

"Oh, why that . . ." Evelyn said with an awkward show of carelessness, "why that's my allotment check, of course."

"Where is your husband?" Mr. Quinn said in a voice that was thunderous, separating each word one from the other.

"Why, Mr. Quinn, nobody knows."

"Why didn't you tell me you had a living husband, Evelyn Oakes? What made you want to make me commit such a sin without my knowing what I was doing?"

"Oh, Mr. Quinn, honey," Evelyn whined. "Don't go. Don't leave me now. I ain't heard from Edward for months and months. I been faithful to him all along and would go right on but nobody knows where he is any more. I just wasn't built for a celibate, Mr. Quinn, I just wasn't built."

"I loathe adultery," Mr. Quinn said, "and involuntary sin is a judgment."

"Oh, shucks," Mable said. "We ain't had a letter from Edward for God knows how long. He's probably dead. If you was to ask me, Mr. Quinn, I'd say God led you to Evelyn."

She gave him this last for what it might be worth. She chewed her gum and watched him speculatively.

Mr. Quinn gave her a quizzical look.

"The devil takes many shapes," he said. He let his eyes travel coldly over Mable.

"Not mine, thank you."

Evelyn began to cry. She ran into the bedroom and threw herself onto the bed. She had no real hope her tears would get her anything, but she knew better than to try to cope with a preacher in the field of argument. She should have told Mr. Quinn the whole truth to begin with, but she had known from the first that her mere doubts as to the reappearance of

Edward would never have had sufficient weight with Mr. Quinn.

Occasionally she stopped sobbing to listen to what the two of them were saying. They seemed to be preparing dinner together while Mable wove Mr. Quinn a web of theological subtleties from which he repeatedly withdrew himself with amazing skill. They were both being very skillful.

Mable called her to dinner but she refused to go. Finally she fell asleep. When she woke, she heard Mable's voice saying, "As I see it, God led you to Evelyn for his own purposes. If you'd known about Edward you'd never have come. Otherwise why did God keep Evelyn's mouth closed? You may be struggling against something much bigger than yourself, Mr. Quinn, if you walk out that door."

Mr. Quinn was still quiet a while. Finally he came into the bedroom.

"Nobody knows," he said, "what the temptation really is. Sometimes it can take the shape even of charity and love."

"Oh, Mr. Quinn, he's dead. I'm sure he is," Evelyn said. She was beginning to cry again. In the state she was in she couldn't at all understand anything he said.

"He might just be lost."

"He might just as well be dead. I've written and asked and they just don't know. They don't know at all."

Mr. Quinn sat down on the bed.

"Well," he said, "whether I go away or stay here the sin won't be any different, neither bigger nor smaller nor any different color. Perhaps I should wait for the truth."

After that things were never quite the same. Mr. Quinn began to refuse his dessert. He would shake his head and say he didn't want any, and sometimes he would look at his meat and say, "I somehow just feel that that meat belongs to Edward Oakes."

That was bad, but then he took to wandering about the house at night. The girls heard him in the living room, muttering to himself and when they went and listened at the door they discovered that he was apparently talking to the hypothetical spirit of Edward Oakes, asking to be forgiven all possible slights.

When the allotment checks came he spoke to them as if they were alive.

One night he reared up in bed and said, "I don't know whether to pray that he's alive or pray that he's dead. I just can't tell what to do."

Shortly after that he seemed to give up sleeping altogether, at least as far as the girls could tell. Whenever one of them went to the bathroom at night they found him sitting nearly naked in the rocking chair by the front window. Sometimes he was mumbling and sometimes just sitting.

One night seeing him there Mable felt she could endure it no longer and let out a wild scream.

"Quinn, for God's sake, Quinn, come to bed," she cried.

"I've come to it at last," he said in a quiet way. "I've been asked to meet this problem of fornication face to face."

All the while he ate less and less until it seemed he ate nothing at all. He had been preternaturally thin to begin with but he continued to get thinner. He seemed also to be in a slight state of trance and a sharp smell began to come out of him. It hung about him like a loose garment. It was as if there were nothing left in Mr. Quinn but his sense of sin, the sense manifesting itself as odor.

"Some day we'll come in here and find him dead," Mable said.

"It scares me just something awful," Evelyn said.

"I just can't imagine what the papers will make of it," Mable wondered. "They'll say we kept this guy naked in here and starved him to death, and, of course, they'll want to know why."

They were both of them getting terribly nervous. They wanted him to leave, but they were afraid to ask him now. When he had been of a mind to go, at the very beginning, and then later when the trouble began, they had begged him to stay and now the thought of leaving never seemed to cross his mind at all.

"I can't stand it a minute longer," Evelyn said. She was losing weight over the matter herself. "I'm just going to write Washington a real strong letter."

And she did.

"I wish to God," the letter said, "you would write and tell me for sure if my husband Edward Oakes is really dead as the man I am living with won't eat or sleep or do anything until he knows for sure. We are just about crazy here and maybe there will be a tragedy. As one word from you could put a stop to everything, it seems to me that a country who has gone to such limits saving the world from everything could at least spare that and put one woman's mind at ease."

"That's fine," Mable said. "That's exactly how it is, and you might add that any tragedy that happens would be on Uncle Sam's head."

They told Mr. Quinn about the letter. He stared at them for a while, hung his head and said nothing.

Every day they looked for the letter that would release Mr. Quinn's mind, which seemed to have got locked up inside him, but it didn't come and nearly a month passed before Mr. Quinn collapsed. The doctor came and carried him off to the hospital. It looked as if the bill would be tremendous. Mr. Quinn had to be force fed and it looked as if they were never going to get his mind to come back out of whatever dark hole it had crawled into. And the government went right on taking its time.

"What in God's name will we do about this bill?" Evelyn asked Mable. It often made her cry when she thought of the expense she was being put to and of how all she had got or was going to get for her money was just a lot more grief.

"Don't worry, dear, we can manage it in time," Mable told her, "only you're going to have to stop moping and come back to work."

Secretly they both thought it would have been nicer if Mr. Quinn had just starved to death, but since they were responsible in a way for his staying with them against his will, and since his being with them had brought on his state, they both felt a kind of responsibility for him that they didn't like to talk or even think about.

In a little, Mr. Quinn was feeding all right, but it took a while longer for his mind to return to natural objects.

"We have all paid kind of heavy for our sins," he said when they brought him home, "now maybe we can just await the outcome."

By outcome he meant the letter which, when it came, merely said: "We are sorry to inform you there is still no news of Edward Oakes."

They passed it round and looked at it very hard as if trying to make something more helpful rise up from the simple words. A black look came into Mr. Quinn's face.

"What am I going to do?" he said, looking at them helplessly. They shook their heads.

Since Mr. Quinn had been back Mable had been sleeping with Evelyn and Mr. Quinn had had her room to himself.

One night Evelyn shook Mable awake.

"Listen," she said. "He's at it again."

They got up and tiptoed through the front room to Mr. Quinn's door. He was not in bed and at first they couldn't see him. Evelyn who had been awake the longer of the two spotted him first. He had pushed up the rug and was lying on the bare floor next the bed. He was so occupied with his thoughts and his muttering that he didn't hear them.

They went back to their room.

"Do you think he'll stop eating again?" Mable asked.

"I don't know," Evelyn said. "I just don't know." She was beginning to cry. "Do you think I'd better write the government again?" she asked.

But Mable only made a scornful sound in her throat.

Charles Morrow Wilson

Charles Morrow Wilson (1905–   ) was born in Fayetteville, Arkansas, where he attended the University of Arkansas. He has taken a special interest in the backwoods and mountain people of the United States. His books include RABBLE ROUSER *(1936),* CORNBREAD AND CREEK WATER: THE LANDSCAPE OF RURAL POVERTY *(1940), and* MIDDLE AMERICA *(1944). "Essence of Rural Humor" is reprinted from* BACKWOODS AMERICA.

Essence of Rural Humor

SPEAKING generally, the peasant American is a kindly soul and a neighborly one, a keen observer and a good listener. He laughs at ambling drolleries, at stray turns of irony, at verbal horseplay. He possesses a jocundity so vital, tethered so securely to earth, that it endures even as the generations fade. Therefore his humor is not likely to be new or sparklingly original.

It suffices grandfather and father as well as son that Uncle Ameriky Hansen got religion at the Schooner Bald revival meeting only to lose it again when his buggy bounced down a couple of ledge boulders and broke a left fore wheel; that Aunt Marthy Pippitt set twenty-six hens and hatched three pullets and three hundred and ninety-six roosters or that Parson Milsap absent-mindedly ate a mink in place of a gray squirrel.

The scene is Kennicott's store at Blue Eye, a situation but slightly commercial. The group includes Dave Beatty, Forgy Dell, Marcus Feitz, Henstep Creaseley, Tola Summerlin, Homer Bullteeter, Homer's hired boy Bill Skeats, and the storekeeper. These occupy poultry crates and such. They whittle matches into infinitesimal slivers. They draw strange diagrams on the dusty porch floor and whistle tunes that take after nothing in particular. They indulge in slight sounds, slow gyrations, slight parleyings, patterings of feet, uproarious yawnings, and stretchings in the form of capital Xs and Ys.

Their relish for the wisecrack inevitably forthcoming is enhanced a dozenfold by such interludes of speculative waiting. The first spiel is by Bill Skeats, since hired boys are among the most cherished perpetrators of store-porch mirth.

Bill Skeats, then, sitting in sunny oblivion on the lowest estate of the store-porch steps, opens in dialect at his boss:

"Homer, how's hit do for me to ride your hoss home?"

The employer quivers slightly.

"It wouldn't do so good, I've got to ride him myse'f." Then a soft ripple of merriment: "Mought be you could walk alongside me though."

"No, I reckon I'd better jest be pattin' down the road now by myself. If I was to walk aside you, I'd have to open and shet ever' gate and fence-gap between here and thar."

There is freely given laughter. The afternoon flow of jocundity has started. Homer faces unsteadily towards his lolling hired help.

"By the way, how come you ain't workin' today?"

The youth deliberately readjusts his battered felt hat and leers.

"W'y, I was workin' but I got hurt. You see I was plowin' corn in that fur squirrel patch and drekly I come to the field— I fell off—and wrenched my knee."

Backbrush humor hangs upon pegs that are unashamedly obvious: the old gentleman who can't get any satisfaction out of reading the dictionary because it changes the subject too often; the itinerant parson who agrees that a spring wagon and a span of mules are fool proof, but not necessarily damn-fool proof; the upbrush politician who craves a postmastership within easy walking distance of a distillery; the clodhopper who overwhelms the schoolteacher's suggestion that the burning of Mart Miller's barn must have been the work of an incendiary with, "Incendiary, hell! Somebody sot it."

The humor carries an amiable plentitude, too, of anecdotes of stupidity.

The sheriff of a brush county in Southwestern Missouri was forming a posse to recapture a depraved culprit who had broken jail while the defender of justice was away investigating. A store-porch commentator reported that the fugitive had spent half the afternoon strolling about the village; that he had last been seen taking out westward down the old wire road. Then the observing countryman added that he had seen the sheriff pass by the escaped prisoner not an hour before. The upholder of sovereign justice admitted it.

"Oh, yes, yes! I seed him all right—passed him on the town branch bridge a while after dinner time—passed him and spoke howdy to him. But I didn't know the low hound reprobate was out of jail."

The store-porcher relishes so simple an episode as that of the rural lad and his first banana. The youth from Alpena was taking his first train ride, and when the newsman came through acclaiming "chawklets—bernanners!" the mountain lad invested readily in the latter. On the next round the caller stopped to ask after the qualities of his wares.

"Well, Mister, I can't say so bodaciously much for it. In the first place it was mainly all cob; and when I'd throwed that away, what little they was left was bitter and sort of ornery to eat."

Sometimes the gentleman of the store-porch is tickled almost beyond endurance by ignorance of rural ways, by unfamiliarity with the dictates of soil and season which he himself knows so well. The newcomer who figures to get rich off a few slanting acres of stump ground; who would bear down on his plow handles, tie up fodder with string, buckle the throat-latch of a bridle before he set the bit, undertake to keep the birds from his cherries or the squirrels from his corn —such a yahoo provides material for slow perceptive smiles based upon first-hand understanding of the ways and wiles of wooded hill and brushy dale.

*   *   *

The conversation on the store-porch drifted around to the chinch bugs, which had descended upon the tasseling corn in

leeching multitudes. The drummer from Saint Looie wanted
to know what a chinch bug looked like.

"You say it's no bigger than a seed tick?"

Nods and salivary assent.

"Why, I wouldn't have my crops wiped out by a little
thing like that."

The sitters nudged one another and one soberly asked what
the commercial ambassador might figure to do about it.

"Do about it? Why, I'd get me a good two-handed brush
and frail 'em off my place."

*　　*　　*

The store-porch humorist is not, of course, above a pun.
An old codger from Red Star was telling of his family.

"Yes, suh, they come three boys, then a girl, then another
boy. So I named 'em Matthew, Mark, Luke, Ann, John."

And he knows the value of hyperbole. One time I asked an
old countryman why he preferred cushaws (large hooked
squashes) to pumpkins. He spat.

"Well suh, if I was to grow punkins on them slopin' fields,
they'd likely break loose from the vines and roll down and
kill somebody. But cushaws—they hook theirselves to corn
stalks and ketch on."

Nor is the store humorist immune to the potency of slap-
stick. There is no good reason why he should be. Mimicry
can also put him into the high rhapsodies of mirth. And the
countryside idiot is a dependable source of laughter.

The rural commoner likewise is amused at the plight of the
singing master who started to cross Brush Creek by means
of a log bridge, and went to where the log bridge wasn't.
There moonlight and a black shadow had fallen across the
way, so the singing master, mistaking the shadow for the
bridge, decided that he would just hunker down and 'coon
across it. So he knelt, putting his elbows forward and pain-
stakingly plunged head first into a stream of ice-cold water.

Backwoods fondness for burlesque mingles mirthfully with the liking for the humor of ignorance. For that very reason countrymen enjoy country jokes and relish the opportunity for embellishment and parody.

"You know, over at Post Oak Hill where we come from, that there's the reel brush. Pap Eason he's about the only feller down that there creek bend as knows how to read and write. So about seven or eight of us chipped in an taken the Springfield newspaper, figgerin' as how Pap could read it to us.

"Well, we done hit, and one day we was settin' around listenin' and Pap was readin' about where the paper said as how ever'body ought to plant a lot of corn and plow hit a lot because some mighty bad droughts was comin'. Mart Miller set and puzzled awhile and then he says:

" 'Pap, what's a drought?'

"Pap chawed his terbaccer a minute and stroked his chin-whiskers and then says,

" 'Well, I couldn't be jest shore, but if I ain't mighty mistaken, a drought is one of them new-fangled varmints that's a cross betwixt a coon and a wildcat. Anyhow they shore is hell on corn.' "

*   *   *

Another tale of the same timbre tells of a rural countryside in the throes of a summertime political campaign. Squire Techstone was running for circuit clerk against a slicked-up county seat lawyer. The two were orating at an August picnic. The legal member was offering belligerent argument.

"That man is as ignorant of the law as he is of the responsibilities of office. I would even defy my opponent to define so simple a legal term as *habeas corpus*."

Squire Techstone lifted off his battered felt hat and cogitated.

"Well, unless I'm mighty fur wrong that term means a red Jersey heifer fresh with a first calf."

There are rural epics of the sort that came about when Newt Finnen's wife prevailed upon Newt to take all their children to the protracted meeting.

"Newt said he couldn't rightfully bear to set and listen to preachin's, but one time his wife got come over with holiness and she hawg-an'-pantered him till he had to take her an' the young 'uns to meetin'. Newt set out on the back porch till the preachin' was all over, then he commenced gettin' oneasy about was the young 'uns still there. He figgered he'd better round 'em up. So he strolled inside and brushed back the black bristles from his forehead and says,

" 'Emmy, Dan'l, Sady, Jude, Prosey, Tom, Virgil, Dessie, Newtie, Violeeny, you-all here?'

"They says, 'Yes, Pa, we're here.'

"So then Newt lined 'em up and struck out for home."

*   *   *

There are times when the edge of satire may become a bit cutting. A countryside revival meeting had reached the stage of spiritual orgies. The parson preached, the congregation rolled and grovelled and kicked up straw. Then came the hour for testifying.

Brother Amos, the countryside cripple, squatted upon a convenient corner bench. He was a paralytic, an invalid hopelessly cramped and drawn, with gangling and unruly limbs. During the course of the testifying the parson called upon the crippled one to rise and tell what the Lord had done for him.

Brother Amos roused jerkily, raised his chin a bare inch from his chest in painful deliberation and struggled to manipulate his lagging limbs. There was a silence of expectation and awaited revelation. Then the lame one shrilled:

"You was askin' what the Lord done for me. Well, I'll tell you. He jest blamed near ruint me."

*   *   *

The run of store-porch humor is withal a gentle humor, a garnishment for extensive leisure, cornmeal mush, sun and rain, dew and moonlight, and backwoods stillness. It rarely carries bitterness. It may be brusque but it is seldom vengeful. It is rarely ulterior. A man does not use it to sell his hen's eggs, or to acquire a soft job, or to swarm with the village social bees. The peasant laughs because he sees no reason why he shouldn't.

As an example of the kindliness of the humor, there is a recitation dealing with a lad from Gulch Hollow, who on first coming to Eureka, was lured by the tempting yellowness of the store-window lemons. The youth had never seen lemons before and he figured to sample them. So he bought a dime's worth and proceeded to try out the purchase. A first attempt to bite through the tough rind revealed an appalling mistake. But in the sight of a half-dozen onlookers the lad from Gulch Hollow did not once hesitate. He ate the first lemon whole; then the second and third. Nobody laughed. There was not even the suggestion of a smile. The rural youth addressed a sober audience.

"Yessir, fer a considerable spell I've been honin' to get my fill of these here tropical fruits because I shorely do pleasure in the flavor of 'em and now I aim to revel in it."

Then with puckering lips he retreated toward the village pump, his departure unmarred by laughter, his sensitive spirit unchafed.

* * *

And one time the folks were having a moonlight supper up at the Brush Ford schoolhouse. Uncle Zeb Hatfield, who hadn't been out to any manner of funmaking in a month of moons, was a bit unsteady about his etiquette, and in consequence chanced to pour buttermilk into his coffee instead of cream. An observing farm wife moved to fetch him another cup. But Uncle Zeb would be the subject of no such bother.

He blew at the murky fluid and assured the company that taking buttermilk in coffee was to him an invariable habit. Steady faces accepted that declaration. There was not even an adolescent snigger.

*   *   *

Backwoods humor has its subtle side, too. The commoner from Low Gap is capable of a cerebral chuckle now and then, fully as capable of it as his brethren of the town.

He enjoys his Aunt Lulu Pettigrew's complaint of pains in her abominable muscles, or that most of her family have died of nobility, or that with one of them New Fords her son Wid can climb any manner of mountain in neutral. He relishes such picturesque generalities as those of Judge Patton of Kentucky, who once offered these instructions to his jury:

"Gentlemen, whenever you see a big overgrown buck a-settin' at the mouth of some holler or the fork of some road, with a big slouch hat on, a blue collar, a celluloid rose in his coat lapel and a banjo strung acrost his chist, fine that man, gentleman. Fine him! Because if he ain't done somethin' already, he blame soon will."

He enjoys hearing the Tannehill child assure a younger brother that if he will only stop hollerin' he can watch the old gentleman fall off the hay wagon.

He enjoys the strategy of the thrifty old lady of didactic leanings who in remonstrating with some little boys for their stealing a pocketful of pears, assured them that if they would only be forward and honest about it and bring along something in which to carry the fruit home, she would be glad to give them the pears. Five minutes later she was faced by the pack of youngsters who brought an old-style clothes basket capable of holding at least four bushels.

There is an ephemeral freshness to backwoods humor due in part to its nearness to earth; in part to the ways of its perpetrators—their slowness of speech and droll maneuverings of expression; their posture and inflections which cannot be adequately reproduced even in the most accommodating of type.

The great majority of upcountry jests are neither scrupulously original nor sparklingly clever. Often enough a rustic gem will shine for generations. And this fact is easier to understand when one understands that in Elizabethan America one generation is very much like another.

Howard Wolf

Howard Wolf (1902–   ), long a resident of Akron, Ohio, where he was columnist and city editor of the BEACON-JOURNAL, *wrote, with his wife Geraldine,* THE WORLD, THE FLESH, AND THE HOLY GHOSTS *(1933), poems.* RUBBER: A STORY OF GLORY AND GREED *(1936), a painstaking and massive (though somewhat critical) study of the rubber industry, is a collaboration with his brother Ralph.* GREENER PASTURES *(1936), a satire, is solo. In 1939 Wolf received a Guggenheim Award for the purpose of writing a history of the press associations of the United States. Some of the fruits of his investigations have appeared in various magazines and a volume is forthcoming. "Odyssey," in a slightly different form, appeared as "The Old Man's Odyssey" in the September, 1939, issue of* ESQUIRE.

Odyssey

THIS was The Day. The old man suddenly recalled that as he sat on the bed edge, slowly and conscientiously pulling up one baggy old trouser leg over one skinny old limb. "Just let her try an' stop me," he muttered malevolently. "I'd like to see anybody try an' stop me. Guess I ain't a-goin' today! Oh, no! An' if she thinks she's a-goin to stop—"

The muttered monologue continued as he bent perilously to pant-leg two, creaked erect to maneuver galluses over shoulders, buttoned the fly with great deliberation. Shuffling to the washbowl he stuck out his tongue at the ostentatiously placed cake of soap, flirted a dribble of water at his face and assaulted the hanging towel with much unnecessary sputtering and blowing. It was heard below stairs. It was designed to be.

"That you, grandpa?" came the expected Voice. "That's right. Wash nice. And don't forget the ears." The old man made a face of disgust. Then, hoisting one leg with great difficulty, he pantomimed the breaking of wind. In her direction.

Chuckling over this feat, he remembered the one about the Irishman and the Devil. "Let's see you catch that an' paint it green," he chanted under his breath. And fortified by his secret knowledge of his secret gibe, he went clumping down the steps in measured descent to that Terrible Woman, Wife of his son's son.

"Let's see those hands," demanded this bustling, masterful one.

Obediently, the old man showed them. The ejaculation was uttered with the customary horror, the comments with the customary satire and irony, the command to march-right-over-to-the-kitchen-sink with the customary peremptoriness.

"Ain't a-goin' to do it," said the old man.

"Not one bite of breakfast till you do," replied the tyrant.

From the kitchen table drifted the scent of sausage, hot cakes and coffee. The old man made his way to the sink. Picking up the soap, he whirled suddenly about. The intent was to catch her gloating. Instead, she was heaping hot cakes on his plate. Mollified, the old man turned to his task.

"I'm comin' as fast as I kin, ain't I?" he demanded. That was to preserve his self respect.

Replete long later, he tongued the last of the syrup from lips, chin and moustache. And called for his overcoat, his cap and his brown, gnarled cane, the third leg that had come to fit so familiarly into his brown, gnarled hand.

"That will be enough of that," said the Terrible Woman. "You're not going up to That Old Corner today."

All the old man's rooster blood boiled to the surface. "Ed said I could," he screamed. "Ed said I could today," he thumped the table with his knuckles. "Night before last he said it, and you heard him. You heard him!"

"So Ed is a weather prophet now" (scornfully). "And you're to go out in that raw wind and catch your death of cold" (bitingly). "And I'm to work and slave and dance attendance on you after all I've been through working and slaving and nursing these last two months just because you *would* go out on a day no more suitable than this" (self-pityingly). "Now you waltz right into that living room and listen to all those nice radio programs you like so much only you're too stubborn to admit it" (imperiously).

Tears came to the old man's eyes and cut the argument short. Not for anything would he have had her see them. Stumbling, he made his way into the living room. And with the radio going full blast, he sat for a time in his easy chair indulging in outright blubbering.

For two months he hadn't been able to make the daily adventurous expedition around which he had built his life through the eighties and on past his ninetieth birthday. For a month he had nightly pestered his grandson for permission to resume his chartered hazarding. Two nights ago Ed had admitted full convalescence and agreed to his faring forth if he would wait another day. And now That Woman—

A last sniffle. The old man couldn't keep on being heart-broken. In spite of himself he was being caught up by the wireless serial. Let's see now, this would be the *Oleo House* continued story sponsored by the Better'n Butter people. The chirpy voice would be pretty Kitty Clancy's and the deep one that of the gypsy kidnaper. Not quite up to *The Solitary Ranger* but, for a morning program, it would do. The old man settled back to enjoy it although remembering to register disgusted boredom whenever his foe swished through the room in going about her business of housekeeping.

An hour later he was listening with somnolent satisfaction to the *Crackerbox House* program sent out by the Reduso Wafer folks. Just as the gypsy kidnaper advanced on pretty Katey Kelly the aristocratic voice of the lady announcer took it away. "Do you have easy chair spread?" the cultured accents condescended. The old man snorted and came to himself. Listening, he heard the water running in the bathroom.

Moving with an astonishingly light-footed agility, he crossed to the hall, lifted overcoat, cap and cane from the rack and eased himself out the front door. Not until the hedge was between him and the house did he pause for the long and involved struggle of getting himself into the coat. Tilting the cap at a rakish angle then, he gave the stick a preliminary twirl and launched himself towards the delights of The Corner four and one-half long blocks away.

Shuffle, shuffle, shuffle went the hardly-lifted shoes in a noise as of miniature side-wheel steamers. Chuckle, chuckle, chuckle went the old man. As cocky as they come, he showed in the glory of ten o'clock sunshine making his way west on that spring morning. The cap was jaunty, the head carried at the perkiest of angles, the walrus moustache drooping not sadly but with the incongrous air of something pasted on for a masquerade. The old man was humming *Loch Lomond* and swinging it.

Down the curb he went and in unconcerned slow scuffle across the intersecting street. A speeding motorist bore down on him in smug and righteous satisfaction at possessing the right-of-way. The old man never missed a shuffle nor did he deign to turn his head. The brakes went on with a shriek, the car jolted to a shivering stop, the old man continued his imperturbable progress past it as a head stuck out to bawl bitter, witty remarks in his direction.

The rejoinder came to him as he reached the opposite curb. "An' paint it green," he sassed, halting for the slow business of hauling one foot and then the other up to the elevation. Firmly planted upon the sidewalk he paused in momentary triumph. Block one had been met and it was his.

"Just wish he'd got out o' that driver's seat," went the monologue as the shoes again shoved grittily forward. " 'Take that an' that an' that' I'd 'a said." Here he furiously fanned the air with his stick.

It was this, probably, that attracted the cur. A snotty, little soiled white one, it had been slinking across the yard, all the ends of the world seeming to have come upon the head, and the tail more than a little weary. Now it stiffened to attention, both ends up.

"Hope it goes on by," thought the old man.

"Wonder if I dare try a bark," thought the dog.

The man hesitated in his shuffle. The dog ventured a yip, not too loud but a bit on the nasty side.

"Oh, oh, oh," thought the old man, coming definitely to a standstill.

"I think I've got him scared," the dog decided, "but I'd best go a little slow yet."

It closed in on the quarry, sniffing the pant legs in what

was designed to be construed as a friendly fashion. This was just in case there had been an error of canine judgment. There had been no error. The two-legged one was palpably nervous. The cur put a world of contempt into the final sniff. Then it fell back an inch or so and opened up.

"Rou, rou, rou," went the little bully's big voice.

"Go 'way," said the old man. "Go 'way."

"Rou, rou, rou," rejoiced his enemy, circling.

Panicky, he swished at it with his cane. The cur tore back into the yard, yelping in surprise and sorrow. The old man put himself into motion. But he just couldn't help looking back over a shoulder to see if the god damned thing was sneaking up. It wasn't. But the backward look was fatal.

"He's got the wind up!" the dog deduced. "Oh, mama, will this be fun!"

Racing at top speed, it drew a great circle around its prey, loosing meanwhile an ecstasy of barking. Now it had the old man in a dither.

"Go 'way, go 'way," he quavered, loosing a stiff, minute kick like a mechanical toy.

Flattening itself to the sidewalk before him, the dog began to worm in his direction to the accompaniment of a continuous fierce, low growling meant to convey the impression that this time it really meant business.

The old man got the idea. He took a shuffling step backward. Then another. The dog hurled itself into the air in a very delirium of bliss and rapture. Another bound carried it right to the victim and, all the time giving tongue lickety-split, it leaped up and down snapping at palpitating hand and wavering stick.

The cap jounced from the old man's head in his frantic lurching and turning. His tormentor was on it like a flash. With the cloth waving from its mouth, it swaggered up into the yard trying its best to look as officious as a road repair flagman or at least as terrible as an army with banners. There it settled down to easeful chewing and snarling. The old man stood on the sidewalk, whimpering.

Cap possibilities exhausted, the dog rolled a speculative eye and saw him still wavering impotently in that spot.

"Rou, rou, rou," it announced and had the satisfaction of seeing him cringe.

Shaking itself to all fours, the cur prepared to start in again. Then, across the street, it saw the man with the leather sack making his appointed rounds. There's no closed season on letter carriers, the comrades long ere this had revealed. Every dog is chartered to bark and snap at those dopes, said the comrades, and they have to like it. The cur never had accumulated the courage. But flushed now with victory, it fairly flew across the street intending to rack up another triumph and return to the old man at leisure. The carrier paid no attention to its approach.

"Everything all right, pappy?" he shouted across the street.

"O.K., O.K.," said the old man. "Wind blew off my cap and I'm just a-goin' to pick it up."

The dog went into its leap and snap. The carrier caught it with the toe of a heavy shoe. The dog turned a flipflop and, torn between pain and astonishment, went scuttling down the street giving tongue to a profound sorrow and despair.

To the accompaniment of that sweet music, the old man doddered into the yard, retrieved his muddied head-piece, and triumphantly chuffed across the second intersection. Two down, he mentally noted as he plucked a leaf from the hedge bordering the sidewalk and tentatively chewed.

He had progressed about half the hedge's length when there was a shrill screech and a face-overshadowing hat popped up above the foliage. Bam! Bam! Bam! went the blanks in the cap-gun covering the old man and not a yard away.

Startled, he froze and a small, terrified yip escaped him. Peals of laughter, a treble whoop of "Heigh-yo, Silver!